COMPREHENSIVE
STRUCTURAL
DESIGN GUIDE

COMPREHENSIVE STRUCTURAL DESIGN GUIDE

MAX KURTZ, P.E.

Consulting Engineer; Instructor for American Society of
Mechanical Engineers and Cooper Union Alumni
Association; Member, National Society of Professional
Engineers; Editor, *Kings County Professional Engineer;*
Author, *Structural Engineering for Professional Engineers'
Examinations, Engineering Economics for Professional
Engineers' Examinations, Framing of Hip and Valley Rafters;*
Contributing Author, *Standard Handbook of Engineering
Calculations*

McGRAW-HILL BOOK COMPANY

New York   St. Louis   San Francisco   London   Sydney
Toronto   Mexico   Panama

COMPREHENSIVE STRUCTURAL DESIGN GUIDE

1 2 3 4 5 6 7 8 9 0 M A M M 7 5 4 3 2 1 0 6 9

To my wife Ruth

" . . . and the rain fell, and the floods came, and the winds blew and beat upon that house, but it did not fall, because it had been founded on the rock."

Matt. 7:25.

Preface

This book is intended primarily to serve as a guide and reference source for structural designers by presenting detailed solutions to a vast number of problems in structural engineering. The problems included in this book are typical of those that arise most frequently in design practice, and each step in the solution is carefully explained to ensure that the solution will be readily understood. To illustrate the use of this book, let us assume that an individual is required to design a plate girder in compliance with the Specification of the American Institute of Steel Construction. He may use the design in Example 12-8 as a model, merely replacing the numerical values in this example with those that apply in his case. This book should also prove of great benefit to engineers and architects preparing for examinations for state licensure or civil service positions.

A book that encompasses a very wide area of structural engineering possesses many important advantages. It offers a unified, integrated treatment of the material, presenting all relevant definitions, concepts, and equations in one compact, self-contained volume while maintaining a uniform notational system and consistent approach. For example, in studying a problem in soil mechanics that requires the construction of Mohr's circle of stress, the reader need merely refer to Article 3-4 for a review of Mohr's circle if he finds this review necessary.   The work of a structural designer requires that he be intimately familiar with a wide variety of subjects.   If he is compelled to refer to several books to review these subjects or extract the pertinent equations, the absence of both a uniform notational system and a consistent approach may be a source of considerable difficulty and confusion.

This book presents a concise but thorough review of the engineering theory underlying each topic.   Much of this material, such as that pertaining to the plastic design of steel structures and the design of prestressed-concrete beams, has been prepared by assuming that the reader has had no prior exposure to these subjects.   A diligent study of this book will afford the reader an intimate familiarity with the standard design codes and the principles upon which the various provisions of these codes are based.   For example, Article 14-1 explains why the AISC Specification assigns a higher allowable bending stress to a flexural member of rectangular or circular cross section than to a wide-flange beam; Article 12-4 explains why the AISC Specification recognizes a redistribution of bending moments in a continuous beam; and Article 15-2 explains why the distribution of shearing stress in a timber beam differs from that in a solid member.

Because of its steadily increasing importance, the subject of prestressed-concrete design is treated at considerable length in this book.   The subject is developed systematically by a method that relies mainly on engineering logic rather than abstruse mathematics.   Each principle of design is illustrated by means of a numerical example, and graphs are used extensively to depict the manner in which stresses vary across the span or to demonstrate the relationship that exists between the eccentricity of the prestressing force and the required magnitude of that force. Structural designers have been reluctant to take advantage of the great economy inherent in the use of continuous beams because of the alleged mathematical complexity of the subject.   It is hoped that the treatment of continuous beams presented in Chapter 22 will overcome this objection, for the principles underlying continuous-beam design are developed in a relatively simple manner and then applied to the solution of typical problems.

In Chapter 14, the plastic design of steel structures is presented in a manner that seeks to make the subject as readily comprehensible as possible and to minimize the mathematical work entailed in the design. For example, the theorem of composite mechanisms developed in Article 14-3 establishes a criterion that enables us to determine at the outset whether or not a particular composite mechanism warrants investigation as a potential mode of failure.   Similarly, the theorem of virtual displacements developed in the same article simplifies the analysis of a gable frame by the mechanism method.

Accuracy of calculation is stressed throughout. Since many calculations in a design project are based upon preceding calculations, it is important that calculated results be submitted to verification wherever possible. Many designers are content to test the accuracy of their results merely by repeating their calculations, but this procedure does not constitute a reliable method of detecting errors. Calculated results may be accepted as accurate if identical answers are obtained by two completely independent methods, or if it is demonstrated that the results are compatible with the given data or with one another. Example 16-7 illustrates how results obtained by substitution in a set of equations may be tested for self-consistency, and Example 22-17 illustrates how results stemming from a quadratic equation may be tested by computing their "second differences."

Structural members are often designed by a trial and error method that consists of using an assumed size of member, calculating the stresses, and then revising the size until eventually an adequate and economical member is obtained. This type of design is highly time-consuming and often unnecessary, for in many instances it is possible to arrive at the correct size of member by a straightforward method. This book applies direct design wherever feasible. Example 12-4 illustrates the direct design of the reinforcing plates for a steel beam, and Examples 20-1 and 20-2 illustrate the direct determination of the required depth of an isolated and combined column footing, respectively.

The author is indebted, in the writing of this book, to the many individuals who have encouraged him in the pursuit of engineering knowledge.

Max Kurtz

Contents

COMPREHENSIVE
STRUCTURAL
DESIGN GUIDE

ONE

Principles of Statics

1-1 Analysis of Force Systems   A force has three characteristics: magnitude, position of its action line, and sense or direction (southward, northeastward, etc.).   The *moment* of a force with respect to a given axis is its tendency to rotate the body on which it acts about that axis.   The moment equals the product of the magnitude of the force and the perpendicular distance from its action line to the axis of rotation, this distance being called the *lever arm*.

It is often convenient to represent a force graphically by means of a vector.   This is a line segment that is parallel to the action line and has a length proportional to the magnitude of the force, with an arrowhead to indicate the sense.

Two systems of forces acting on a body are said to be *equivalent* if they produce an identical external effect on the body.   Assume that a given system of forces may be replaced with an equivalent single force.   The latter is termed the *resultant* of the system, and a substitution of this nature is called the *composition of forces*.   Conversely, consider that a single force is replaced with an equivalent system composed of two forces. The members of this system are referred to as *components* of the single

1

force, and a substitution of this nature is referred to as the *resolution of a force*.

Example 1-1   The body in Fig. 1-1*a* is acted upon by three forces represented by vectors A, B, and C.   Draw the vector representing the resultant R of this system.

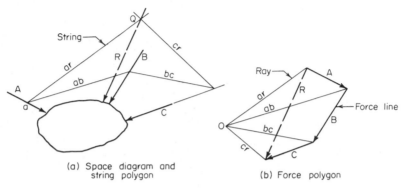

(a) Space diagram and
string polygon

(b) Force polygon

fig. 1-1 Resultant of force system.

Solution. The magnitude and direction of R are found by the following procedure: In Fig. 1-1*b*, draw the vector chain ABC, making the terminal point of one vector the initial point of its successor.   This chain is termed the *force line*.   The resultant is represented by the vector extending from the initial point to the terminal point of the force line.

The action line of R is found by replacing the given force system with an equivalent system composed of only two forces.   This substitution is effected by resolving each given force into components in such a manner that one component of A nullifies one component of B, and the other component of B nullifies one component of C.   The procedure is as follows: In Fig. 1-1*b*, select an arbitrary point O as pole, draw the rays from O to the ends of the vectors, and label the rays in the manner shown.   The forces have thus been resolved into the indicated components and the system itself has been resolved into components ar and cr.

In Fig. 1-1*a*, select an arbitrary point a on the action line of A, and draw lines (termed *strings*) parallel to rays ar and ab.   At the point where the string ab intersects the action line of B, draw a string parallel to ray bc.   At the point where the string bc intersects the action line of C, draw a string parallel to cr.   Let Q denote the point of intersection of strings ar and cr.   Since the moment of the force system with respect to Q is zero, it follows that the action line of R passes through Q.

The resultant is now established with respect to its magnitude, direction, and position of action line.   The polygon formed by the strings in Fig. 1-1*a* is termed a *string polygon*.

A force system that has a zero resultant is described as *balanced*, and the body on which it acts is said to be *in equilibrium*.   Consider that all forces in a coplanar system are resolved into components parallel to two axes, x and y, and that moments are taken with respect to an arbitrary axis. Algebraic signs are employed to denote the sense of the forces and of the moments (clockwise or counterclockwise). A balanced force system satisfies the *equations of equilibrium*, which are as follows:

$$\Sigma F_x = 0 \qquad \Sigma F_y = 0 \qquad \text{(1-1)}$$
$$\Sigma M = 0 \qquad \text{(1-2)}$$

where ΣF_x = sum of x components

ΣF_y = sum of y components

ΣM = sum of moments about given axis

By convention, forces are usually resolved into their horizontal and vertical components. In this text, we shall adopt the following sign convention:

Horizontal forces are positive if they are directed to the right and negative if directed to the left. Vertical forces are positive if they are directed upward and negative if directed downward. Clockwise moments are positive, and counterclockwise moments negative.

1-2 Static Friction In Fig. 1-2a, body A transmits to body B a force that has components N and H normal and parallel, respectively, to the surface of contact. Motion of A relative to B is resisted by the frictional

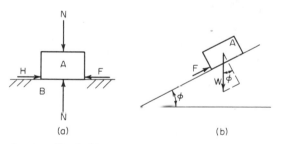

(a)   (b)

fig. 1-2 Static friction.

force F. If the body remains in equilibrium, $F = H$. However, the maximum value that F may assume is

$$F_{max} = \mu N \qquad \text{(1-3)}$$

where μ is the coefficient of static friction of abutting surfaces.

In Fig. 1-2b, body A tends to slide down the inclined plane under the parallel component of its weight, but this tendency is counteracted by the frictional resistance. Assume that angle ϕ is gradually increased until A is on the verge of sliding. The angle of inclination at the instant of impending motion, or the maximum value of ϕ if motion is to be prevented, is termed the *angle of repose.* From the geometry of the drawing, we obtain

$$\tan \phi_{max} = \mu \qquad (1\text{-}4)$$

1-3   Analysis of Internal Forces   The internal forces induced in a structure by a given load system may be evaluated by considering a portion of the structure as a free body and applying the equations of equilibrium. The effect of cutting the structure is to transmute internal forces to external forces.

Example 1-2   The frame in Fig. 1-3a consists of two inclined members and a tie rod.   What is the tension in the rod when a load of 1000 lb is applied at the hinged apex?   Neglect the weight of the frame, and consider the supports to be smooth.

   Solution.   The free-body diagram of the frame is shown in Fig. 1-3b.   Since friction is absent, the reactions at the supports are vertical.   The frame forms a

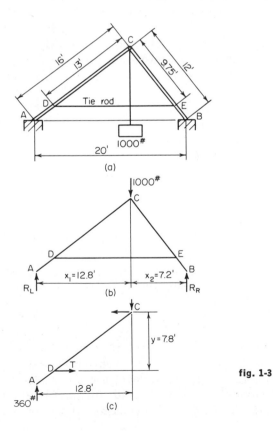

fig. 1-3

3-4-5 right triangle, and we therefore have the following:

$$x_1 = 16 \times \tfrac{4}{5} = 12.8 \text{ ft} \qquad x_2 = 12 \times \tfrac{3}{5} = 7.2 \text{ ft}$$
$$\Sigma F_V = R_L + R_R - 1000 = 0$$

Taking moments about B, we have

$$\Sigma M_B = 20R_L - 1000 \times 7.2 = 0$$
$$\therefore R_L = 360 \text{ lb} \qquad \text{and} \qquad R_R = 640 \text{ lb}$$

The free-body diagram of member AC is shown in Fig. 1-3c.   We shall take moments about C.

$$y = 13 \times \tfrac{3}{5} = 7.8 \text{ ft}$$
$$\Sigma M_C = 360 \times 12.8 - 7.8T = 0$$
$$\therefore T = \textbf{591 lb}$$

Alternatively, T may be found by analyzing member BC as a free body.

TWO

Properties of Areas—
Parabolic Arcs

The stresses induced within a member are functions of both the external forces acting on the member and the properties of its cross section. It is therefore necessary to define and analyze certain fundamental properties of areas.

2-1 Definition of Properties   In Fig. 2-1, x and y are rectangular coordinate axes and S is the origin.   Consider the area shown in the drawing to be divided into elemental areas.   Let x and y denote the coordinates of

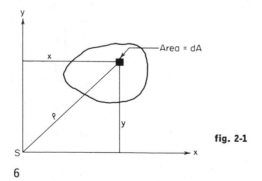

fig. 2-1

the center of an elemental area and ρ the corresponding polar distance. The notational system pertaining to the properties of the area is as follows:

A = total area
Q_x = statical moment (or first moment) of area with respect to x axis
I_x = moment of inertia (or second moment) of area with respect to x axis
r_x = radius of gyration of area with respect to x axis
P_{xy} = product of inertia of area with respect to x and y axes
J_s = polar moment of inertia of area with respect to axis through S perpendicular to plane of area

The properties are defined by the following equations:

$$Q_x = \int y\, dA \tag{2-1}$$
$$I_x = \int y^2\, dA \tag{2-2}$$

$$r_x = \sqrt{\frac{I_x}{A}} \quad \text{or} \quad I_x = Ar_x^2 \tag{2-3}$$

$$P_{xy} = \int xy\, dA \tag{2-4}$$
$$J_s = \int \rho^2\, dA \tag{2-5}$$

but
$$\rho^2 = y^2 + x^2$$
$$\therefore\ J_s = I_x + I_y \tag{2-6}$$

The statical moment and product of inertia may be positive, negative, or zero; the moment of inertia, radius of gyration, and polar moment of inertia are always positive.

The following principle stems from Eq. (2-3): If several areas all have the same radius of gyration with respect to a given axis, the radius of gyration of their combined area equals that of the individual areas.

2-2 Properties of an Area with Respect to Parallel Axes In evaluating the properties of an area, it is often necessary to transfer from one set of rectangular axes to a parallel set. With reference to the area in Fig. 2-2, the following relationships obtain:

$$Q_{x'} = Q_x + Ab \tag{2-7}$$
$$I_{x'} = I_x + 2Q_x b + Ab^2 \tag{2-8a}$$
$$I_{y'} = I_y + 2Q_y a + Aa^2 \tag{2-8b}$$
$$P_{x'y'} = P_{xy} + Q_x a + Q_y b + Aab \tag{2-9}$$

If the statical moment of an area with respect to a particular axis is zero, the latter is called a *centroidal axis*. In Fig. 2-2, let o denote the centroidal axis parallel to the x axis and y_m denote the distance between these axes. By setting $Q_o = 0$ and making the appropriate substitutions in Eqs. (2-7) and (2-8), we obtain these results:

$$Q_x = Ay_m \qquad (2\text{-}10)$$
$$I_x = I_o + Ay_m^2 \qquad (2\text{-}11)$$

Then
$$r_x = \sqrt{r_o^2 + y_m^2} \qquad (2\text{-}12)$$

Since there is a centroidal axis corresponding to every direction of the x axis, it follows that an area has an infinite number of centroidal axes. It can be demonstrated that all centroidal axes of an area are concurrent; their point of intersection is termed the *centroid* of the area.

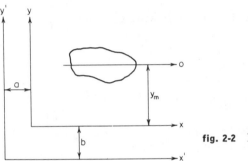

fig. 2-2   Parallel axes.

Assume that an area has an axis of symmetry. From the defining equations, it follows that:

1. An axis of symmetry is a centroidal axis.
2. The product of inertia of the area with respect to the axis of symmetry and any axis perpendicular thereto is zero.

The radius of gyration of an area with respect to a centroidal axis may be regarded as an index of the dispersion of the area about that axis.

The properties of the simpler geometrical figures are presented on pages 6-22 to 6-28 of the American Institute of Steel Construction Manual. The reader should commit to memory the following properties of a tri-

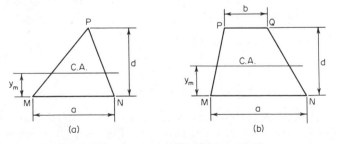

fig. 2-3   Centroidal axis of triangle and trapezoid.

angle and trapezoid: In Fig. 2-3a

$$y_m = \tfrac{1}{3}d \qquad Q_{MN} = \tfrac{1}{6}ad^2 \tag{2-13}$$

In Fig. 2-3b

$$y_m = \frac{d}{3}\frac{a + 2b}{a + b} \qquad Q_{MN} = \frac{d^2}{6}(a + 2b) \tag{2-14}$$

2-3 Properties of an Area with Respect to Concurrent Axes It is often necessary to transfer from one set of rectangular axes to a concurrent set. With reference to the area in Fig. 2-4, the following relationships obtain:

$$I_{x'} = \frac{I_x + I_y}{2} + \frac{I_x - I_y}{2}\cos 2\theta - P_{xy}\sin 2\theta \tag{2-15a}$$

$$I_{y'} = \frac{I_x + I_y}{2} - \frac{I_x - I_y}{2}\cos 2\theta + P_{xy}\sin 2\theta \tag{2-15b}$$

$$P_{x'y'} = \frac{I_x - I_y}{2}\sin 2\theta + P_{xy}\cos 2\theta \tag{2-16}$$

Consider that the moment of inertia I of an area is evaluated with respect to a group of concurrent axes. There is a distinct value of I

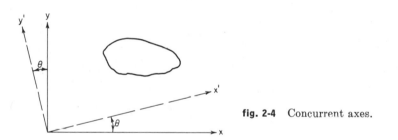

fig. 2-4 Concurrent axes.

associated with each axis, as given by Eq. (2-15a). The *major* axis is the one for which I is maximum; the *minor* axis is the one for which I is minimum. The major and minor axes are referred to collectively as the *principal* axes.

The orientation of the principal axes relative to the given x axis is found by differentiating Eq. (2-15a) with respect to θ, equating $dI/d\theta$ to zero, and solving for θ. The result is

$$\tan 2\theta = \frac{2P_{xy}}{I_y - I_x} \tag{2-17}$$

The following conclusions emerge:

1. The principal axes through a given point are mutually perpendicular, since the two values of θ that satisfy this equation differ by 90°.

2. The product of inertia of an area with respect to its principal axes is zero, since P_{xy} is zero if θ is zero.

3. Conversely, if the product of inertia of an area with respect to two mutually perpendicular axes is zero, these are principal axes.

4. An axis of symmetry is a principal axis, since the product of inertia of the area with respect to this axis and one perpendicular thereto is zero.

2-4 Properties of Parabolic Arcs   Assume that we are given a parabolic arc described by the equation

$$y = ax^2 + bx + c$$

where a, b, and c are constants. In designing continuous prestressed-concrete beams, it is necessary to determine the properties of this arc when we are given the coordinates at the ends and at the midpoint as measured along the x axis. With reference to the parabolic arc $P_1P_2P_3$ in Fig. 2-5,

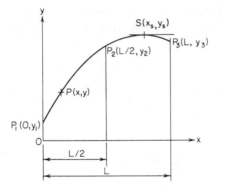

fig. 2-5   Parabolic arc.

let P denote an arbitrary point on the arc and S the summit point; let m denote the slope of the arc.

The ordinate and slope at P are as follows:

$$y = 2(y_1 - 2y_2 + y_3)\left(\frac{x}{L}\right)^2 - (3y_1 - 4y_2 + y_3)\frac{x}{L} + y_1 \quad (2\text{-}18)$$

$$m = \frac{dy}{dx} = 4(y_1 - 2y_2 + y_3)\frac{x}{L^2} - \frac{3y_1 - 4y_2 + y_3}{L} \quad (2\text{-}19)$$

The change in slope is constant along the arc and has the following value:

$$\frac{dm}{dx} = \frac{4}{L^2}(y_1 - 2y_2 + y_3) \quad (2\text{-}20)$$

At the endpoints P_1 and P_3, respectively, the slope has the following values:

$$m_1 = -\frac{3y_1 - 4y_2 + y_3}{L} \tag{2-21a}$$

$$m_3 = \frac{y_1 - 4y_2 + 3y_3}{L} \tag{2-21b}$$

The coordinates at the summit are as follows:

$$x_s = \frac{L}{4}\frac{3y_1 - 4y_2 + y_3}{y_1 - 2y_2 + y_3} \tag{2-22a}$$

$$y_s = -\frac{1}{8}\frac{(3y_1 - 4y_2 + y_3)^2}{y_1 - 2y_2 + y_3} + y_1 \tag{2-22b}$$

THREE

Analysis of Stress and Strain

3-1 Definitions   Consider that a force is applied to a straight member. If the action line of the force coincides with the longitudinal axis of the member, the force is said to be *axial* or *concentric*.   If the action line does not coincide with the longitudinal axis but is parallel thereto, the force is described as *eccentric*, and the perpendicular distance from the action line to the longitudinal axis is called the *eccentricity* of the force.

The force transmitted across a unit area is called the *stress*.   The stress on a given plane may be resolved into two components, one perpendicular to and the other parallel to the plane.   The former is called a *normal*, *direct*, or *axial* stress, and the latter is called a *shearing* stress.

A normal stress changes the dimensions of the body in which it is present.   The ratio of the change in a given dimension to the original dimension is termed the *strain*.   We shall refer to a strain caused by a given stress as a *direct* strain if it occurs in the same direction as the stress, and a *lateral* strain if it occurs in a direction perpendicular to that of the stress. The direct and lateral strains are of opposite character.   For example, when tensile forces are applied at the ends of a bar, there is an increase in the length of the bar and a reduction in the dimensions of the cross section.   The ratio of lateral to direct strain, in absolute value, is known as *Poisson's ratio.*

12

For most structural materials, the ratio of a normal stress to its accompanying direct strain is constant if the stress does not exceed a certain limiting value called the *proportional limit*. The stress-strain ratio is termed the *modulus of elasticity* of the material.

A shearing stress induces a slight rotation of the body in which it exists. Consider two lines in the body that were originally perpendicular to one another. The change in the angle between these lines caused by the shearing stress, measured in radians, is termed the *shearing strain*. The ratio of the shearing stress to its accompanying shearing strain is called the *modulus of rigidity* (or *shearing modulus of elasticity*) of the material.

3-2 Axially Loaded Members   Consider that axial forces are applied at the two ends of a straight prismatic member of homogeneous composition. We shall assume in the absence of any statement to the contrary that the induced stresses are below the proportional limit of the material. The notational system is as follows:

A = cross-sectional area of member
L = original length of member
ΔL = increase in length
P = axial force
s = normal stress on cross section
ϵ = direct strain = $\Delta L/L$
E = modulus of elasticity of material = s/ϵ

The following are the basic equations of axial stress and strain:

$$s = \frac{P}{A} \tag{3-1}$$

$$\Delta L = \frac{sL}{E} = \frac{PL}{AE} \tag{3-2}$$

3-3 Thermal Effects   If a body is free to expand or contract, its volume is modified by a variation in temperature. In the following material, we shall consider the change in size of the body in one direction only. Let

c = coefficient of thermal expansion of material
L = original length of body
ΔL = increase in length caused by increase in temperature
ΔT = increase in temperature

Then
$$\Delta L = cL\,\Delta T \tag{3-3}$$

Assume that a given member is prevented from undergoing its natural change in length corresponding to a change in temperature. Let ΔL_t and

ΔL_r denote the deformation caused by the temperature increase and the restraining forces, respectively, if each acted independently of the other. The restraining forces or the stresses they induce may be evaluated by superposing these deformations.

Example 3-1   A steel member 18 ft long is set snugly between two walls and then heated 80°F.   If each wall yields 0.015 in., what is the compressive stress in the member?   Use $c = 6.5 \times 10^{-6}$ per °F and $E = 30 \times 10^6$ psi.

Solution.   Let s denote the compressive stress. $\Delta L_t + \Delta L_r =$ expansion of member $= 2 \times 0.015 = 0.030$ in.   Equation (3-3) yields

$$\Delta L_t = 6.5 \times 10^{-6} \times 18 \times 12 \times 80 = 0.1123 \text{ in.}$$

Then $\Delta L_r = 0.030 - 0.1123 = -0.0823$ in.

Equation (3-2) yields

$$s = \frac{30 \times 10^6 \times 0.0823}{18 \times 12} = \textbf{11,430 psi}$$

3-4   Analysis of Stresses on Collinear Planes; Mohr's Circle

Consider a group of planes to be passed through a given line in a stressed body. Although the state of stress on each plane is unique, the various stresses are related to one another in accordance with certain basic laws, which we shall now develop.

A plane on which there is a normal stress but not a shearing stress is termed a *principal plane*, and the normal stress on this plane is called a *principal stress*.   We shall adopt the following sign convention:

A tensile stress is positive; a compressive stress is negative.

A shearing stress is positive if it tends to rotate the body on which it acts in a clockwise direction, and negative if it tends to rotate the body in a counterclockwise direction.

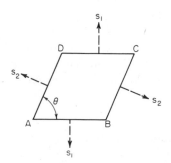

fig. 3-1   Assumed principal planes.

With reference to the body in Fig. 3-1, assume that AB and AD are principal planes subjected to the indicated stresses, where $s_1 \neq s_2$.   (The dashed vectors represent stresses in contrast to forces.)   It is apparent that the equation of equilibrium $\Sigma M = 0$ is satisfied only if $\theta = 90°$.   It therefore follows that the principal planes through a given line are mutually perpendicular.   A body is said to be in a state of *biaxial* or *triaxial stress* according to whether there are two or three principal planes through a given point in the body.   For the present, we shall confine our study to a biaxial-stress condition.

With reference to the body $ABCD$ in Fig. 3-2a, AB and AD are the principal planes through A.   We wish to evaluate the stresses on an oblique plane AE that makes an angle θ with the x axis, measured in a counterclockwise direction.   Let

s_x and s_y = normal stress on x and y axis, respectively, where $s_x > s_y$
s_n and s_s = normal stress and shearing stress, respectively, on plane AE

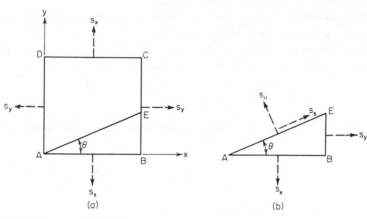

fig. 3-2   Stresses in body.

By analyzing ABE as a free body, we obtain the following results:

$$s_n = s_y + (s_x - s_y) \cos^2 \theta \tag{3-4a}$$

or

$$s_n = \frac{s_x + s_y}{2} + \frac{s_x - s_y}{2} \cos 2\theta \tag{3-4b}$$

$$s_s = \frac{s_x - s_y}{2} \sin 2\theta \tag{3-5}$$

These stresses may conveniently be represented by Mohr's circle of stress, which is constructed in the following manner: In Fig. 3-3, draw $OA = s_x$ and $OB = s_y$; locate C, the midpoint of AB.   Draw a circle having C as center and AC as radius.   Draw the radius CD making an

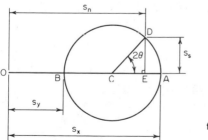

fig. 3-3   Mohr's circle of stress.

angle 2θ with the baseline, and drop the perpendicular DE. Then OE represents s_n and ED represents s_s.

The following conclusions stem from this analysis:

1. The principal planes through a given line are mutually perpendicular, as previously stated.

2. A principal stress is either the maximum or the minimum normal stress on the planes through a given line.

3. The shearing stresses on two mutually perpendicular planes are numerically equal but opposite in sign.

4. The maximum shearing stress occurs on the plane lying midway between the principal planes, and its value is

$$s_{s,\text{max}} = \frac{s_x - s_y}{2} \tag{3-6}$$

Example 3-2   With reference to Fig. 3-4a, find the normal and shearing stress on plane AE, and verify the results.

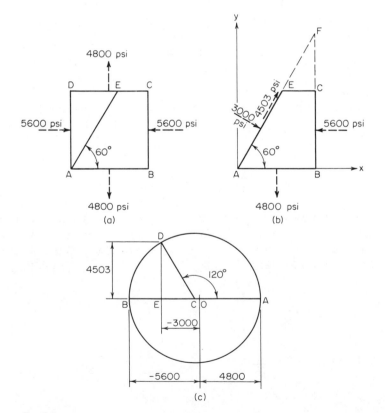

fig. 3-4

Solution

$$s_x = 4800 \text{ psi} \qquad s_y = -5600 \text{ psi} \qquad \theta = 60°$$

Applying Eqs. (3-4a) and (3-5), we have

$$s_n = -5600 + [4800 - (-5600)] \cos^2 60°$$
$$= -5600 + 10,400 \times 0.5^2 = -3000 \text{ psi}$$

$$s_s = \frac{4800 - (-5600)}{2} \sin 120° = 5200 \times 0.866 = 4503 \text{ psi}$$

The results may be verified in this manner: In Fig. 3-4b, let AF represent one unit of length. Then

$$AB = \cos 60° = 0.5 \qquad BF = \sin 60° = 0.866$$
$$\Sigma F_H = -5600 \times 0.866 + 3000 \times 0.866 + 4503 \times 0.5 = 0 \qquad \text{OK}$$

The Mohr's circle for this body is shown in Fig. 3-4c.

With reference to Fig. 3-5, let s_{n1} and s_{n2} denote the normal stresses on two mutually perpendicular planes, and let s_{s1} denote the shearing stress

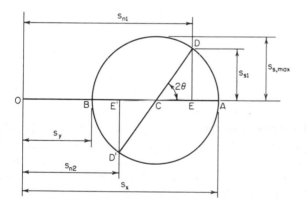

fig. 3-5 Determination of principal stresses and maximum shearing stress.

accompanying s_{n1}. From the geometry of the drawing, we obtain the following results:

$$s_{s,\text{max}} = \sqrt{\left(\frac{s_{n1} - s_{n2}}{2}\right)^2 + s_{s1}^2} \qquad (3\text{-}7)$$

$$s_x = \frac{s_{n1} + s_{n2}}{2} + s_{s,\text{max}} \qquad (3\text{-}8a)$$

$$s_y = \frac{s_{n1} + s_{n2}}{2} - s_{s,\text{max}} \qquad (3\text{-}8b)$$

$$\theta = \tfrac{1}{2} \arcsin \frac{s_{s1}}{s_{s,\text{max}}} \qquad (3\text{-}9)$$

FOUR

Pressure Vessels—
Torsion of Shafts

4-1 Thin-walled Cylinders and Spheres When a hollow body is subjected to an internal pressure directed radially outward, tension is induced in the shell of the body. The tensile stress at a given point acts normal to the radius of curvature of the shell at that point, and the stresses caused.by the internal pressure are accordingly designated as *hoop tension*. The existence of hoop tension is illustrated in Fig. 4-1a, which is a free-body diagram of a portion of a hollow cylindrical vessel. *F* denotes the resultant of the radial pressure on the body; this is balanced by the radial components of the hoop tension *T*. As shown in Fig. 4-1b, a cylindrical vessel with closed ends is also subjected to longitudinal tension.

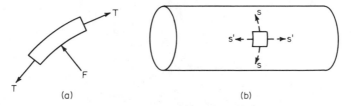

(a)   (b)

fig. 4-1 Tensile stresses in cylinder shell.

18

We shall confine our study to hollow cylinders and spheres. The notational system is as follows:

s = hoop stress
s' = normal stress in longitudinal direction in closed cylindrical vessel
p = radial pressure
D = internal diameter
ΔD = increase in diameter caused by radial pressure
t = thickness of shell
ν = Poisson's ratio

If the ratio t/D is less than about $\frac{1}{15}$, the vessel is described as *thin-walled*, and the stresses s and s' are assumed to be uniform across the shell. The following equations apply to a thin-walled, closed cylindrical vessel:

$$s = \frac{pD}{2t} \tag{4-1}$$

$$s' = \frac{pD}{4t} \tag{4-2}$$

$$\Delta D = \frac{D}{E}(s - \nu s') \tag{4-3a}$$

or $$\Delta D = \frac{pD^2}{2tE}\left(1 - \frac{\nu}{2}\right) \tag{4-3b}$$

The following equations apply to a thin-walled spherical vessel:

$$s = \frac{pD}{4t} \tag{4-4}$$

$$\Delta D = \frac{Ds}{E}(1 - \nu) \tag{4-5a}$$

or $$\Delta D = \frac{pD^2}{4tE}(1 - \nu) \tag{4-5b}$$

Example 4-1 A steel pipe 5 ft in diameter and $\frac{3}{8}$ in. thick sustains a fluid pressure of 200 psi. Calculate the hoop stress, the longitudinal stress, and the increase in diameter. Use $E = 30 \times 10^6$ psi and $\nu = 0.25$.

Solution

$$p = 200 \text{ psi} \qquad D = 60 \text{ in.} \qquad t = \frac{3}{8} \text{ in.}$$

Applying Eqs. (4-1), (4-2), and (4-3a), we obtain the following results:

$$s = \frac{200 \times 60}{2 \times \frac{3}{8}} = \textbf{16,000 psi} \qquad s' = \frac{1}{2}s = \textbf{8000 psi}$$

$$\Delta D = \frac{60(16,000 - 0.25 \times 8000)}{30 \times 10^6} = \textbf{0.0280 In.}$$

Example 4-2   A spherical vessel 7 ft in diameter and ½ in. thick sustains a fluid pressure of 240 psi.   Calculate the hoop stress and increase in diameter, using the same values as in Example 4-1.

Solution. Applying Eqs. (4-4) and (4-5a), we obtain the following results:

$$s = \frac{240 \times 84}{4 \times \frac{1}{2}} = 10{,}080 \text{ psi}$$

$$\Delta D = \frac{84 \times 10{,}080 \times 0.75}{30 \times 10^6} = 0.0212 \text{ in.}$$

4-2   Torsion of Shafts   The right cylindrical shaft shown in Fig. 4-2 has a fixed support at its left end and is free or floating at its right end.   If a

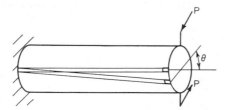

fig. 4-2   Deformation of cylindrical shaft due to torque.

twisting moment, or torque, is applied at the free end, each transverse section rotates slightly about the longitudinal axis, the angle of rotation varying uniformly from its maximum value at the free end to zero at the fixed end.   These unequal rotations engender shearing stresses, and the assumption is made that the shearing stress at a given point is directly proportional to the distance from that point to the longitudinal axis. The notational system is as follows:

T = torque
R = radius of cylinder
J = polar moment of inertia of transverse section with respect to longitudinal axis
L = length of shaft
G = modulus of rigidity
s_s = shearing stress at outermost fibers
θ = angle of twist at free end

Then
$$s_s = \frac{TR}{J} \tag{4-6}$$

$$\theta = \frac{TL}{JG} \tag{4-7}$$

For a hollow circular section having an external diameter D and internal diameter d

$$J = \frac{\pi}{32} (D^4 - d^4)$$

Then
$$s_s = \frac{16TD}{\pi(D^4 - d^4)} \qquad\qquad (4\text{-}6a)$$

Example 4-3 A torque of 8000 ft-lb is applied at the ends of a 14-ft cylindrical shaft having an external and internal diameter of 5 and 3 in., respectively. Calculate the maximum shearing stress and the angle of twist, using $G = 6 \times 10^6$ psi.

Solution

$$J = \frac{\pi}{32} (5^4 - 3^4) = 53.4 \text{ in.}^4$$

$$s_s = \frac{8000 \times 12 \times 2.5}{53.4} = \textbf{4500 psi}$$

$$\theta = \frac{8000 \times 12 \times 14 \times 12}{53.4 \times 6{,}000{,}000} = \textbf{0.050 radian}$$

$$= 0.050 \times 57.3 = 2.9°$$

FIVE
Stresses in Beams

The following analysis of beams is based upon these assumptions: the beam is composed of elastic material, and the bending stresses are always below the proportional limit. The method of structural design that evolves from these assumptions is known as *elastic* design.

5-1 Definitions A *beam* is a member that sustains forces whose action lines are normal to the longitudinal axis of the member. In the absence of any statement to the contrary, it is understood that the forces lie in an axis of symmetry of the transverse section; for convenience of terminology, it is assumed that the longitudinal axis is horizontal. These conditions are illustrated in Fig. 5-1.

There are two types of beam supports: simple and fixed. A *simple* support is one that merely prevents vertical displacement; a *fixed* support is one that prevents both linear displacement and rotation. The distance between supports is called the *span*.

A beam that rests on two simple supports is described as *simple*, or *simply supported*, and one that has two fixed supports is called a *fixed*, or *fixed-ended*, beam. A *cantilever* beam is one that has a fixed support at one end and is free or floating at the other end; a *propped-cantilever* beam is one that has a fixed support at one end and a simple support at the other end.   A beam that overhangs one or both supports is referred to as an *overhanging* beam.   A *continuous* beam is one having more than two supports.

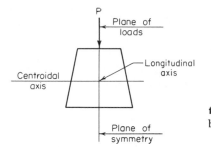

fig. 5-1   Transverse section of beam.

5-2 Vertical Shear and Bending Moment   In order to evaluate the stresses at a given section of the beam, we may remove the portion of the beam to the left of the section, provided we replace it with the resultant force and moment that this exerts on the right portion.   It is therefore advantageous to introduce the concepts of vertical shear and bending moment.

The *vertical shear V* at a given section is the algebraic sum of all vertical forces to the left of the section, an upward force being considered positive.

The *bending moment M* at a given section is the algebraic sum of the moments of all forces to the left of the section with respect to that section, a clockwise moment being considered positive.

Assume that the beam carries a distributed load.   Let w denote the load intensity at a given section, a downward load being considered positive.   Let x denote the distance from the left end of the beam to a given section.   By considering a portion of the span of length dx as a free body, we arrive at the following equations for the rate of change in vertical shear and bending moment:

$$\frac{dV}{dx} = -w \qquad (5\text{-}1)$$

$$\frac{dM}{dx} = V \qquad (5\text{-}2)$$

Let a and b denote the boundary sections of an interval of the span; let M_a and M_b denote the bending moment at the indicated section.   As a consequence of Eq. (5-2), we have

$$M_b - M_a = \int_a^b V \, dx \qquad (5\text{-}3)$$

It also follows from Eq. (5-2) that the bending moment has a local maximum or minimum value where the shear is zero or passes through zero in an abrupt reversal of sign.

Example 5-1 Construct the shear and bending-moment diagrams for the beam in Fig. 5-2, and indicate the values of shear and bending moments at all significant sections.

   Solution. To compute the reactions, it is necessary to replace the distributed load on each interval of the span with its equivalent concentrated load.   Where the load is uniformly distributed, this equivalent load acts at the center of the interval.

$$W_{AB} = 2 \times 4 = 8 \text{ kips} \qquad W_{BC} = 2 \times 6 = 12 \text{ kips} \qquad W_{AC} = 8 + 12 = 20 \text{ kips}$$
$$W_{CD} = 3 \times 15 = 45 \text{ kips} \qquad W_{DE} = 1.4 \times 5 = 7 \text{ kips}$$

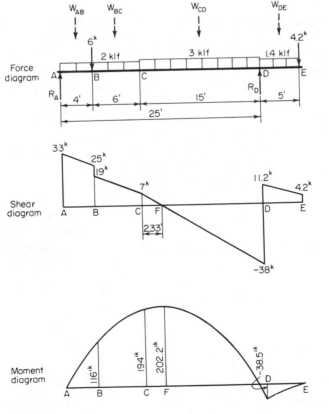

fig. 5-2

By taking moments of all forces about either support, we secure an equation containing only one unknown quantity. Subscripts are used to identify the moment center.

$$\Sigma M_D = 25R_A - 6 \times 21 - 20 \times 20 - 45 \times 7.5 + 7 \times 2.5 + 4.2 \times 5 = 0$$
$$\Sigma M_A = 6 \times 4 + 20 \times 5 + 45 \times 17.5 + 7 \times 27.5 + 4.2 \times 30 - 25R_D = 0$$

Solving, $\qquad R_A = 33$ kips $\qquad R_D = 49.2$ kips

$$\Sigma F_V = 33 + 49.2 - 8 - 12 - 45 - 7 - 6 - 4.2 = 0 \qquad \text{OK}$$

We shall determine the shear at every significant section, or directly to the left and right of that section if a concentrated load is present.

V_A at right $= 33$ kips
V_B at left $= 33 - 8 = 25$ kips
V_B at right $= 25 - 6 = 19$ kips
$V_C = 19 - 12 = 7$ kips
V_D at left $= 7 - 45 = -38$ kips
V_D at right $= -38 + 49.2 = 11.2$ kips
V_E at left $= 11.2 - 7 = 4.2$ kips
V_E at right $= 4.2 - 4.2 = 0$

The points representing these values are plotted in the shear diagram. Since the shear diminishes at a uniform rate between the significant sections, the shear diagram is rectilinear.

We shall compute the bending moment at every significant section by summing the moments of the forces to the left of the section.

$$M_A = 0$$
$$M_B = 33 \times 4 - 8 \times 2 = 116 \text{ ft-kips}$$
$$M_C = 33 \times 10 - 8 \times 8 - 6 \times 6 - 12 \times 3 = 194 \text{ ft-kips}$$

Similarly, $\qquad M_D = -38.5$ ft-kips $\qquad M_E = 0$

The points representing these values are plotted in the bending-moment diagram. In accordance with Eq. (5-2), the moment changes at a uniformly varying rate between the significant sections, and the diagram therefore consists of a series of parabolic arcs. The maximum moment occurs at F, where the shear is zero.

$$CF = \tfrac{7}{3} = 2.33 \text{ kips} \qquad M_F = 202.2 \text{ ft-kips}$$

We shall now compute the bending moment at the significant sections by an alternative method. Equation (5-3) may be written in this form:

$$M_b - M_a = \text{area under shear diagram in interval } ab$$

By summing the areas under the shear diagram, we obtain the following results:

$$M_A = 0$$
$$M_B = M_A + \tfrac{1}{2} \times 4(33 + 25) = 116 \text{ ft-kips}$$
$$M_C = 116 + \tfrac{1}{2} \times 6(19 + 7) = 194 \text{ ft-kips}$$
$$M_D = 194 + \tfrac{1}{2} \times 15(7 - 38) = -38.5 \text{ ft-kips}$$
$$M_E = -38.5 + \tfrac{1}{2} \times 5(11.2 + 4.2) = 0$$
$$M_F = 194 + \tfrac{1}{2} \times 2.33 \times 7 = 202.2 \text{ ft-kips}$$

5-3 Bending Stresses   The bending moments in a beam cause each transverse section to rotate about an axis that is normal to the plane of the loads, compressing the longitudinal fibers on one side of this axis and distending those on the other side.   The axis of rotation is referred to as the *neutral axis*.   If the beam is homogeneous, the neutral axis coincides with the centroidal axis of the section.

The normal stress in a fiber caused by the bending moment is termed the *bending, flexural,* or *fiber* stress.   We wish to evaluate the bending stress in a given fiber at a given section.   The notational system is as follows:

y = distance from neutral axis to given fiber
f = bending stress in this fiber at given section
c = distance from neutral axis to outermost fiber
I = moment of inertia of transverse section with respect to its centroidal axis
S = section modulus = I/c
M = bending moment at given section
V = vertical shear at given section
x = distance from left end of beam to given section

The strain of the given fiber is directly proportional to y.   Since we are assuming that stress is directly proportional to strain, it follows that the bending stress is also directly proportional to y.   Its value is

$$f = \frac{My}{I} \tag{5-4}$$

If the bending moment is positive, the fibers above the neutral axis are in compression and those below are in tension.   At the given section, the maximum numerical value of bending stress is

$$f_{\max} = \frac{Mc}{I} = \frac{M}{S} \tag{5-5}$$

By differentiating Eq. (5-4) with respect to x and applying Eq. (5-2), we obtain the following equation for the rate of increase in bending stress with respect to distance along the span:

$$\frac{df}{dx} = \frac{Vy}{I} \tag{5-6}$$

Example 5-2   A simply supported beam having the trapezoidal cross section shown in Fig. 5-3*a* carries the loads indicated in 5-3*b*.   What is the maximum bending stress at the top and at the bottom of this member?

Solution. Taking moments about the right support, we obtain

$$\Sigma M_R = 10R_L - 500 \times 10 \times 5 - 1600 \times 2.5 = 0 \qquad R_L = 2900 \text{ lb}$$

The maximum bending moment occurs at the section A of zero shear.

$$V_A = 2900 - 500x = 0 \qquad x = 5.8 \text{ ft}$$
$$M_A = \tfrac{1}{2} \times 2900 \times 5.8 = 8410 \text{ ft-lb} = 100{,}900 \text{ in.-lb}$$

The properties of a trapezoidal area are presented on page 6-25 of the AISC Manual.

$$y_t = \frac{9}{3}\frac{2 \times 6 + 3}{6 + 3} = 5 \text{ in.} \qquad y_b = 4 \text{ in.}$$

$$I = \frac{9^3}{36}\frac{6^2 + 4 \times 6 \times 3 + 3^2}{6 + 3} = 263.3 \text{ in.}^4$$

$$f_{\text{top}} = \frac{100{,}900 \times 5}{263.3} = \textbf{1916 psi compression}$$

$$f_{\text{bottom}} = \frac{100{,}900 \times 4}{263.3} = \textbf{1533 psi tension}$$

A structural member generally carries both permanent and transient loads. The former are referred to as *dead* loads and the latter as *live* loads. For example, consider the case of a steel beam supporting a roof. With respect to this member, the weight of the beam and the weight of the roof construction are dead loads; the weight of the snow is a live load.

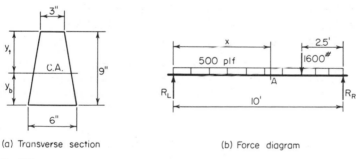

(a) Transverse section   (b) Force diagram

fig. 5-3

5-4 Composite Beams   In computing the stresses in a composite beam, it is expedient to replace the given beam with a homogeneous beam that is equivalent to the given one with respect to flexure. This equivalent homogeneous beam is termed a *transformed beam*, and its cross section is referred to as a *transformed section*.

Consider the timber beam in Fig. 5-4a, which is reinforced with steel side plates.   Let E_s and E_t denote the modulus of elasticity of steel and timber, respectively, and n the modular ratio E_s/E_t.   At any line parallel to the neutral axis, the stress f_s in a steel fiber is n times the stress f_t in a timber fiber, since the fibers have equal strains.   To secure the transformed section, we shall replace each steel fiber of area dA_s with a timber fiber of area dA_t at the same distance from the neutral axis.   Let dF

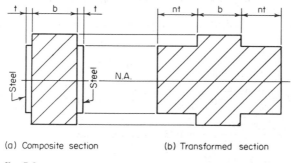

(a) Composite section   (b) Transformed section

fig. 5-4

denote the axial force in the fiber resulting from bending.   Since dF remains constant during the transformation, we have

$$dF = f_t \, dA_t = f_s \, dA_s = nf_t \, dA_s$$
$$\therefore \ dA_t = n \, dA_s \tag{5-7}$$

The transformed section is shown in Fig. 5-4b.

Each material in a composite beam has its particular allowable stress, and it is therefore necessary to determine which of the two allowable stresses limits the capacity of the member.

Example 5-3   An 8 × 12 in. timber beam (exact size) is reinforced by the addition of a 7 × ½ in. steel plate at the top and a 7-in. 9.8-lb steel channel at the bottom, as shown in Fig. 5-5a.   The moduli of elasticity and allowable bending stresses have the following values:

$$E_s = 30 \times 10^6 \text{ psi} \qquad E_t = 1.2 \times 10^6 \text{ psi}$$
$$f_s = 22{,}000 \text{ psi} \qquad f_t = 1200 \text{ psi}$$

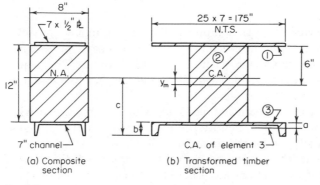

(a) Composite
     section

(b) Transformed timber
     section

fig. 5-5

How does the flexural strength of the reinforced beam compare with that of the original timber beam? Disregard shearing stresses.

Solution. Let M_1 and M_2 denote the allowable bending moment in the original and the reinforced beam, respectively. The transformed section, which is shown in Fig. 5-5b, is resolved into its three elements.

$$n = \frac{30}{1.2} = 25$$

ELEMENT 1

$$A = 25 \times 7 \times \tfrac{1}{2} = 87.5 \text{ sq in.} \qquad I_o \text{ negligible}$$

ELEMENT 2

$$A = 8 \times 12 = 96 \text{ sq in.}$$
$$I_o = \tfrac{1}{12} \times 8 \times 12^3 = 1152 \text{ in.}^4$$

ELEMENT 3. (Refer to AISC Manual, pages 1-26, 1-27.)

$$A = 25 \times 2.85 = 71.25 \text{ sq in.}$$
$$I_o = 25 \times 0.98 = 25 \text{ in.}^4$$
$$a = 0.55 \text{ in.} \qquad b = 2.09 \text{ in.}$$

To locate the centroidal axis of the transformed section, we shall compute the statical moment of the area with respect to the centerline of element 2 and apply Eq. (2-10):

$$y_m = \frac{87.5 \times 6.25 - 71.25 \times 6.55}{87.5 + 96 + 71.25} = 0.31 \text{ in.}$$

By Eq. (2-11), the moment of inertia of the transformed section is as follows:

$$I = 1152 + 25 + 87.5(6.25 - 0.31)^2 + 96 \times 0.31^2$$
$$+ 71.25(6.55 + 0.31)^2 = 7626 \text{ in.}^4$$
$$c = 0.31 + 6 + 2.09 = 8.40 \text{ in.}$$

We must now identify the material in the composite beam that first reaches its allowable stress as the load on the member is gradually increased. Assume that the steel is stressed to its allowable value; the corresponding stress in the transformed beam is as follows:

$$f = \frac{22,000}{25} = 880 < 1200 \text{ psi}$$

In the actual beam, the maximum timber stress, which occurs at the back of channel, is even less than 880 psi. The capacity of the member is therefore governed by the steel rather than the timber.

$$M_1 = \frac{fI}{c} = \frac{1200 \times 1152}{6} = 230,000 \text{ in.-lb}$$

$$M_2 = \frac{880 \times 7626}{8.40} = 799,000 \text{ in.-lb}$$

$$\frac{M_2}{M_1} = \frac{799,000}{230,000} = \textbf{3.47}$$

5-5   Shearing Stresses   With reference to the beam in Fig. 5-6*a*, consider that we extract the element bounded by planes *a*, *b*, and *c*, where *c* lies above the neutral plane.   The free-body diagram of this element appears in Fig. 5-6*b*.   Let C_a and C_b represent the resultants of the bend-

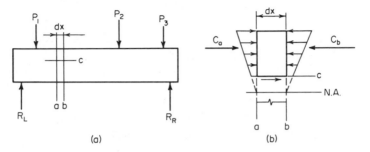

fig. 5-6   Horizontal shear in beam.

ing stresses on the boundary sections.   Since the bending moment at *b* exceeds that at *a*, C_b exceeds C_a.   We therefore conclude that a horizontal shearing force is present on plane *c*.   If planes *a* and *b* are a unit distance apart, this force on *c* is termed the longitudinal *shear flow*.

Assume that the vertical shear remains constant across this element and that the shearing stress is uniform across the width of the section.   Let

q = shear flow on *c*
v = shearing stress on *c*
V = vertical shear at *a*
Q = statical moment of cross-sectional area above *c* with respect to centroidal axis of section
I = moment of inertia of section with respect to its centroidal axis
t = thickness of section at *c*

By applying Eq. (5-6), we obtain

$$q = \frac{VQ}{I} \tag{5-8}$$

Then
$$v = \frac{VQ}{It} \tag{5-9}$$

As demonstrated in Art. 3-4, the shearing stresses on two mutually perpendicular planes are numerically equal.   It therefore follows that *v* also represents the vertical shearing stress at the intersection of planes *a* and *c*.

Example 5-4 A timber beam was formed by securely bolting a 3 × 6 in. member to a 6 × 8 in. member (exact size), as shown in Fig. 5-7. If the beam carries a uniform load of 600 plf on a simple span of 13 ft, calculate the longitudinal shear flow and the shearing stress at the juncture of the two elements at a section 3 ft from the support.

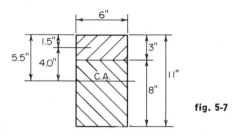

fig. 5-7

Solution

$$V = 600(\tfrac{1}{2} \times 13 - 3) = 2100 \text{ lb}$$
$$I = \tfrac{1}{12}bd^3 = \tfrac{1}{12} \times 6 \times 11^3 = 666 \text{ in.}^4$$
$$Q = Ay = 3 \times 6 \times 4 = 72 \text{ in.}^3$$
$$q = \frac{VQ}{I} = \frac{2100 \times 72}{666} = 227 \text{ pli}$$

$$v = \frac{q}{t} = \frac{227}{6} = 38 \text{ psi}$$

5-6 Combined Bending and Axial Loads Many structural members are subjected simultaneously to axial loads and loads that induce bending. If the deformation of the member in bending is relatively small, we may superpose the effects of these two sets of loads.

Consider the special case of a member of rectangular cross section supporting an eccentric longitudinal load P. Let x and y denote the centroidal axes parallel to the sides of the rectangle. We shall assume that the member is capable of resisting both tensile and compressive stresses. The stress at a given corner may be obtained by applying the following equation:

$$f = \frac{P}{A}\left(1 \pm \frac{6e_x}{d_x} \pm \frac{6e_y}{d_y}\right) \tag{5-10}$$

where e_x and e_y = eccentricity of load with respect to x and y axes, respectively

d_x and d_y = side of rectangle normal to x and y axes, respectively

Example 5-5   A post having the cross section shown in Fig. 5-8 carries a concentrated longitudinal load of 100 kips applied at R.   Calculate the stress induced at each corner.

Solution. We shall consider a compressive stress to be positive and a tensile stress to be negative.

METHOD 1. The eccentric load may be replaced with an equivalent system comprising a concentric load of 100 kips and two couples having the following moments

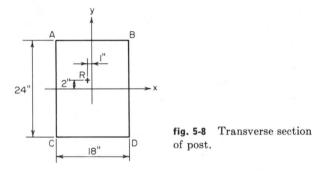

fig. 5-8   Transverse section of post.

with respect to the coordinate axes:

$$M_x = 100,000 \times 2 = 200,000 \text{ in.-lb}$$
$$M_y = 100,000 \times 1 = 100,000 \text{ in.-lb}$$

The section moduli are as follows:

$$S_x = \tfrac{1}{6}bd^2 = \tfrac{1}{6} \times 18 \times 24^2 = 1728 \text{ in.}^3$$
$$S_y = \tfrac{1}{6} \times 24 \times 18^2 = 1296 \text{ in.}^3$$

The stresses due to axial load and flexure are as follows:

$$f_1 = \frac{P}{A} = \frac{100,000}{18 \times 24} = 231 \text{ psi}$$

$$f_x = \frac{M_x}{S_x} = \frac{200,000}{1728} = 116 \text{ psi}$$

$$f_y = \frac{M_y}{S_y} = \frac{100,000}{1296} = 77 \text{ psi}$$

The stresses at the corners are as follows:

$$f_A = 231 + 116 + 77 = \mathbf{424 \text{ psi}}$$
$$f_B = 231 + 116 - 77 = \mathbf{270 \text{ psi}}$$
$$f_C = 231 - 116 + 77 = \mathbf{192 \text{ psi}}$$
$$f_D = 231 - 116 - 77 = \mathbf{38 \text{ psi}}$$

These stresses are all compressive.

METHOD 2. This problem lends itself to solution by Eq. (5-10).

$$\frac{6e_x}{d_x} = \frac{6 \times 2}{24} = 0.5 \qquad \frac{6e_y}{d_y} = \frac{6 \times 1}{18} = 0.33$$

$$f_A = 231(1 + 0.5 + 0.33) = 231 \times 1.83 = 424 \text{ psi}$$
$$f_B = 231(1 + 0.5 - 0.33) = 231 \times 1.17 = 270 \text{ psi}$$
$$f_C = 231(1 - 0.5 + 0.33) = 231 \times 0.83 = 192 \text{ psi}$$
$$f_D = 231(1 - 0.5 - 0.33) = 231 \times 0.17 = 38 \text{ psi}$$

As an aid in the stress analysis of an eccentrically loaded post, it is convenient to establish the *kern* of the transverse section. This is the central region within which the load may be applied without causing tension anywhere in the member. For a rectangular section, the boundaries of the kern may be located by the following method: In Fig. 5-9, let J denote

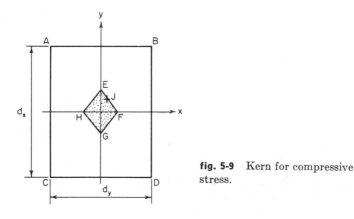

fig. 5-9 Kern for compressive stress.

a point having the characteristic that when a load P is applied at this point the stress at the most distant corner C is zero. Let x and y denote the coordinates of J. In accordance with Eq. (5-10),

$$f = \frac{P}{A}\left(1 - \frac{6y}{d_x} - \frac{6x}{d_y}\right) = 0$$

Then

$$y = \frac{d_x}{6} - \frac{d_x}{d_y} x$$

This is the equation of the straight line EF, which intersects the centroidal axes at $y = d_x/6$ and $x = d_y/6$. The kern of the section is the shaded area $EFGH$, where

$$EG = \tfrac{1}{3}d_x \qquad \text{and} \qquad HF = \tfrac{1}{3}d_y$$

SIX

Deflection of Beams

6-1 Introduction When loads are applied to a beam, the longitudinal axis is bent into a curve called the *elastic curve*. It is frequently necessary to establish the properties of this curve.

The notational system is as follows:

θ = slope of elastic curve at given section
y = deflection of elastic curve at given section
x = distance from left end of beam to given section
E = modulus of elasticity of material
I = moment of inertia of cross section with respect to its centroidal axis
M = bending moment at given section

Assuming that the longitudinal axis of the beam is initially horizontal, we shall consider a downward deflection to be positive; θ is therefore positive if the beam slopes downward to the right.

When the bending moment at a given section is positive, the fibers above the neutral axis are in compression and those below are in tension. Consequently, the elastic curve at this section is concave upward; i.e., the center of curvature lies above the curve. The reverse is true when the bending moment is negative.

The elastic curve of a beam may be investigated by a variety of methods, and it will usually be found that there is one particular method that is simplest to apply in a given situation. In all instances, we shall assume that the bending stresses are below the proportional limit.

In the examples that follow, it is to be understood that the beam is prismatic. The elastic curve is drawn in hyperbolic fashion to accentuate its characteristics.

6-2 Double-integration Method By analyzing the geometry of an element of the beam of length dx, we arrive at this result:

$$EI \frac{d\theta}{dx} = -M \tag{6-1}$$

But

$$\theta = \frac{dy}{dx}$$

$$\therefore EI \frac{d^2y}{dx^2} = -M \tag{6-2}$$

Example 6-1 The simply supported beam in Fig. 6-1 is subjected to a counterclockwise moment N applied at the right support. Determine the slope of the elastic curve at each support and the maximum deflection of the beam.

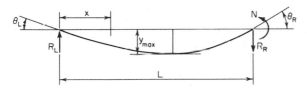

fig. 6-1 Deflection of simple beam under end moment.

Solution

$$R_L = \frac{N}{L} \qquad M = \frac{Nx}{L}$$

$$EI \frac{d^2y}{dx^2} = -M = -\frac{Nx}{L}$$

Integrating twice, we obtain the following results, in which c_1 and c_2 denote the constants of integration.

$$EI \frac{dy}{dx} = EI\theta = -\frac{Nx^2}{2L} + c_1$$

$$EIy = -\frac{Nx^3}{6L} + c_1x + c_2$$

The constants of integration are evaluated by applying the following boundary conditions:

$$\text{When } x = 0, y = 0 \qquad \therefore c_2 = 0$$

$$\text{When } x = L, y = 0 \qquad \therefore c_1 = \frac{NL}{6}$$

The substitution of these values yields

$$\theta = \frac{N}{6EIL}(L^2 - 3x^2) \qquad y = \frac{Nx}{6EIL}(L^2 - x^2)$$

Setting $x = 0$ and $x = L$, we obtain

$$\theta_L = \frac{NL}{6EI} \qquad \theta_R = -\frac{NL}{3EI}$$

The section of maximum deflection is located by setting $\theta = 0$. Then

$$L^2 - 3x^2 = 0 \qquad x = \frac{L}{\sqrt{3}}$$

When this value of x is substituted, the result is

$$y_{\text{max}} = \frac{NL^2}{9\sqrt{3}\,EI}$$

6-3   Moment-area Method   Let A and B denote two points on the elastic curve of a beam. By applying Eq. (6-1), we arrive at the following theorems:

1. The difference between the slope at A and the slope at B is numerically equal to the area of the M/EI diagram within the interval AB.

2. The vertical distance from A to the tangent to the elastic curve through B is numerically equal to the statical moment of the area of the M/EI diagram within the interval AB with respect to A. (This vertical distance is referred to as the *tangential deviation*.)

Example 6-2 Solve Example 6-1 by applying the moment-area method.
   Solution. Refer to Fig. 6-2.

$$t_1 = \text{moment of } \triangle ABC \text{ about } B$$

$$= \frac{NL}{2EI}\frac{L}{3} = \frac{NL^2}{6EI}$$

$$\theta_L = \frac{t_1}{L} = \frac{NL}{6EI}$$

The value of θ_R is found in a similar manner.

Let x denote the horizontal distance from A to the point E' where $\theta = 0$.

$$\text{Area } \triangle AED = \text{area } \triangle ABC \left(\frac{x}{L}\right)^2 = \frac{Nx^2}{2EIL}$$

$$\theta_E = \theta_L - \text{area } \triangle AED = \frac{NL}{6EI} - \frac{Nx^2}{2EIL} = 0$$

Solving,

$$x = \frac{L}{\sqrt{3}}$$

$$\text{Area } \triangle AED = \theta_L = \frac{NL}{6EI}$$

$$y_{\max} = t_2 = \frac{NL}{6EI}\frac{2x}{3} = \frac{NL}{6EI}\frac{2L}{3\sqrt{3}} = \frac{NL^2}{9\sqrt{3}\,EI}$$

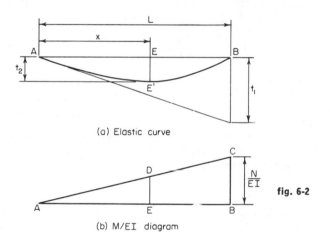

(a) Elastic curve

(b) M/EI diagram

fig. 6-2

6-4 Unit-load Method   With reference to Fig. 6-3, the solid vectors represent the true loads that are to be supported by the beam and the

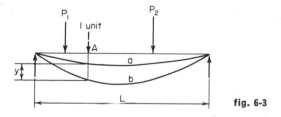

fig. 6-3

dashed vector represents an imaginary unit load that is introduced to enable us to calculate the deflection at A.   Consider that the unit load is applied first, causing the elastic curve to assume the position a.   While this load is present, the true loads are applied, causing the elastic curve to assume the position b.   The indicated distance y equals the deflection that would occur at A if the true loads alone were present.

With respect to any section along the span, let

M = bending moment induced by true loads
m = bending moment induced by unit load

The deflection y may be found by equating the work performed by the unit load during the application of the true loads to the increase in strain energy of the beam caused by the presence of the unit load.   The result is as follows:

$$y = \int_0^L \frac{Mm}{EI}\, dx \tag{6-3a}$$

Similarly, if we apply a unit moment at A, we obtain the following equation for the slope of the elastic curve at A caused by the true loads:

$$\theta = \int_0^L \frac{Mm}{EI}\, dx \tag{6-3b}$$

where m is the bending moment induced by the unit moment.

The foregoing results suggest that the elastic curve of a beam may be investigated by introducing imaginary unit loads and unit moments.

Example 6-3   The cantilever beam in Fig. 6-4a carries a load that varies uniformly from w plf at the free end to zero at the fixed end.   Determine the slope and deflection of the elastic curve at the free end.

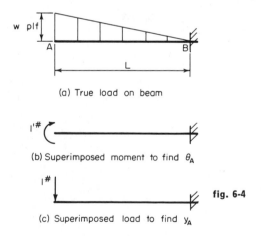

(a) True load on beam

(b) Superimposed moment to find θ_A

fig. 6-4

(c) Superimposed load to find y_A

Solution. Let w_x denote the load intensity at a section at a distance x from A. By proportion,

$$w_x = w\,\frac{L - x}{L}$$

$$M = -\frac{x^2}{6}(2w + w_x) = -\frac{wx^2}{6}\left(2 + \frac{L - x}{L}\right)$$

$$= -\frac{wx^2(3L - x)}{6L}$$

Apply a unit clockwise moment at A, as shown in Fig. 6-4b. Then

$$m = 1$$

Applying Eq. (6-3b),

$$EI\theta_A = -\int_0^L \frac{wx^2(3L - x)}{6L}\,dx = -\frac{w}{6L}\int_0^L (3Lx^2 - x^3)\,dx$$

$$= -\frac{w}{6L}\left(\frac{3Lx^3}{3} - \frac{x^4}{4}\right)\Big]_0^L = -\frac{w}{6L}\left(L^4 - \frac{L^4}{4}\right)$$

$$\theta_A = -\frac{1}{8}\frac{wL^3}{EI}$$

Now apply a unit downward load at A, as shown in Fig. 6-4c. Then

$$m = -x$$

Applying Eq. (6-3a),

$$EIy_A = \int_0^L \frac{wx^3(3L - x)}{6L}\,dx = \frac{w}{6L}\int_0^L x^3(3L - x)\,dx$$

$$y_A = \frac{11}{120}\frac{wL^4}{EI}$$

6-5   Maxwell's Theorem of Reciprocal Deflections   Assume that unit loads are applied to a given beam at two points, designated A and B. With respect to any section along the span, let

m_A = bending moment induced by unit load at A

m_B = bending moment induced by unit load at B

In accordance with Eq. (6-3a), the deflection at A caused by a load P applied at B is

$$y_A = \int_0^L \frac{Pm_Bm_A}{EI}\,dx = P\int_0^L \frac{m_Am_B}{EI}\,dx$$

Similarly, the deflection at B caused by a load P applied at A is

$$y_B = \int_0^L \frac{Pm_Am_B}{EI}\,dx = P\int_0^L \frac{m_Am_B}{EI}\,dx$$

Thus, the deflection at A caused by a load P applied at B equals the deflection at B caused by a load P applied at A. This analysis illustrates a general relationship known as the *theorem of reciprocal deflections*. In many instances, the investigation of the deformation of a structure may be simplified considerably by applying this theorem.

SEVEN
Framed Structures

7-1 Introduction   A *truss* is a frame composed of members arranged in the form of contiguous triangles, as illustrated in Fig. 7-1.   It is assumed

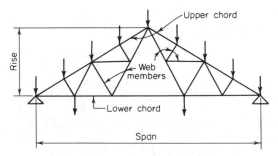

fig. 7-1   Fink truss.

in theory that each member terminates at a joint, that all joints are flexible, and that the external forces are applied solely at the joints.

As a consequence of these assumptions, every member in a truss is subjected solely to a force applied at each end.   The equations of equilibrium require that these forces lie on the longitudinal axis of the member and that they be equal in magnitude but oppositely sensed. Thus, a truss member resists axial forces but not flexure. Since the assumed conditions never exist in reality, bending stresses are invariably present. However, they are usually of secondary importance.

The sign convention is as follows: A tensile force is positive, a compressive force is negative.

7-2 Truss Analysis by Graphical Methods   Graphical analysis is a simple, rapid, and reasonably accurate method of determining the internal forces of a truss. It consists of constructing the force polygon at every joint, the polygons being juxtaposed so that every internal vector forms the side of two adjacent polygons. In this manner, the duplication of lines is obviated entirely, and we obtain a composite force polygon for the truss itself.

Example 7-1   With reference to the cantilever truss in Fig. 7-2a, apply graphical analysis to evaluate the forces induced in the truss members.

Solution.   The joints are assigned the indicated numbers. In accordance with Bow's notation, every region bounded by either external or internal forces is assigned an uppercase letter, and the forces and their corresponding members are designated by the regions they delimit. For example, the lower-chord member at the extreme right is FP, and the load at joint 4 is BC. In the force polygon, however, the forces are represented by the corresponding lowercase letters.

Resolve the reactions R_U and R_L into their horizontal and vertical components. Taking moments with respect to joint 8, we have

$$\Sigma M_8 = 12R_{UH} - 3(8 + 16 + 24) - 5(6 + 12 + 18) = 0$$
$$R_{UH} = 27 \text{ kips to right}$$

Since R_U is collinear with the force DE,

$$\frac{R_{UV}}{R_{UH}} = \frac{12}{24} \qquad \therefore R_{UV} = 13.5 \text{ kips up}$$

$$R_U = 30.2 \text{ kips}$$

Applying the equations of equilibrium to the truss, we obtain

$$R_{LH} = 27 \text{ kips to left} \qquad R_{LV} = 10.5 \text{ kips up}$$
$$R_L = 29.0 \text{ kips}$$

In Fig. 7-2b, construct the polygon of external forces in this manner: Using a suitable scale, draw vector fg to represent force FG; draw vector gh to represent force GH; etc. (Omit the arrowheads.) The polygon should close. The forces are taken in the order in which they appear as we proceed around the truss in a clockwise direction.

Starting at joint 1, where there are two unknown forces, draw a line through a in the force polygon parallel to member AJ in the truss, and one through h parallel to member HJ, these lines intersecting at j. Triangle haj is the force polygon for joint 1. Vector aj represents the force in AJ, and vector hj represents the force in HJ.

Proceed to joint 2, where there are now only two unknown forces (BK and JK). Draw a line through b in the force polygon parallel to BK, and one through j

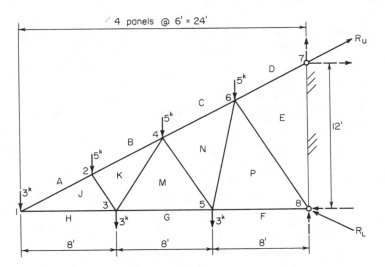

(a) Truss diagram

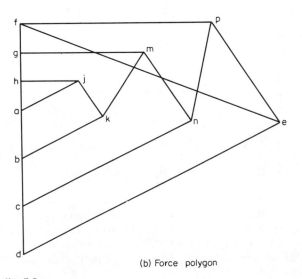

(b) Force polygon

fig. 7-2

parallel to *JK*, these lines intersecting at *k*. Quadrilateral *abjk* is the force polygon for joint 2, and the forces *BK* and *JK* are thus determined.

Proceed to joints 3, 4, 5, and 6, in that order, and complete the force polygon by continuing this process. If the construction has been accurately performed, it will be found that *pe* in the force polygon is parallel to member *PE*. Scale the vector lengths to obtain the magnitude of the internal forces. The results are recorded in Table 7-1.

Table 7-1　Forces in Truss Members (Fig. 7-2)

Member	Force, kips
AJ	+6.7
BK	+9.5
CN	+19.8
DE	+30.2
HJ	−6.0
GM	−13.0
FP	−20.0
JK	−4.5
KM	+8.1
MN	−8.6
NP	+10.4
PE	−12.6

The character of the internal forces (tension or compression) is established in this manner: Selecting a particular joint, proceed around the joint in a clockwise direction, listing the letters in the order in which they appear. Then refer to the force polygon pertaining to that joint, and proceed along the polygon in the same order. This procedure reveals the direction in which each force at that joint is acting.

For example, proceeding around joint 4 in the prescribed manner, we obtain *CNMKB*. Tracing a path along the force polygon in the order in which these letters appear, we find that force *CN* is acting upward to the right, *NM* is acting upward to the left, and *MK* and *KB* are acting downward to the left. Therefore, *CN*, *MK*, and *KB* are directed away from the joint; this condition discloses that they are tensile forces. *NM* is directed toward the joint, and it is therefore compressive.

The validity of the foregoing procedure for finding the character of the internal forces lies in the fact that the external-force polygon is drawn by proceeding around the truss in a clockwise direction.

7-3　Method of Joints　　The internal forces of a truss may be determined analytically by two distinct methods: the method of joints and the method of sections.   The former consists of applying the equations of equilibrium to all truss joints in succession.

Example 7-2   Applying the method of joints, determine the forces in the truss in Fig. 7-3a.   The inclined load at joint 4 has a horizontal component of 4 kips and a vertical component of 3 kips.

  Solution. The data are recorded in Table 7-2 as they are computed.   Each internal force will be resolved into its horizontal and vertical components, with a subscript to identify each.   The ratio of the vertical to the horizontal component of a force equals the slope of the member, which is recorded in the second column of this table.   The unknown forces will be assumed to be directed away from their joints.   Hence, if a computed value is positive, the truss member is in tension; otherwise it is in compression.

$$R_{LV} = 19 \text{ kips} \qquad R_{LH} = 4 \text{ kips} \qquad R_R = 21 \text{ kips}$$

JOINT 1. The free-body diagram appears in Fig. 7-3b.

$$\Sigma F_H = 4.0 + AJ_H + HJ = 0 \qquad\qquad (a)$$
$$\Sigma F_V = 19.0 + AJ_V = 0$$
$$\therefore AJ_V = -19.0 \text{ kips} \qquad AJ_H = -\frac{19.0}{0.75} = -25.3 \text{ kips}$$

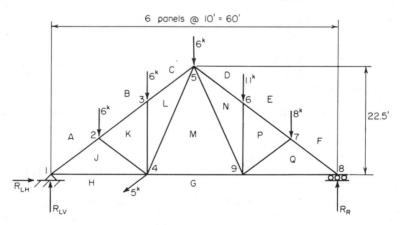

(a) Truss diagram

(b) Free-body diagram
of joint I

(c) Free-body diagram
of joint 2

fig. 7-3

Table 7-2   Forces in Truss Members (Fig. 7-3)

Member	Slope	Horizontal component	Vertical component	Force, kips
AJ	0.75	25.3	19.0	-31.7
BK	0.75	21.3	16.0	-26.7
CL	0.75	21.3	16.0	-26.7
DN	0.75	22.7	17.0	-28.3
EP	0.75	22.7	17.0	-28.3
FQ	0.75	28.0	21.0	-35.0
HJ	0	21.3	0	$+21.3$
GM	0	16.0	0	$+16.0$
GQ	0	28.0	0	$+28.0$
JK	0.75	4.0	3.0	-5.0
KL	∞	0	6.0	-6.0
LM	2.25	5.3	12.0	$+13.1$
MN	2.25	6.7	15.0	$+16.4$
NP	∞	0	11.0	-11.0
PQ	0.75	5.3	4.0	-6.7

From Eq. (a), $HJ = 21.3$ kips

JOINT 2. The free-body diagram appears in Fig. 7-3c; the known force AJ is now shown as compressive. We shall express the vertical components of BK and JK in terms of the horizontal components.

$$\Sigma F_H = 25.3 + BK_H + JK_H = 0$$
$$\Sigma F_V = -6.0 + 19.0 + 0.75BK_H - 0.75JK_H = 0$$

Solving these simultaneous equations, we obtain

$$BK_H = -21.3 \text{ kips} \qquad JK_H = -4.0 \text{ kips}$$
$$BK_V = -16.0 \text{ kips} \qquad JK_V = -3.0 \text{ kips}$$

JOINT 3. Since there are no external horizontal forces at this joint and member KL is vertical, we have

$$CL_H = BK_H = 21.3 \text{ kips compression}$$
and
$$KL = 6 \text{ kips compression}$$

JOINT 4

$$\Sigma F_H = -4.0 - 21.3 + 4.0 + LM_H + GM = 0 \qquad (b)$$
$$\Sigma F_V = -3.0 - 3.0 - 6.0 + LM_V = 0$$

$$LM_V = 12.0 \text{ kips} \qquad LM_H = \frac{12.0}{2.25} = 5.3 \text{ kips}$$

From Eq. (*b*), $GM = 16.0$ kips

JOINT 5

$$\Sigma F_H = 21.3 - 5.3 + DN_H + MN_H = 0$$
$$\Sigma F_V = -6.0 + 16.0 - 12.0 - 0.75DN_H - 2.25MN_H = 0$$
$$DN_H = -22.7 \text{ kips} \qquad MN_H = 6.7 \text{ kips}$$
$$DN_V = -17.0 \text{ kips} \qquad MN_V = 15.0 \text{ kips}$$

JOINT 6

$$EP_H = DN_H = 22.7 \text{ kips C}$$
$$NP = 11.0 \text{ kips C}$$

JOINT 7

$$\Sigma F_H = 22.7 - PQ_H + FQ_H = 0$$
$$\Sigma F_V = -8.0 - 17.0 - 0.75PQ_H - 0.75FQ_H = 0$$
$$PQ_H = -5.3 \text{ kips} \qquad FQ_H = -28.0 \text{ kips}$$
$$PQ_V = -4.0 \text{ kips} \qquad FQ_V = -21.0 \text{ kips}$$

JOINT 8

$$\Sigma F_H = 28.0 - GQ = 0 \qquad GQ = 28.0 \text{ kips}$$
$$\Sigma F_V = 21.0 - 21.0 = 0 \qquad \text{OK}$$

JOINT 9

$$\Sigma F_H = -16.0 - 6.7 - 5.3 + 28.0 = 0 \qquad \text{OK}$$
$$\Sigma F_V = 15.0 - 11.0 - 4.0 = 0 \qquad \text{OK}$$

With the horizontal and vertical components of the internal forces established, the forces themselves may now be found.   For example,

$$AJ = -\sqrt{25.3^2 + 19.0^2} = -31.7 \text{ kips}$$

The results are recorded in the last column in Table 7-2.

7-4   Method of Sections   To determine the force in a given truss member by the method of sections, we cut the truss along a surface that intersects the given member and then apply the equations of equilibrium to either part of the truss.   (We shall in all instances use the left part.)

Example 7-3   With reference to the truss in Fig. 7-3*a*, determine the forces in the members *BK* and *LM* by applying the method of sections.
    Solution. Cut the truss at plane *aa*, as shown in Fig. 7-4*a*, and draw a free-body diagram of the left part of the truss.   Assume that *BK* is tensile.   We shall apply the equation $\Sigma M = 0$.   By selecting joint 4 as the moment center, we secure an equation containing *BK* as the only unknown.   Since each half of the truss forms a 3-4-5 right triangle,

$$d = 20 \times \tfrac{3}{5} = 12 \text{ ft}$$
$$\Sigma M_4 = 19 \times 20 - 6 \times 10 + 12BK = 0 \qquad BK = -26.7 \text{ kips}$$

The negative result signifies that the assumed direction of BK is incorrect; the force is therefore compressive.

Alternatively, BK may be found by the following method: Consider this force (again assumed to be tensile) to be resolved into its horizontal and vertical

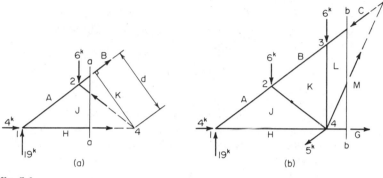

fig. 7-4

components, the resolution being made at joint 1. With respect to joint 4, these components have arms of zero and 20 ft, respectively.

$$\Sigma M_4 = 19 \times 20 + 20BK_V - 6 \times 10 = 0$$
$$BK_V = -16.0 \text{ kips} \qquad BK = -16.0 \times \tfrac{5}{3} = -26.7 \text{ kips}$$

To evaluate LM, cut the truss at plane bb, as shown in Fig. 7-4b, and draw a free-body diagram of the left part. Assume that LM is tensile. Resolve this force into its horizontal and vertical components at joint 4, and take moments with respect to joint 1.

$$\Sigma M_1 = 6(10 + 20) + 3 \times 20 - 20LM_V = 0$$
$$LM_V = 12.0 \text{ kips} \qquad LM_H = \frac{12.0}{2.25} = 5.3 \text{ kips}$$
$$LM = 13.1 \text{ kips}$$

7-5   Space Frames   The analytical techniques for investigating plane trusses may be readily extended to cover three-dimensional structures and force systems. Let us establish three rectangular coordinate axes, denoted by x, y, and z. The equations of equilibrium are

$$\Sigma F_x = 0 \qquad \Sigma F_y = 0 \qquad \Sigma F_z = 0$$
$$\Sigma M = 0$$

Let d denote the length of a member, and d_x, d_y, and d_z denote its length as projected on the x, y, and z axes, respectively. Then

$$d = \sqrt{d_x{}^2 + d_y{}^2 + d_z{}^2}$$

The ratio d_x/d is termed the *direction cosine* of the member with respect to the x axis because it represents the cosine of the angle between the member and the x axis, or an axis parallel thereto.

Let F denote the axial force in a member, and F_x, F_y, and F_z denote the x, y, and z components of the force, respectively. Since this force has the same direction as the member itself, a direction cosine also represents the ratio of the component of a force along the designated axis to the total force. For example,

$$\frac{F_x}{F} = \frac{d_x}{d}$$

Example 7-4   With reference to the space frame in Fig. 7-5a, A lies in the xy plane, B and C lie on the z axis, and D lies on the x axis. A horizontal load of 4000 lb lying in the xy plane is applied at A. Determine the force induced in each member by applying the method of joints, and verify the results by taking moments with respect to convenient axes.

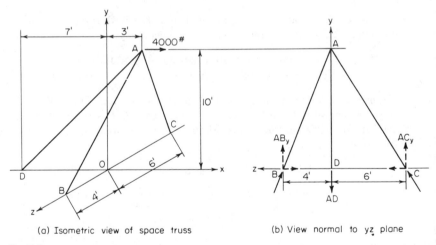

(a) Isometric view of space truss   (b) View normal to yz plane

fig. 7-5

Solution. It is first necessary to determine the projected lengths, true length, and direction cosines of each member. The results are recorded in Table 7-3.

We shall consider joint A as a free body. Assuming that all three members are in tension, we obtain the following results:

$$\Sigma F_x = 4000 - AB_x - AC_x - AD_x = 0$$
$$\Sigma F_y = \qquad\quad - AB_y - AC_y - AD_y = 0$$
$$\Sigma F_z = \qquad\quad\ AB_z - AC_z \qquad\quad = 0$$

When each component of a force is expressed in terms of the total force, the

Table 7-3   Data for Space Frame (Fig. 7-5)

Member	AB	AC	AD
d_x, ft	3	3	10
d_y	10	10	10
d_z	4	6	0
d	11.18	12.04	14.14
d_x/d	0.268	0.249	0.707
d_y/d	0.894	0.831	0.707
d_z/d	0.358	0.498	0
Force, lb......	-3830	-2750	$+8080$

equations of equilibrium assume the following forms:

$$\Sigma F_x = 4000 - 0.268AB - 0.249AC - 0.707AD = 0$$
$$\Sigma F_y = \quad\quad - 0.894AB - 0.831AC - 0.707AD = 0$$
$$\Sigma F_z = \quad\quad 0.358AB - 0.498AC \quad\quad = 0$$

The forces are found by solving these three simultaneous equations.   A positive result signifies tension; a negative result, compression.

$$AB = \textbf{3830 lb C} \quad\quad AC = \textbf{2750 lb C}$$
$$AD = \textbf{8080 lb T}$$

To verify these results, it is necessary to select moment axes that yield equations independent of those previously developed.   Figure 7-5b shows the reactions at the supports B, C, and D, each reaction being numerically equal to and collinear with the force in the member at that support.   The reactions are resolved into their components.   Taking moments with respect to the axis through C parallel to the x axis, we have

$$\Sigma M = 10AB_y - 6AD_y$$
$$= 10 \times 0.894 \times 3830 - 6 \times 0.707 \times 8080 = 0$$

Taking moments with respect to the x axis, we have

$$\Sigma M = 4AB_y - 6AC_y$$
$$= 4 \times 0.894 \times 3830 - 6 \times 0.831 \times 2750 = 0$$

The calculated results are thus confirmed.

Example 7-5   The compound space frame in Fig. 7-6a has the dimensions recorded in the orthographic projections, Fig. 7-6b and c.   A load of 5000 lb, which lies in the xy plane and makes an angle of 30° with the vertical, is applied at A.   Calculate the force induced in each member, and verify the results.

Solution. The projected lengths and true length of each member are recorded in Table 7-4.   The components of the applied load, in absolute value, are as follows:

$$P_x = 5000 \sin 30° = 2500 \text{ lb}$$
$$P_y = 5000 \cos 30° = 4330 \text{ lb}$$

50

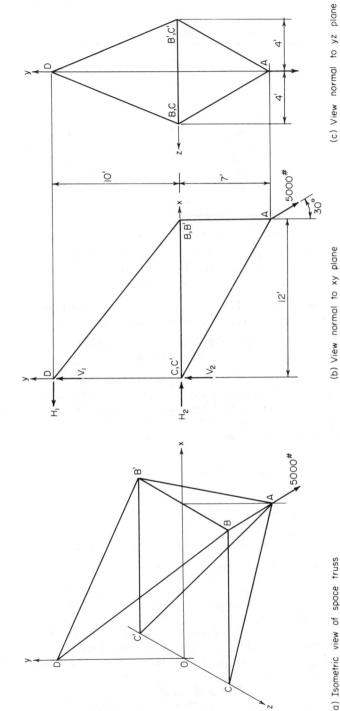

(a) Isometric view of space truss

fig. 7-6

(b) View normal to xy plane

(c) View normal to yz plane

Table 7-4   Data for Space Frame (Fig. 7-6)

Member	AB	AC	BC	BD	BB'
d_x, ft	0	12	12	12	0
d_y	7	7	0	10	0
d_z	4	4	0	4	8
d	8.06	14.46	12.00	16.12	8
F_x, lb	0	1250	1723	1723	0
F_y	1436	729	0	1436	0
F_z	821	417	0	574	1395
F	+1653	+1506	−1723	+2315	−1395

Since the truss and load system are symmetrical with respect to the xy plane, the internal forces are also symmetrical. As one component of an internal force becomes known, it will be convenient to calculate the other components at once, as well as the total force. We shall assume in all instances that an unknown force is tensile.

The first step in the solution consists of finding the x and y components of the reactions; the z components are not required in this solution. Refer to Fig. 7-6b. Forces H_2 and V_2 represent the sum of the horizontal and vertical reactions, respectively, at C and C'. Taking moments with respect to the z axis, we have

$$\Sigma M = 4330 \times 12 - 2500 \times 7 - 10H_1 = 0$$
$$H_1 = 3446 \text{ lb} \qquad H_2 = 3446 - 2500 = 946 \text{ lb}$$

At joint D,

$$\Sigma F_x = -H_1 + 2BD_x = 0 \qquad BD_x = 1723 \text{ lb T}$$
$$BD_y = 1723 \times \tfrac{10}{12} = 1436 \text{ lb}$$
$$\Sigma F_y = V_1 - 2BD_y = V_1 - 2 \times 1436 = 0$$
$$V_1 = 2872 \text{ lb}$$

For the entire frame,

$$\Sigma F_y = V_1 + V_2 - 4330 = 0$$
$$V_2 = 4330 - 2872 = 1458 \text{ lb}$$

The internal forces may now be evaluated. The remaining calculations for BD are as follows:

$$BD_z = 1723 \times \tfrac{4}{12} = 574 \text{ lb}$$
$$BD = 1723 \times \frac{16.12}{12} = 2315 \text{ lb}$$

At joint C,

$$\Sigma F_x = \tfrac{1}{2}H_2 + AC_x + BC = 0 \tag{a}$$
$$\Sigma F_y = \tfrac{1}{2}V_2 - AC_y = 0 \tag{b}$$

From Eq. (b), $AC_y = 729 \text{ lb T}$
Then $AC_x = 729 \times \tfrac{12}{7} = 1250 \text{ lb}$

From Eq. (a),
$$BC = 1723 \text{ lb C}$$
$$AC_z = 729 \times \tfrac{3}{7} = 417 \text{ lb}$$
$$AC = 729 \times \frac{14.46}{7} = 1506 \text{ lb}$$

At joint B,

$$\Sigma F_y = BD_y - AB_y = 0 \qquad AB_y = 1436 \text{ lb T}$$
$$AB_z = 1436 \times \tfrac{4}{7} = 821 \text{ lb}$$
$$AB = 1436 \times \frac{8.06}{7} = 1653 \text{ lb}$$
$$\Sigma F_z = -AB_z - BD_z - BB' = 0$$
$$BB' = -821 - 574 = 1395 \text{ lb C}$$

The internal forces are now determined. To verify the results, we shall write a new set of equilibrium equations that includes all internal forces. At joint A,

$$\Sigma F_x = -2AC_x + 2500 = -2 \times 1250 + 2500 = 0$$
$$\Sigma F_y = 2AB_y + 2AC_y - 4330$$
$$= 2 \times 1436 + 2 \times 729 - 4330 = 0$$

Consider the forces acting at joint B, and refer to Fig. 7-6c. Taking moments of these forces with respect to the axis through A parallel to the x axis, we have

$$\Sigma M = -7BB' + 7BD_z + 4BD_y$$
$$= -7 \times 1395 + 7 \times 574 + 4 \times 1436 = 0$$

Consider the structure to be cut along a plane parallel to the yz plane. For the right part, we have

$$\Sigma F_x = -2BD_x + 2BC - 2AC_x + 2500$$
$$= -2 \times 1723 + 2 \times 1723 - 2 \times 1250 + 2500 = 0$$
$$\Sigma F_y = 2BD_y + 2AC_y - 4330$$
$$= 2 \times 1436 + 2 \times 729 - 4330 = 0$$

The calculated results are thus confirmed.

7-6 Deflection of Trusses

7-6 Deflection of Trusses   The deformation of a truss under a given load system may be investigated by either an analytical or a graphical method. We shall first consider the analytical method.

Article 6-4 presents the unit-load method of calculating beam deflections. The concept underlying this method is applicable to the analysis of trusses as well as beams. Assume that we wish to determine the displacement of a given point in the truss in a specified direction. Apply an imaginary unit load to the truss at this point in the same direction as the displacement to be evaluated. By equating the work performed by this unit load when the true loads are applied to the increase in strain energy of the truss caused by the presence of the unit load, we obtain the required displacement.

With respect to a given truss member, let

A = cross-sectional area
L = length
E = modulus of elasticity of material
S = force induced by true loads
u = force induced by unit load

The displacement Δ of the point under consideration is

$$\Delta = \sum \frac{SuL}{AE} \tag{7-1}$$

To make this equation dimensionally homogeneous, u should be expressed as a pure number.

Example 7-6 The truss in Fig. 7-7 carries loads applied at B, E, and F, as indicated. The cross-sectional areas of the members are recorded in Table 7-5. Calculate the vertical displcement of C, using $E = 2,000,000$ psi.

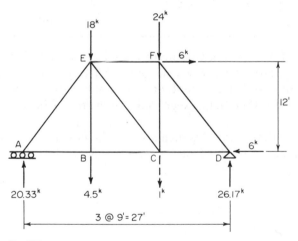

fig. 7-7

Solution. The reactions at A and D are shown in the drawing. The internal forces S may be evaluated by any convenient method. For example, if we cut the truss along a plane passing through EF, CF, and CD, we have

$$20.33 + CF - 18 - 4.5 = 0 \qquad CF = 2.17 \text{ kips}$$

Apply a unit vertical load at C, as indicated, and compute the internal forces u. The reaction at A is 0.333 kip. Cutting the truss in the same manner as before, we have

$$0.333 + CF - 1.0 = 0 \qquad CF = 0.667 \text{ kip}$$

All calculated values are recorded in Table 7-5. Equation (7-1) yields

$$\Delta_C = \frac{1,164,900}{2,000,000} = 0.582 \text{ in.}$$

Since the result is positive, C is displaced downward.

Table 7-5   Calculations for Truss Deflection (Fig. 7-7)

Member	A, sq in.	L, in.	S, kips	u	SuL/A, kips/in.
AB	5	108	+15.25	+0.250	+82.4
BC	5	108	+15.25	+0.250	+82.4
CD	5	108	+13.63	+0.500	+147.2
EF	6	108	−13.63	−0.500	+122.7
BE	4	144	+4.50	0	0
CF	4	144	+2.17	+0.667	+52.1
AE	8	180	−25.42	−0.417	+238.5
CE	4	180	−2.71	+0.417	−50.9
DF	10	180	−32.71	−0.833	+490.5
Total......	...	...	....	....	1164.9

The deformation of a truss may be investigated graphically by constructing a *displacement diagram*, in which we establish both the magnitude and direction of the displacement of each joint. In theory, the method is approximate rather than exact, but the degree of imprecision is negligible.

In Fig. 7-8, consider that point P is displaced to the position Q. Drop perpendiculars QR and QS to the x and y axes, respectively. We may

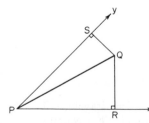

fig. 7-8 Components of displacement of point.

say that P is displaced a distance PR in the x direction and a distance PS in the y direction; we may also refer to PR and PS as the x and y components, respectively, of the displacement of P. Conversely, where we are given the components of the displacement of a point, we may find the displacement itself by reversing this construction.

The following example illustrates the graphical method of analyzing truss deflections.

Example 7-7   The truss in Fig. 7-9a supports a load system that causes the indicated change in length of the members.   Joint A is fixed and joint D is constrained to traverse a horizontal path.   Find the displacement of joints B, C, and D by graphical analysis.

Solution. Since A remains stationary, we select this as our reference point in evaluating displacements.   We shall assume tentatively that member AB does not rotate and shall construct a preliminary displacement diagram that reflects this assumption.

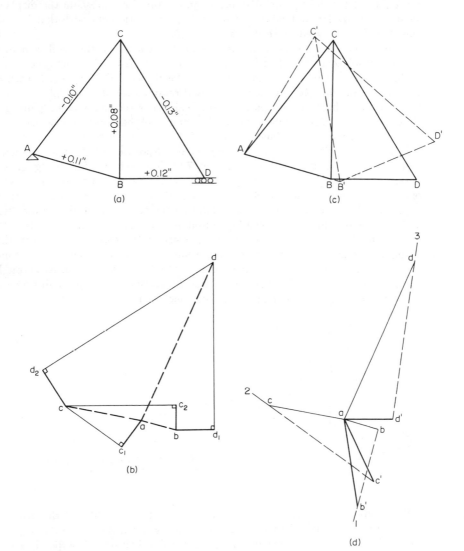

fig. 7-9   Diagrams for deformation of truss.

In Fig. 7-9b, start at the point labeled a.   If AB does not rotate, the displacement of joint B is 0.11 in. along AB, outward from A.   Therefore, draw line ab parallel to member AB and representing 0.11 in., placing b to the right of a.

Joint C has two components of displacement.   The first is a displacement of 0.10 in. along AC, inward toward A.   The second is the displacement of B plus a displacement of 0.08 in. along BC, outward from B.   Therefore, draw line ac_1 parallel to AC and representing 0.10 in., placing c_1 below a; draw line bc_2 parallel to BC and representing 0.08 in., placing c_2 above b.   Erect perpendiculars at c_1 and c_2, and label their point of intersection c.   Line ac represents the displacement of C if AB does not rotate.   Comparing the position of c with that of a, we find that C is displaced upward and to the left.

Joint D has two components of displacement.   The first is the displacement of B plus a displacement of 0.12 in. along BD, outward from B.   The other is the displacement of C plus a displacement of 0.13 in. along CD, inward toward C. Therefore, draw line bd_1 parallel to BD and representing 0.12 in., placing d_1 to the right of b; draw line cd_2 parallel to CD and representing 0.13 in., placing d_2 above c.   Erect perpendiculars at d_1 and d_2, and label their point of intersection d. Line ad represents the displacement of D if AB does not rotate.

In Fig. 7-9c, $AB'C'D'$ represents the deformed position of the truss as determined by the displacement diagram in 7-9b, the deformation being grossly exaggerated for emphasis.   Our assumption that AB does not rotate violates the requirement that D traverse a horizontal path, and a correction is therefore required.   This correction consists of rotating the truss in a clockwise direction with A as center until D' lies on a horizontal line through D.   Since in reality the deformation is minuscule in relation to the size of the truss, we may say that during this rotation D' traverses a straight line perpendicular to line AD.   Similarly, B' traverses a straight line perpendicular to AB, and C' traverses a straight line perpendicular to AC.   Moreover, the displacement of a joint during this rotation is directly proportional to the distance of the joint from A.

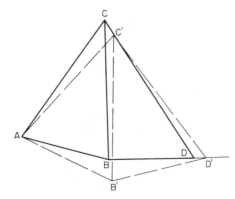

fig. 7-10   Deformation of truss.

We must superpose the displacements previously obtained and the displacements that accompany the truss rotation.   In Fig. 7-9d, reproduce the displacements ab, ac, and ad established in 7-9b.   Draw line 1 through b perpendicular to AB, line 2 through c perpendicular to AC, and line 3 through d perpendicular to line AD. These lines represent the directions in which the respective truss joints are displaced during the rotation about A.

Let ab', ac', and ad' denote the true displacement of the respective joints. Since D is displaced horizontally, d' lies at the intersection of line 3 and a horizontal line through a. Thus, ad is the displacement previously obtained, dd' is the displacement caused by truss rotation, and ad' is the true displacement. Now locate b' on line 1 and c' on line 2 so that

$$\frac{bb'}{dd'} = \frac{AB}{AD} \qquad \text{and} \qquad \frac{cc'}{dd'} = \frac{AC}{AD}$$

The displacements of the joints are now established. The deformed position of the truss is shown in Fig. 7-10, the deformation being grossly exaggerated.

EIGHT

Statically Indeterminate
Structures

A structure or structural member is described as *statically determinate* if it may be completely analyzed by applying solely the equations of equilibrium, and as *statically indeterminate* if these equations do not suffice. Several methods of analyzing an indeterminate structure are available. One method is to supplement the equations of equilibrium with other equations derived from a study of the deformation of the structure. Another method is to transform the given structure to a determinate one and then to apply whatever forces are required to restore the structure to its true condition.

8-1 Two-span Continuous Beams A beam that is continuous across two spans may be readily analyzed by regarding one of the three reactions as a load of unknown magnitude. This device serves to transform the member to a beam having only two supports.

Example 8-1 The beam in Fig. 8-1a is supported at its center by a spring having a constant of 100 kips per in.; i.e., a force of 100 kips will compress the spring 1 in. The EI value of the beam is 35×10^9 lb-in.^{2} Neglecting the weight of member, compute the reactions at the supports.

58

Solution. Figure 8-1*b* is the free-body diagram of the member.   We shall treat R_B as a load rather than a reaction.

Let y denote the deflection at B.   An expression for y is obtained by referring to Cases 7 and 8 on page 2-122 of the AISC Manual.   With respect to the 50-kip load, we have

$$b = 7 \text{ ft} \qquad x = 14 \text{ ft}$$

In substituting numerical values in a deflection equation, it is convenient to express distances along the span in ft, E in psi, and I in in.[4]   To obtain the

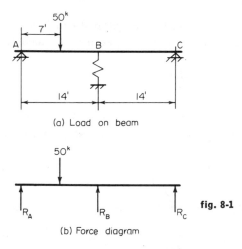

(a) Load on beam

50^k

R_A R_B R_C

fig. 8-1

(b) Force diagram

deflection in in., we must multiply by 12^3, or 1728.

$$y = \frac{50{,}000 \times 7 \times 14(28^2 - 7^2 - 14^2) \times 1728}{6 \times 35 \times 10^9 \times 28} - \frac{R_B \times 28^3 \times 1728}{48 \times 35 \times 10^9}$$

$$= 0.776 - \frac{2.26R_B}{10^5}$$

Another expression for y is obtained by applying the spring constant.   By proportion,

$$\frac{y}{1} = \frac{R_B}{100{,}000} \qquad y = \frac{R_B}{100{,}000}$$

Then
$$\frac{R_B}{10^5} = 0.776 - \frac{2.26R_B}{10^5}$$

$$R_B = \frac{0.776 \times 10^5}{3.26} = \textbf{23{,}800 lb}$$

Taking moments about the supports, we obtain

$$R_A = \textbf{25{,}600 lb} \qquad R_C = \textbf{600 lb}$$

8-2 Moment Distribution   Rigid frames may be analyzed by the method of moment distribution developed by Prof. Hardy Cross.   The method consists of evaluating the bending moments at the joints through a series of successive approximations.

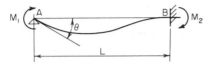

fig. 8-2 Deflection of propped-cantilever beam.

In Fig. 8-2, assume that we wish to rotate the propped-cantilever beam through a unit angle at end A.   The moment M_1 required to accomplish this is

$$M_1 = \frac{4EI}{L} \tag{8-1}$$

The quantity EI/L thus represents the flexural *stiffness* of the span with respect to rotation at A; it is denoted by K.   The moment M_2 induced at B is

$$M_2 = \frac{2EI}{L} = \frac{M_1}{2} \tag{8-2}$$

If the support at B is hinged rather than fixed,

$$M_1 = \frac{3EI}{L} \tag{8-3}$$

Thus, when the support at B is hinged, the value of K is three-fourths of that when the support is fixed.

Example 8-2   With reference to Fig. 8-3, the adjoining beams are rigidly connected to one another at the supports to form a continuous homogeneous beam. The span lengths and moments of inertia have the indicated values.   Calculate the bending moments at the supports by means of moment distribution.

Solution. All computed data are recorded in the drawing as they are obtained.

We must determine the relative stiffness of each span with respect to rotation at B and C.   For spans AB and BC, consider that the far support will be fixed; for CD, consider that the far support will be hinged.   In the present instance, the modulus of elasticity is constant and may therefore be disregarded.

$$K_{AB} = {}^{270}\!/_{18} = 15 \qquad K_{BC} = {}^{192}\!/_{12} = 16 \qquad K_{CD} = 0.75 \times {}^{240}\!/_{20} = 9$$

Consider joints B and C as well as A to be locked against rotation, thus making each member an isolated beam. AB and BC are fixed-ended beams and CD is a propped-cantilever beam.   We shall compute the restraining moments induced at the fixed supports.   These are termed *fixed-end moments* (f.e.m.); a clockwise moment will be regarded as positive.   Refer to Case 14 on page 2-124 and Case 15 on page 2-125 of the AISC Manual. Let M_{AB} and M_{BA} denote the fixed-end moment at A and B, respectively, for span AB.

$$M_{AB} = -\frac{wL^2}{12} = -\frac{2 \times 18^2}{12} = -54.0 \text{ ft-kips}$$

$$M_{BA} = +54.0 \text{ ft-kips}$$

Similarly,

$$M_{BC} = -48.0 \text{ ft-kips} \qquad M_{CB} = +48.0 \text{ ft-kips}$$

$$M_{CD} = -\frac{24 \times 15 \times 5(15 + 20)}{2 \times 20^2} = -78.8 \text{ ft-kips}$$

The net, or *unbalanced*, moments at B and C are as follows:

At B: $+54.0 - 48.0 = +6.0 \text{ ft-kips}$
At C: $+48.0 - 78.8 = -30.8 \text{ ft-kips}$

These artificial moments must be eliminated by introducing opposing, or balancing, moments at these joints. In applying the balancing moment at B,

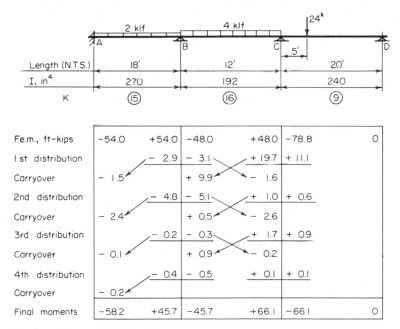

fig. 8-3 Moment distribution.

consider that joint B is unlocked but joints A and C remain locked. The balancing moment at B is therefore distributed to the two adjoining spans in proportion to their relative stiffnesses. The distributed moments are as follows:

$$M_{BA} = -6.0 \times {}^{15}\!/_{31} = -2.9 \text{ ft-kips}$$
$$M_{BC} = -6.0 \times {}^{16}\!/_{31} = -3.1 \text{ ft-kips}$$

Similarly,

$$M_{CB} = +30.8 \times {}^{16}\!/_{25} = +19.7 \text{ ft-kips}$$
$$M_{CD} = +30.8 \times {}^{9}\!/_{25} = +11.1 \text{ ft-kips}$$

When the balancing moment was applied at B, restraining moments were induced at joints A and C, which we had considered as remaining locked. Similarly, when the balancing moment was applied at C, a restraining moment was induced at B. These restraining moments are called *carryover* moments; they are computed by applying Eq. (8-2). The values of the carryover moments are as follows:

$$M_{AB} = \tfrac{1}{2}(-2.9) = -1.5 \text{ ft-kips} \qquad M_{BC} = \tfrac{1}{2}(+19.7) = +9.9 \text{ ft-kips}$$
$$M_{CB} = \tfrac{1}{2}(-3.1) = -1.6 \text{ ft-kips}$$

The first cycle in the moment-distribution procedure is now completed. There is an unbalanced moment of $+9.9$ ft-kips at B and -1.6 ft-kips at C. The results obtained in the second cycle are recorded in the drawing, and the process is continued until the computed results become negligible. By totaling the values thus obtained, we arrive at the following values of bending moment:

$$M_A = -58.2 \text{ ft-kips} \qquad M_B = -45.7 \text{ ft-kips} \qquad M_C = -66.1 \text{ ft-kips}$$

8-3   Statically Indeterminate Trusses   A truss may be tested for statical determinateness by applying a simple criterion. Resolve the truss reactions into their horizontal and vertical components, and let

j = number of joints
m = number of truss members
r = number of reaction components

Two equations of equilibrium are available for each joint. Therefore, if $2j = m + r$, the truss is determinate; if $2j < m + r$, the truss is indeterminate, and the deficiency represents the degree of indeterminateness.

Assume that a truss has one redundant member and that this member is in tension. Cut the redundant member into two parts, labeled a and b; the structure thus becomes statically determinate. Apply a unit tensile force to a and to b; these forces cause the ends to separate, with a and b overlapping one another. When the true loads are applied, the ends are displaced in the reverse direction and a gap forms between a and b. The true force in the redundant member is of such magnitude as to make these two displacements equal, thus preventing the formation of a gap.

With respect to the truss that has been cut, let

S = force in given member caused by true loads
u = force in given member caused by unit tensile forces on parts a and b

With respect to the actual truss, let

S' = force in given member caused by true loads

By applying Eq. (7-1) to evaluate the two displacements, we obtain the following value for the force in the redundant member:

$$S'_{red} = -\frac{\sum \dfrac{SuL}{AE}}{\sum \dfrac{u^2 L}{AE}} \qquad (8\text{-}4)$$

Example 8-3 With reference to the truss in Fig. 8-4a, the members are made of the same material and their cross-sectional areas have the relative values recorded in Table 8-1. Calculate the forces in the truss members.

Solution. The reactions are shown in Fig. 8-4b.

$$j = 5 \qquad m = 8 \qquad r = 3$$
$$2j = 10 \qquad m + r = 11$$

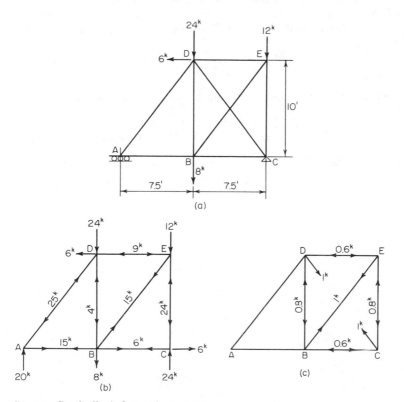

fig. 8-4 Statically indeterminate truss.

Table 8-1   Calculations for Redundant Truss (Fig. 8-4a)

Member	A	L, in.	S, kips	u, kips	SuL/A	u^2L/A	S', kips
AB	5	90	+15	0	0	0	+15.0
BC	5	90	+6	−0.6	−64.8	6.48	+11.8
AD	8	150	−25	0	0	0	−25.0
BD	4	120	−4	−0.8	+96.0	19.20	+3.8
BE	4	150	+15	+1.0	+562.5	37.50	+5.3
CD	6	150	0	+1.0	0	25.00	−9.7
CE	7	120	−24	−0.8	+329.1	10.97	−16.2
DE	4	90	−9	−0.6	+121.5	8.10	−3.2
Total......	...	...	....	.....	+1044.3	107.25	

The truss is therefore statically indeterminate to the first degree; i.e., it contains one redundant member. We shall consider CD as redundant. When this member is cut, the truss in effect becomes that shown in Fig. 8-4b.

The values of S and of u are indicated in Fig. 8-4b and c, respectively, and the results of the remaining calculations are recorded in Table 8-1. A tensile force is considered positive and a compressive force negative. Only the relative values of A, E, and L are significant; since E is constant, it may be disregarded.

$$S'_{CD} = -\frac{1044.3}{107.25} = -9.74 \text{ kips}$$

The true forces in the truss may now be found. For example,

$$S'_{BC} = 6 - 0.6(-9.74) = 11.8 \text{ kips}$$
$$S'_{BD} = -4 - 0.8(-9.74) = 3.8 \text{ kips}$$

The results may be tested by selecting some other member, such as CE, as the redundant member, and making a new set of calculations.

NINE

Moving Loads and Influence Lines

Many structures, such as bridges and crane girders, support groups of concentrated loads that roll across the structure while the loads remain fixed distances apart. In order to analyze a given quantity, such as the bending moment in a beam or the axial stress in a truss member, it is necessary as a preliminary step to identify the position of the load group at which this quantity attains its maximum value. We shall refer to this as the *critical* position.

9-1 Maximum Moment and Shear in Simple Beams   Assume that a simply supported beam carries solely a moving-load group and that the weight of the beam is negligible. The *instantaneous* maximum moment is the maximum bending moment that exists at a given instant; the *absolute* maximum moment is the maximum bending moment induced during transit of the load group. Since the load group consists exclusively of concentrated loads, the vertical shear changes sign under one of these loads, and the instantaneous maximum moment therefore occurs under that load. We shall refer to the load under which the absolute maximum moment occurs as the *dominant* load.

A multiple-load group contains many variable quantities, and it is therefore impossible to formulate a set rule or equation for identifying the dominant load or the critical position.   For a simply supported beam, the following procedure is to be followed:

1. Locate the resultant of the load group.

2. Assume that a particular load is dominant, and place the group in such a position that this load is as far from one support as the resultant is from the other.   If L denotes the span and d the distance from the load under consideration to the resultant, the distance from this load to the adjacent support is $\frac{1}{2}(L - d)$.

3. Compute the bending moment at the section under this load.   This is usually the greatest moment occurring under this load during transit of the group.

4. Repeat steps 2 and 3 for the remaining loads.

Step 3 in this procedure is to be performed only if it is found, after positioning the loads in the prescribed manner, that all loads are present on the span and that the shear changes sign under this load.   Moreover, when the distances between loads are large in relation to the span, the absolute maximum moment may occur when only part of the load group is on the span.

The maximum vertical shear occurs when the entire load group is on the span and the resultant of the group is at its minimum possible distance from a support.

Example 9-1   The moving-load group shown in Fig. 9-1a traverses a beam of 40-ft span.   Calculate the maximum bending moment and maximum shear induced in the beam during transit of these loads.   Disregard the weight of beam.

Solution. The resultant R is 29 kips, and its location may be found by taking moments with respect to A.

$$\Sigma M_A = 29AD = 4 \times 5 + 15 \times 17 \qquad AD = 9.48 \text{ ft}$$

For the 10-kip load,

$$d = 9.48 \text{ ft} \qquad \tfrac{1}{2}(L - d) = \tfrac{1}{2}(40 - 9.48) = 15.26 \text{ ft}$$

$$R_L = 29 \times \frac{15.26}{40} = 11.06 \text{ kips} \qquad (\text{see Fig. 9-1}b)$$

Since the shear does not pass through zero under the 10-kip load, this position lacks significance.

For the 4-kip load,

$$d = 4.48 \text{ ft} \qquad \tfrac{1}{2}(L - d) = 17.76 \text{ ft}$$

$$R_L = 29 \times \frac{17.76}{40} = 12.88 \text{ kips} \qquad (\text{see Fig. 9-1}c)$$

$$M = 12.88 \times 17.76 - 10 \times 5 = 178.7 \text{ ft-kips}$$

For the 15-kip load,

$$d = 7.52 \text{ ft} \qquad \tfrac{1}{2}(L - d) = 16.24 \text{ ft}$$

$$R_R = 29 \times \frac{16.24}{40} = 11.77 \text{ kips} \qquad \text{(see Fig. 9-1}d\text{)}$$

$$M = 11.77 \times 16.24 = 191.1 \text{ ft-kips}$$

Then $$M_\text{max} = \textbf{191.1 ft-kips}$$

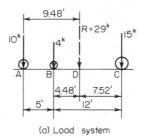

(a) Load system

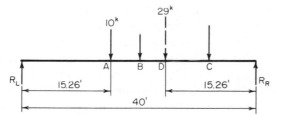

(b) Position I, for I0-kip load

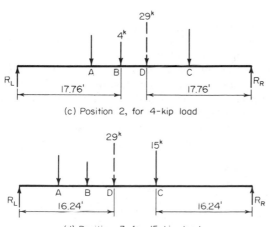

(c) Position 2, for 4-kip load

(d) Position 3, for I5-kip load

fig. 9-1

The absolute maximum shear occurs when the 15-kip load is an infinitesimal distance to the left of the right support.

$$V_{max} = \frac{29(40 - 7.52)}{40} = \textbf{23.5 kips}$$

9-2 Influence Lines for Trusses   When applied to a truss, the terms *vertical shear* and *bending moment* have the same significance as for a beam. Assume that a truss supports only vertical loads.   The vertical shear V at a given transverse plane is the algebraic sum of the forces to the left of the plane, the bending moment M at the plane is the algebraic sum of the moments of those forces with respect to the plane.

The floor of a bridge is carried by transverse beams that frame to the two supporting trusses.   In a *through* bridge, the floor beams are connected to the lower chords; in a *deck* bridge, to the upper chords.   Thus, every bridge load is transmitted to the supporting trusses in the form of concentrated loads at panel points.   It is to be understood that each load specified hereafter represents that portion of the bridge load that is transmitted to the truss under consideration.

Assume that we wish to ascertain the maximum force induced in a truss member during transit of a moving-load group.   As an aid in identifying the critical position of the group, it is advantageous to construct an *influence line*.   This is a diagram that depicts the variation in a given quantity as a unit concentrated load traverses the structure.   The ordinate at a given point in the diagram represents the value of this quantity when the unit load occupies the corresponding point in the structure.   The following examples illustrate the construction of influence lines.

Example 9-2   With reference to the through truss in Fig. 9-2a, construct the influence line for the vertical shear in panel *cd* caused by a moving load traversing the bridge floor.   Compute the slope of the influence line.

Solution. Figure 9-2b shows the unit load lying in panel *ef*.   The load is transmitted to the truss as a concentrated load at *e* and another at *f*.   However, since the panel-point loads are merely components of the unit load, we may apply the unit load itself in determining the truss reactions.

Let V_{cd} denote the shear in panel *cd*; let x denote the distance from the unit load to the right support.   Place the load to the right of *d*, as shown.

$$R_L = \frac{x}{120} \qquad V_{cd} = R_L = \frac{x}{120} \tag{a}$$

Place the load to the left of *c*.

$$V_{cd} = R_L - 1 = \frac{x}{120} - 1 \tag{b}$$

Place the load within panel cd; let P_c denote the panel-point load at c.

$$P_c = \frac{x - dg}{20} = \frac{x - 60}{20} = \frac{x}{20} - 3$$

$$V_{cd} = R_L - P_c = \frac{x}{120} - \left(\frac{x}{20} - 3\right)$$

$$= -\frac{x}{24} + 3 \qquad (c)$$

Applying the foregoing equations, we obtain the diagram in Fig. 9-2c. The point j at which this line intersects the base is known as the *neutral point*. The slopes are as follows:

Lines (a) and (b): $\qquad\qquad\qquad \dfrac{dV}{dx} = \frac{1}{120}$

Line (c): $\qquad\qquad\qquad\qquad\quad \dfrac{dV}{dx} = -\frac{1}{24}$

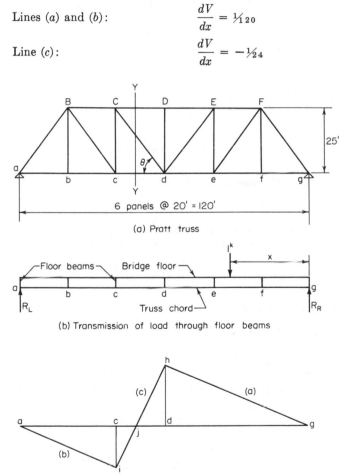

(a) Pratt truss

(b) Transmission of load through floor beams

(c) Influence line for shear in panel cd

fig. 9-2

Example 9-3   With reference to the deck truss in Fig. 9-3*a*, construct the influence line for bending moment at *b* caused by a moving load traversing the bridge floor. Compute the slope of the influence line.

Solution. The unit load is transmitted to the truss in the form of concentrated loads at two adjacent panel points at the upper chord.

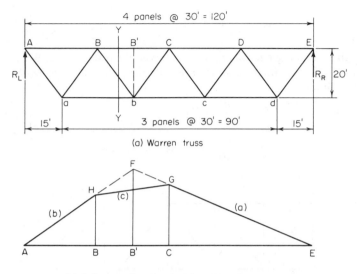

(a) Warren truss

(b) Influence line for bending moment at b

fig. 9-3

Let M_b denote the bending moment at *b*; let *x* denote the distance from the unit load to the right support.   Place the unit load to the right of *C*.

$$R_L = \frac{x}{120} \qquad M_b = 45R_L = \frac{3x}{8} \qquad (a)$$

Place the unit load to the left of *B*.

$$M_b = 45R_L - (x - B'E) = 45R_L - (x - 75)$$

$$= -\frac{5x}{8} + 75 \qquad (b)$$

Place the unit load within panel *BC*; let P_B denote the panel-point load at *B*.

$$P_B = \frac{x - CE}{30} = \frac{x - 60}{30} = \frac{x}{30} - 2$$

$$M_b = 45R_L - 15P_B = \frac{3x}{8} - 15\left(\frac{x}{30} - 2\right)$$

$$= -\frac{x}{8} + 30 \qquad (c)$$

Applying the foregoing equations, we obtain the diagram in Fig. 9-3*b*. The slopes are as follows:

Line (*a*): $$\frac{dM}{dx} = \tfrac{3}{8}$$

Line (*b*): $$\frac{dM}{dx} = -\tfrac{5}{8}$$

Line (*c*): $$\frac{dM}{dx} = -\tfrac{1}{8}$$

If *EG* and *AH* are prolonged, they intersect above *B'*.

9-3 Forces in Bridge Trusses　The force induced in a member of a bridge truss may be readily evaluated by constructing the appropriate influence line and thereby discerning the critical position of the loads. We shall analyze these structures without recourse to any set rule or equation in order to illumine the principles involved in designing for moving loads. The sign convention is as follows: A tensile force is positive, a compressive force is negative. By convention, it is assumed that locomotion proceeds from right to left.

In the following examples, the subscripts *u* and *c* placed to the left of the main symbol will be used to distinguish between a shear or bending moment caused by a uniform load and that caused by concentrated loads, respectively.

Example 9-4　The truss in Fig. 9-4*a* supports a bridge that transmits the following live loads to its bottom chord: a moving uniform load of 1.2 klf, and the moving-load group shown in Fig. 9-4*b*. Establish the limiting values of the force in member *De* caused by these loads.

Solution.　By cutting the truss along a vertical plane through *De*, we find that the force in this member is a function of the vertical shear in that panel. The influence line for this shear appears in Fig. 9-4*c*; its properties are as follows:

$$ek = {}^{100}\!/_{200} = 0.5$$

$$\text{slope of } ik = \text{slope of } ma = \tfrac{1}{200} \qquad \text{slope of } km = -\tfrac{1}{200}$$

$$ej = \frac{0.5}{\tfrac{1}{200}} = 14.3 \text{ ft} \qquad ij = 114.3 \text{ ft}$$

We shall first evaluate the extreme values of V_{de} associated with the moving uniform load. This shear is maximum when the load extends continuously from *i* to *j*, and its value is found by multiplying the load intensity by the area under the influence line across this interval.

$$_u V_{de,\text{max}} = 1.2 \times \tfrac{1}{2} \times 114.3 \times 0.5 = 34.29 \text{ kips}$$

The shear is minimum when the load extends continuously from j to a. By similar triangles,

$$\frac{\text{Area } \Delta jam}{\text{Area } \Delta ijk} = -\left(\frac{da}{ie}\right)^2 = -\left(\frac{3}{4}\right)^2 = -0.5625$$

Then $_uV_{de,\min} = -0.5625 \times 34.29 = -19.29$ kips

These values may be tested in the following manner: Consider the bottom chord to be a beam carrying a uniformly distributed load of 1.2 klf along the entire span. Calculate the shear at the center of panel de. This result should equal the algebraic sum of the two calculated values.

$$V = 12.5 \times 1.2 = 15.00 \text{ kips} \qquad 34.29 - 19.29 = 15.00 \text{ kips} \qquad \text{OK}$$

We shall now evaluate the extreme values of V_{de} associated with the loads in Fig. 9-4b. The resultant R is 50 kips, and its location is as follows:

$$\Sigma M_1 = 12 \times 6 + 18 \times 16 + 15 \times 22 = 50x \qquad x = 13.8 \text{ ft}$$

By convention, we assume that bridge traffic flows from right to left, but in reality it also flows in the opposite direction. In the present instance, it is not manifest which direction of motion induces the maximum or minimum shear in de.

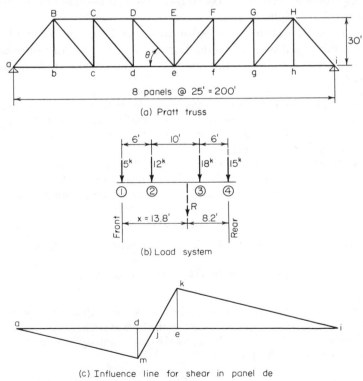

(a) Pratt truss

(b) Load system

(c) Influence line for shear in panel de

fig. 9-4

Assume first that the load group is moving from left to right; let $_cV_{de}$ denote the shear in panel de when the resultant is x feet from the left support. Now assume that the load group is moving from right to left; let $_cV_{ef}$ denote the shear in panel ef when the resultant is x feet from the right support. Since the truss is symmetrical, $_cV_{de} = -_cV_{ef}$. Hence the maximum shear in panel de with left-to-right motion equals the minimum shear in panel ef with right-to-left motion. This principle enables us to assume a single-track movement and calculate the internal forces accordingly.

It is therefore necessary to evaluate the following quantities associated with right-to-left motion:

1. MAXIMUM SHEAR IN PANEL de. Consider that load 1 lies within panel de and the remaining loads lie to the right of e. As motion continues, the shear changes at the following rate:

$$\frac{d\,_cV_{de}}{dx} = -\tfrac{7}{200} \times 5 + \tfrac{1}{200} \times 45 > 0$$

The shear therefore increases. Now consider that loads 1 and 2 lie within panel de and the remaining loads lie to the right of e. Then

$$\frac{d\,_cV_{de}}{dx} = -\tfrac{7}{200} \times 17 + \tfrac{1}{200} \times 33 < 0$$

The shear therefore decreases. It is apparent that the shear attains its maximum value at the instant load 2 is at e. For this position,

$$R_L = \frac{50(100 + 6 - 13.8)}{200} = 23.05 \text{ kips}$$

The load at panel-point d is

$$P_d = \frac{5 \times 6}{25} = 1.20 \text{ kips}$$

$$_cV_{de} = 23.05 - 1.20 = 21.85 \text{ kips}$$

2. MAXIMUM SHEAR IN PANEL ef. From the foregoing analysis, it is seen that this occurs when load 2 is at f.

$$R_L = \frac{50(75 + 6 - 13.8)}{200} = 16.80 \text{ kips}$$

$$_cV_{ef} = 16.80 - 1.20 = 15.60 \text{ kips}$$

3. MINIMUM SHEAR IN PANEL de. Consider that load 4 lies within panel de and the remaining loads lie to the left of d. Then

$$\frac{d\,_cV_{de}}{dx} = \tfrac{1}{200} \times 35 - \tfrac{7}{200} \times 15 < 0$$

The shear therefore decreases as motion continues until load 4 is at d. For this position,

$$R_L = \frac{50(125 + 8.2)}{200} = 33.30 \text{ kips}$$

$$_cV_{de} = 33.30 - 50 = -16.70 \text{ kips}$$

4. MINIMUM SHEAR IN PANEL *ef*. This occurs when load 4 is at e.

$$R_L = \frac{50(100 + 8.2)}{200} = 27.05$$

$$_cV_{ef} = 27.05 - 50 = -22.95 \text{ kips}$$

A comparison of the results in (1) and (4) reveals that

$$_cV_{de,\max} = 22.95 \text{ kips}$$

A comparison of the results in (2) and (3) reveals that

$$_cV_{de,\min} = -16.70 \text{ kips}$$

The extreme values of the live-load shear in panel *de* are therefore as follows:

$$V_{de,\max} = 34.29 + 22.95 = 57.24 \text{ kips}$$
$$V_{de,\min} = -19.29 - 16.70 = -35.99 \text{ kips}$$
$$\csc \theta = \frac{39.05}{30} = 1.302$$
$$De_{\max} = 57.24 \times 1.302 = \textbf{74.5 kips T}$$
$$De_{\min} = 35.99 \times 1.302 = \textbf{46.9 kips C}$$

Example 9-5 The truss in Fig. 9-3*a* supports a bridge that transmits the following live loads to its upper chord: a moving uniform load of 1.2 klf, and the moving loads shown in Fig. 9-5.   Calculate the maximum force in member *BC* caused by these loads.

Solution. By cutting the truss along the vertical plane *YY*, we find that the force in this member is a function of the bending moment at b.   Refer to Example 9-3.   The ordinates of the influence line are as follows:

$$CG = 22.5 \text{ ft-kips} \qquad BH = 18.75 \text{ ft-kips}$$

We shall first calculate the maximum value of M_b associated with the moving uniform load.   The moment at b is maximum when the entire bridge is loaded. Multiplying the load intensity by the area under the influence line, we have

$$_uM_{b,\max} = 1.2 \times \tfrac{1}{2}[60 \times 22.5 + 30(22.5 + 18.75) + 30 \times 18.75]$$
$$= 1890 \text{ ft-kips}$$

Alternatively, considering the actual forces at A and B, we obtain the following:

$$\text{Load on panel} = 1.2 \times 30 = 36 \text{ kips} \qquad R_L = 72 \text{ kips}$$
$$_uM_{b,\max} = 72 \times 45 - 36 \times 30 - 18 \times 15 = 1890 \text{ ft-kips}$$

We shall now calculate the maximum value of M_b associated with the loads in Fig. 9-5. The resultant is 65 kips, and its location is shown in the drawing. Assume right-to-left motion. With loads 1, 2, and 3 in panel BC and load 4 in panel CD, we have

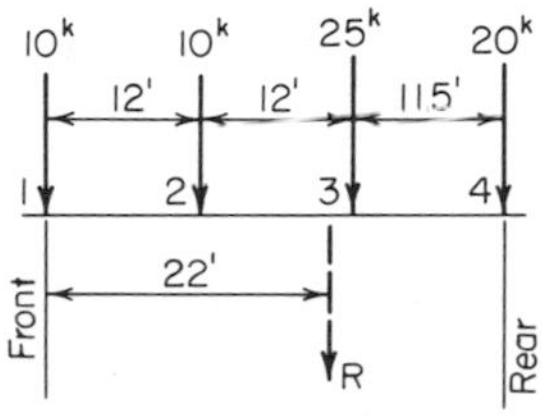

fig. 9-5

$$\frac{d\,_cM_b}{dx} = -\tfrac{1}{8} \times 45 + \tfrac{3}{8} \times 20 > 0$$

With load 1 in panel AB, loads 2 and 3 in panel BC, and load 4 in panel CD, we have

$$\frac{d\,_cM_b}{dx} = -\tfrac{5}{8} \times 10 - \tfrac{1}{8} \times 35 + \tfrac{3}{8} \times 20 < 0$$

The moment at b is therefore maximum when load 1 is at B. For this position,

$$R_L = \frac{65(90-22)}{120} = 36.83 \text{ kips}$$

The panel-point load at B is

$$P_B = 10 + \frac{10 \times 18 + 25 \times 6}{30} = 21 \text{ kips}$$

Then $\qquad _cM_b = 36.83 \times 45 - 21 \times 15 = 1342 \text{ ft-kips}$

By symmetry, the maximum moment at b with left-to-right motion equals the maximum moment at c with right-to-left motion. The influence line for the latter moment is opposite hand to that in Fig. 9-3b. The moment at c with right-to-left motion attains its maximum value when load 2 is at C. For this position,

$$R_R = \frac{65(60 - 12 + 22)}{120} = 37.92 \text{ kips}$$

$$P_D = \frac{25 \times 12 + 20 \times 23.5}{30} = 25.67 \text{ kips}$$

Then $\qquad _cM_c = 37.92 \times 45 - 25.67 \times 15 = 1321 \text{ ft-kips}$

$$\therefore \; _cM_{b,\text{max}} = 1342 \text{ ft-kips}$$

$$M_{b,\text{max}} = 1890 + 1342 = 3232 \text{ ft-kips}$$

Assume BC is tensile. Taking moments about b, we have

$$\Sigma M_b = 20BC + 3232 = 0 \qquad BC = \textbf{161.6 kips C}$$

9-4 Influence Lines for Statically Indeterminate Structures The problem of constructing an influence line for some function in a statically indeterminate structure is most readily solved by applying the Müller-Breslau principle, which transforms the problem to one of constructing an elastic curve for a modified structure. We shall develop the principle by analyzing several illustrative cases.

With reference to the continuous beam in Fig. 9-6*a*, assume that we wish to construct the influence line for the reaction at the center support *B*. To do this, we apply a unit load at an arbitrary section *D*, inducing a reaction R_B at *B*. Our problem is to evaluate R_B. Consider that we

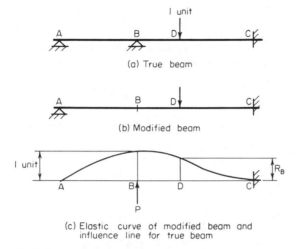

fig. 9-6

remove the center support, thereby obtaining the propped-cantilever beam shown in Fig. 9-6*b*. For this modified beam, let

y_{BB} = deflection at *B* due to unit load at *B*
y_{BD} = deflection at *B* due to unit load at *D*
y_{DB} = deflection at *D* due to unit load at *B*

The reaction R_B in the true beam must be of such magnitude as to cause zero deflection at *B*. Then

$$y_{BD} - R_B y_{BB} = 0 \qquad \therefore R_B = \frac{y_{BD}}{y_{BB}}$$

However, in accordance with the theorem of reciprocal deflections presented in Art. 6-5, $y_{BD} = y_{DB}$. We may therefore write

$$R_B = \frac{y_{DB}}{y_{BB}}$$

This equation expresses R_B in the true beam as a ratio of deflections in the modified (propped-cantilever) beam. Since deflections are proportional to loads, it is apparent that R_B equals the ratio of the deflection at *D* to the deflection at *B* caused by *any* vertical load applied at *B*. For simplicity, consider that we apply an upward load *P* at *B* that causes a unit displacement at that point, as shown in Fig. 9-6c.   The value of R_B is now represented by the deflection at D caused by this load.   Consequently, the elastic curve in Fig. 9-6c is the influence line for the reaction at support B in the true beam.

With reference to the fixed-ended beam in Fig. 9-7a, assume that we wish to construct the influence line for the bending moment at a given section C.   We apply a unit load at an arbitrary section D, inducing a bending moment M_C at C; our problem is to evaluate M_C.   Consider that we make the beam partially discontinuous at C in a manner that permits the two parts AC and CB to rotate relative to one another at C but constrains them to undergo an identical deflection at this section.   (This may be done by inserting a hinge at C.)   We now apply a unit moment to AC and CB at C, causing the elastic curve to assume a form similar to that shown in Fig. 9-7b.   For the modified beam, let

θ_{CC} = relative rotation at C due to unit moments at C
θ_{CD} = relative rotation at C due to unit load at D
y_{DC} = deflection at D due to unit moments at C

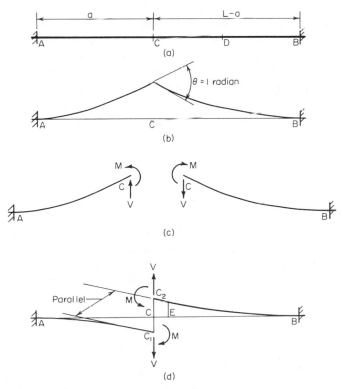

fig. 9-7   Influence lines for fixed-ended beam.

The bending moment M_C in the true beam must be of such magnitude as to cause zero relative rotation at C.   Then

$$\theta_{CD} - M_C\theta_{CC} = 0 \qquad \therefore M_C = \frac{\theta_{CD}}{\theta_{CC}}$$

However, in accordance with the theorem of reciprocal deflections, θ_{CD} and y_{DC} are equal in numerical value.   Then

$$M_C = \frac{y_{DC}}{\theta_{CC}}$$

If we apply moments M at C that cause a unit relative rotation at that section, we obtain the elastic curve shown in Fig. 9-7b.   This is the influence line for the bending moment at C in the true beam.   If M alone were acting at C, the longer part CB would deflect more than the shorter part AC.   Consequently, there must be a transverse force V transmitted across C, as shown in Fig. 9-7c.

Now assume that we wish to construct the influence line for shear at section C in Fig. 9-7a.   Consider that we make the beam partially discontinuous at C in a manner that permits the parts AC and CB to be displaced vertically relative to one another at C but constrains them to undergo an identical rotation at this section, as shown in Fig. 9-7d.   It may be demonstrated that if we apply vertical forces V at these ends to make the relative vertical displacement C_1C_2 equal to one unit, the resulting elastic curve of the modified beam is the influence line for shear at C in the true beam.   To satisfy the requirement that the two elastic curves have equal slopes at C, it is necessary to apply the moments M, which have the indicated directions.   Curve C_2B is concave downward above CE and concave upward above EB.

The foregoing results illustrate the Müller-Breslau principle, which may be expressed in this manner:

Consider that a structure is modified by removing the restraint exerted by a given function (reaction, bending moment, shear) at a given section. If the modified structure is subjected to a unit deformation (vertical deflection, relative rotation, relative vertical displacement) at this section, the resulting elastic curve is the influence line for the given function in the original structure.

It is important to observe that the modified structure is subjected solely to the deformation associated with removal of the restraint.   For example, when a vertical reaction is removed, we impose a vertical deflection on the modified structure; when a bending moment is removed, we impose a relative rotation.

Example 9-6   The prismatic beam in Fig. 9-7a is 45 ft long and AC is 20 ft.   Compute the values of M and V that are required to produce the unit rotation shown in Fig. 9-7b.

Solution. Figure 9-8 presents the bending-moment diagrams for AC and CB by parts; i.e., the moments caused by M and by V are represented by separate diagrams.   The slope and vertical deflection at C may be readily found by applying the moment-area method, taking into account the fact that the elastic curves are

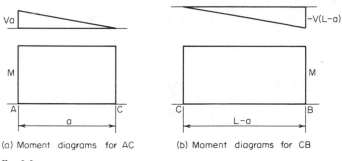

(a) Moment diagrams for AC   (b) Moment diagrams for CB

fig. 9-8

horizontal at the fixed supports A and B.   The slope at C is therefore equal to the area of the M/EI diagram between C and the fixed support, and the deflection at C equals the statical moment of this area with respect to C.   Taking absolute values only, we obtain the following results for AC:

$$EI\theta_c = \frac{Va^2}{2} + Ma$$

$$EIy_c = \frac{Va^2}{2}\frac{2}{3}a + Ma\frac{a}{2} = \frac{Va^3}{3} + \frac{Ma^2}{2}$$

For CB,

$$EI\theta_c = -\frac{V(L-a)^2}{2} + M(L-a)$$

$$EIy_c = -\frac{V(L-a)^3}{3} + \frac{M(L-a)^2}{2}$$

By equating the two expressions for y_c, we obtain the following relationship:

$$V = \frac{3}{2}\frac{(L-a)^2 - a^2}{(L-a)^3 + a^3}M$$

$$L = 45 \text{ ft} \qquad a = 20 \text{ ft} \qquad L - a = 25 \text{ ft}$$

Then

$$V = \frac{M}{70}$$

By summing the two expressions for the rotation at C and equating the relative rotation to unity, we obtain

$$EI\theta = M\left(\frac{1}{70}\frac{20^2}{2} + 20 - \frac{1}{70}\frac{25^2}{2} + 25\right) = EI \times 1$$

$$M = \frac{140}{6075}EI \quad \text{and} \quad V = \frac{2}{6075}EI$$

Having established the values of M and V, we may proceed to write the equations of the elastic curves in Fig. 9-7b. From the relationship between M and V, it follows that the elastic curve for CB has a point of inflection if $a < L/3$, and part of the curve therefore falls below the base line.

Where the modified structure is itself highly indeterminate, the problem of deriving the equations of the influence line for a given function becomes formidable. In this situation, it is helpful to construct a model of the modified structure and then subject it to the required deformation.

TEN

Stability of Structures

The loads applied to a structure must be transmitted to the underlying soil in such a manner that the maximum soil pressure shall not be excessive and that the structure shall be safe against horizontal displacement, over-turning, and uplift.

10-1 Distribution of Soil Pressure Assume that the resultant force acting on the base of a structure is eccentric with respect to the base. If the base is rigid, the deformation of the underlying soil varies uniformly across the length of base, and we therefore usually assume that the soil pressure also varies uniformly. By analogy, the prism of soil lying between the base and bedrock may be regarded as a beam-column, and the soil pressures are computed by means of the flexure formula.

Example 10-1 A pedestal-type footing weighing 50 kips supports a column with a load of 200 kips. At the base of the column, which is 5 ft above the base of the footing, there is a longitudinal horizontal force of 15 kips and a transverse horizontal force of 10 kips. The footing base is 10 × 12 ft. Compute the soil pressure at each corner of the footing.

Solution. Refer to Fig. 10-1.   We shall apply Eq. (5-5).

$$S_x = \tfrac{1}{6}bd^2 = \tfrac{1}{6} \times 12 \times 10^2 = 200 \text{ ft}^3$$
$$S_y = \tfrac{1}{6} \times 10 \times 12^2 = 240 \text{ ft}^3$$
$$f = \frac{P}{A} = \frac{250,000}{10 \times 12} = 2083 \text{ psf}$$
$$f_x = \frac{M_x}{S_x} = \frac{10,000 \times 5}{200} = 250 \text{ psf}$$
$$f_y = \frac{M_y}{S_y} = \frac{15,000 \times 5}{240} = 313 \text{ psf}$$
$$f_a = 2083 + 250 + 313 = \textbf{2646 psf}$$
$$f_b = 2083 + 250 - 313 = \textbf{2020 psf}$$
$$f_c = 2083 - 250 + 313 = \textbf{2146 psf}$$
$$f_d = 2083 - 250 - 313 = \textbf{1520 psf}$$

10-2   Gravity Dams   A *gravity* structure is one that carries little or no vertical load other than its own weight, this weight acting as the ballast for the structure.   Gravity dams usually have trapezoidal profiles, with the upstream face vertical.

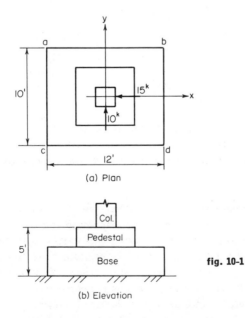

(a) Plan

(b) Elevation

fig. 10-1

Example 10-2   A concrete gravity dam is 20 ft high, 3 ft wide at the top, and 15 ft wide at the base.   The rear face is vertical.   Compute the foundation pressure under the toe and heel of the dam when the water surface is level with the top.   If the coefficient of friction is 0.6, what is the factor of safety (FS) against sliding?   What is the factor of safety against overturning?

Solution. Refer to Fig. 10-2. We shall use a 1-ft length of dam as epitomizing the entire structure. The weight of concrete is 150 pcf; the horizontal thrust of the impounded fluid is represented by the hydrostatic pressure triangle CBF. We shall determine the resultant force R on the base.

$$W_1 = \tfrac{1}{2} \times 12 \times 20 \times 150 = 18,000 \text{ lb}$$
$$W_2 = 3 \times 20 \times 150 = \underline{9,000}$$
$$R_V = 27,000 \text{ lb}$$
$$R_H = H = \tfrac{1}{2}wh^2 = \tfrac{1}{2} \times 62.4 \times 20^2 = 12,480 \text{ lb}$$

Take moments about the toe.

$$R_V x = 18,000 \times 8 + 9000 \times 13.5 - 12,480 \times 6.67$$
$$= 144,000 + 121,500 - 83,200 = 182,300 \text{ ft-lb}$$
$$\therefore x = 6.75 \text{ ft} \qquad e = 7.50 - 6.75 = 0.75 \text{ ft}$$

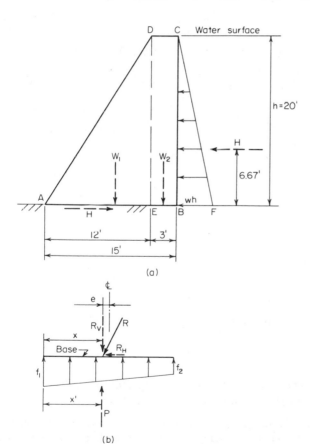

(a)

(b)

fig. 10-2 Soil pressure under dam.

Applying Eq. (5-10),

$$f_1 = \frac{27,000}{15 \times 1}\left(1 + \frac{6 \times 0.75}{15}\right)$$

or
$$f_1 = 1800 \times 1.3 = \textbf{2340 psf}$$
and
$$f_2 = 1800 \times 0.7 = \textbf{1260 psf}$$

Maximum resistance to sliding $= 0.6 \times 27,000 = 16,200$ lb

$$\text{FS against sliding} = \frac{16,200}{12,480} = \textbf{1.3}$$

From the preceding calculations,

Overturning moment $= 83,200$ ft-lb

Stabilizing moment $= 144,000 + 121,500 = 265,500$ ft-lb

$$\text{FS against overturning} = \frac{265,500}{83,200} = \textbf{3.2}$$

The computed values of f_1 and f_2 may be tested by determining the volume of the pressure prism and locating its centroidal axis.

$$P = \tfrac{1}{2} \times 15(2340 + 1260) = 27,000 \text{ lb} \qquad \text{OK}$$

$$x' = \frac{15}{3}\left(\frac{2340 + 2 \times 1260}{2340 + 1260}\right) = 6.75 \text{ ft} \qquad \text{OK}$$

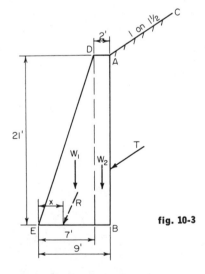

fig. 10-3

10-3   Retaining Walls   The function of a retaining wall is to confine laterally a mass of earth or other granular material.

Example 10-3   With reference to the concrete retaining wall in Fig. 10-3, the pressure on the back of wall has the following horizontal and vertical components:

$$p_H = 69.2y \qquad p_V = 46.2y$$

where y denotes the vertical distance from A to a given point.   Ascertain whether the wall is safe against overturning and uplift at the heel.

Solution. Since the pressure diagram is triangular, the action line of the result-ant earth thrust T intersects AB at a point 7 ft above B.   We shall compute the moment of the loads with respect to the toe.

$$W_1 = \tfrac{1}{2} \times 7 \times 21 \times 150 = 11{,}030 \text{ lb}$$
$$W_2 = 2 \times 21 \times 150 = 6300 \text{ lb}$$
$$T_H = \tfrac{1}{2} \times 69.2 \times 21^2 = 15{,}260 \text{ lb}$$
$$T_V = \tfrac{1}{2} \times 46.2 \times 21^2 = 10{,}190 \text{ lb}$$
$$M_E = 11{,}030 \times 4.67 + 6300 \times 8 + 10{,}190 \times 9 - 15{,}260 \times 7$$
$$= 86{,}760 \text{ ft-lb}$$

Since the moment about the toe is clockwise, the wall is safe against over-turning.   We shall locate the resultant R of the loads.

$$R_V = 11{,}030 + 6300 + 10{,}190 = 27{,}520 \text{ lb}$$

$$x = \frac{M_E}{R_V} = \frac{86{,}760}{27{,}520} = 3.2 \text{ ft}$$

Since the resultant strikes the base within the middle third, the structure is not subject to uplift.   This conclusion stems from the discussion of kern distances in Art. 5-6.

ELEVEN
Riveted and Welded Connections

In the design of riveted and welded connections, we shall apply the Specification of the American Institute of Steel Construction, adopted 1963. It is to be understood that the structural members are made of ASTM A36 steel, which has a yield-point stress of 36,000 psi. (In the Specification, the yield-point stress is denoted by F_y. Where an allowable stress is a function of the yield point, the numerical value is presented in the Appendix to the Specification.)

11-1 Riveted Joints under Concentric Loading Assume that a riveted joint connects plates that carry tensile forces. An investigation of the joint requires consideration of three types of stress: The shearing stress in the rivet, the bearing stress between the rivet and plate, and the tensile stress in the plate. The shearing stress is assumed to be uniform across the transverse section of the rivet. The bearing stress is assumed to be uniform across an area that lies on a plane through the rivet center normal to the load; the effective bearing area is therefore taken as the product of the rivet diameter and thickness of plate.

In the following material, it is to be understood that the connections are made with A141 hot-driven rivets. The allowable stresses in the joint as prescribed by Secs. 1.5.1.1 and 1.5.2 of the AISC Specification are as follows:

Tensile stress in plate............ 22,000 psi
Shearing stress in rivet.......... 15,000
Bearing stress.................. 48,500

As shown in Fig. 11-1, a rivet is said to be in *single shear* if the opposing forces tend to shear the rivet along one plane, and in *double shear* if they

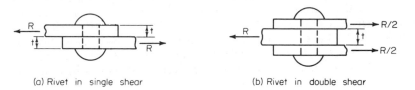

(a) Rivet in single shear   (b) Rivet in double shear

fig. 11-1

tend to shear it along two planes.

The notational system is as follows:

R_{ss} = shearing capacity of rivet in single shear
R_{ds} = shearing capacity of rivet in double shear
R_b = bearing capacity of rivet
t = thickness of connected member

Example 11-1 Compute the values of R_{ss}, R_{ds}, and R_b for ¾- and ⅞-in. rivets.
Solution. For a ¾-in. rivet, we have the following:

$$\text{Area of cross section} = 0.7854 \times 0.75^2 = 0.4418 \text{ sq in.}$$
$$R_{ss} = 0.4418 \times 15,000 = 6630 \text{ lb}$$
$$R_{ds} = 2 \times 0.4418 \times 15,000 = 13,250 \text{ lb}$$
$$\text{Effective bearing area} = 0.75t$$
$$R_b = 0.75t \times 48,500 = 36,380t \quad \text{lb}$$

For a ⅞-in. rivet, we have the following:

$$\text{Area of cross section} = 0.7854 \times 0.875^2 = 0.6013 \text{ sq in.}$$
$$R_{ss} = 0.6013 \times 15,000 = 9020 \text{ lb}$$
$$R_{ds} = 2 \times 0.6013 \times 15,000 = 18,040 \text{ lb}$$
$$\text{Effective bearing area} = 0.875t$$
$$R_b = 0.875t \times 48,500 = 42,440t \quad \text{lb}$$

The capacity of a rivet in shear and in bearing against a plate of given thickness may be obtained directly by referring to the tables on pages 4-4 to 4-7 of the AISC Manual.

Two plates may be connected to one another by means of a *lap splice*, in which one plate overlaps the other, or a *butt splice*, in which the plates are joined through the use of auxiliary plates, termed *cover, strap,* or *splice* plates.   Rivet holes are generally made $\frac{1}{16}$ in. larger than the rivet diameter to provide driving clearance, but punched holes are deemed to be $\frac{1}{8}$ in. larger than the rivet diameter to allow for damage to the surrounding metal.

Example 11-2   The hanger in Fig. 11-2a is spliced with nine $\frac{3}{4}$-in. rivets in the manner shown.   Compute the load P that may be transmitted across this lap splice.

Solution. There are three criteria to be considered: the shearing strength of the connection, the bearing strength of the connection, and the tensile strength of the plate at each row of rivets.   We shall use subscripts to identify each criterion.

Since the load is concentric, it is assumed that the load transmitted through each rivet is $\frac{1}{9}P$.   As plate A deflects, it bears against the upper half of each rivet.   Consequently, the reaction of the rivet on plate A is exerted *above* the horizontal diametral plane of the rivet.

The capacity of the joint in shear and in bearing is as follows:

$$P_{ss} = 9 \times 6630 = 59{,}700 \text{ lb}$$
$$P_b = 9 \times 36{,}380 \times 0.375 = 122{,}800 \text{ lb}$$

Refer to Fig. 11-2b, c, and d.   The capacity of the plate in tension is determined by means of the following calculations, in which s denotes the tensile stress.   The effective diameter of rivet hole is $\frac{7}{8}$ in.

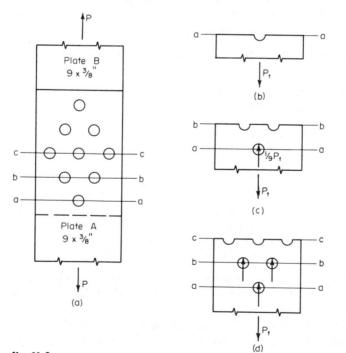

fig. 11-2

At *aa*:

$$\text{Residual tension} = P_t$$
$$\text{Net area} = (9 - 0.875) \times 0.375 = 3.05 \text{ sq in.}$$

$$s = \frac{P_t}{3.05} = 22{,}000 \qquad P_t = 67{,}100 \text{ lb}$$

At *bb*:

$$\text{Residual tension} = \tfrac{8}{9}P_t$$
$$\text{Net area} = (9 - 1.75) \times 0.375 = 2.72 \text{ sq in.}$$

$$s = \frac{\tfrac{8}{9}P_t}{2.72} = 22{,}000 \qquad P_t = 67{,}300 \text{ lb}$$

At *cc*:

$$\text{Residual tension} = \tfrac{2}{3}P_t$$
$$\text{Net area} = (9 - 2.625) \times 0.375 = 2.39 \text{ sq in.}$$

$$s = \frac{\tfrac{2}{3}P_t}{2.39} = 22{,}000 \qquad P_t = 78{,}900 \text{ lb}$$

The allowable load is the lowest of the five computed values, namely, **59,700 lb.**

Example 11-3   A tension member in the form of a $10 \times \tfrac{1}{2}$ in. steel plate is to be spliced with $\tfrac{7}{8}$-in. rivets.   Design a butt splice for the maximum load the member may carry.

Solution. The design load P is established by computing the allowable load at a cross section having one rivet hole.

$$\text{Net area} = (10 - 1) \times 0.5 = 4.5 \text{ sq in.}$$
$$P = 4.5 \times 22{,}000 = 99{,}000 \text{ lb}$$

Since two cover plates are used in a butt splice, the rivets will be in double shear.   Refer to the results in Example 11-1 or to the tables in the AISC Manual.

$$R_{ds} = 18{,}040 \text{ lb} \qquad R_b = 42{,}440 \times 0.5 = 21{,}220 \text{ lb}$$
$$\frac{99{,}000}{18{,}040} = 5.5$$

Use six rivets.

The rivets must be so arranged as to maintain an approximate balance between the drop in plate area and the drop in residual tension, and the rivet spacing must satisfy Secs. 1.16.4 and 1.16.5 of the AISC Specification.   We shall try the pattern shown in Fig. 11-3.   The calculated results are recorded in the accompanying table, and the rivet pattern is found to be satisfactory.

Section	Residual tension in main plate, lb	÷	Net area, sq in.	=	Stress, psi
aa	99,000		4.5		22,000
bb	82,500		4.0		20,600
cc	49,500		3.5		14,100

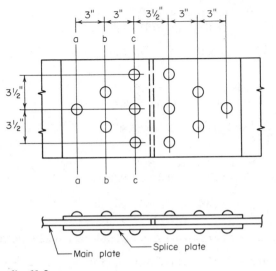

fig. 11-3

We shall now design the splice plates. To the left of the centerline of joint, the splice plates bear against the *left* half of each rivet. Therefore, the entire load has been transmitted to the splice plates at *cc*, which is the critical section.

$$\text{Tension in splice plate} = \tfrac{1}{2} \times 99{,}000 = 49{,}500 \text{ lb}$$

$$\text{Thickness required} = \frac{49{,}500}{22{,}000 \times 7} = 0.321 \text{ in.}$$

Make splice plates **10 × ⅜ in.**

11-2   Torsion on Riveted Joints   Consider that a member is riveted to its support and then subjected to a moment, as illustrated in Fig. 11-4*a*.

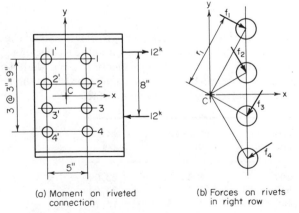

(a) Moment on riveted connection

(b) Forces on rivets in right row

fig. 11-4

This moment causes the member to rotate slightly, thereby exerting a tangential thrust on each rivet. It may be demonstrated that the center of rotation coincides with the centroid of the rivet group. Assume that all rivets are the same size. Let

M = moment on joint
f = force on given rivet
r = distance from centroid of group to center of given rivet
J = polar moment of inertia of rivet group with respect to its centroid, considering the cross-sectional area of rivet as unity

Then
$$f = \frac{Mr}{J} \tag{11-1}$$

Consider that we establish rectangular coordinate axes through the centroid of the rivet group, as shown. Let x and y denote the coordinates of the given rivet. Resolving f into its components, we obtain

$$f_x = \frac{My}{J} \quad \text{and} \quad f_y = \frac{Mx}{J} \tag{11-2}$$

Example 11-4 The channel in Fig. 11-4a is connected to its supporting column with $\frac{3}{4}$-in. rivets and resists the indicated couple. Compute the shearing stress in each rivet.

Solution. Let s denote the shearing stress.

$$M = 12,000 \times 8 = 96,000 \text{ in.-lb}$$
$$r_1 = r_4 = \sqrt{2.5^2 + 4.5^2} = 5.15 \text{ in.}$$
$$r_2 = r_3 = \sqrt{2.5^2 + 1.5^2} = 2.92 \text{ in.}$$
$$J = \Sigma r^2 = \Sigma(x^2 + y^2) = 8 \times 2.5^2 + 4 \times 1.5^2 + 4 \times 4.5^2$$
$$= 140 \text{ sq in.}$$
$$f_1 = f_4 = \frac{96,000 \times 5.15}{140} = 3530 \text{ lb}$$
$$f_2 = f_3 = \frac{96,000 \times 2.92}{140} = 2000 \text{ lb}$$

The directions of these forces are shown in Fig. 11-4b.

$$s_1 = s_4 = \frac{3530}{0.442} = 7990 \text{ psi}$$
$$s_2 = s_3 = \frac{2000}{0.442} = 4520 \text{ psi}$$

The rivet forces may be checked by summing their moments with respect to the centroid.

$$M_1 = M_4 = 3530 \times 5.15 = 18,180 \text{ in.-lb}$$
$$M_2 = M_3 = 2000 \times 2.92 = 5840 \text{ in.-lb}$$
$$\Sigma M = 4 \times 18,180 + 4 \times 5840 = 96,080 \text{ in.-lb} \qquad \text{OK}$$

When a rivet group sustains a load P of eccentricity e, we may supplant this eccentric load with an equivalent system comprising a concentric load P and moment Pe. The AISC Manual recommends that we replace the true eccentricity with an *effective* eccentricity in order to account implicitly for certain secondary effects. The procedure is illustrated on

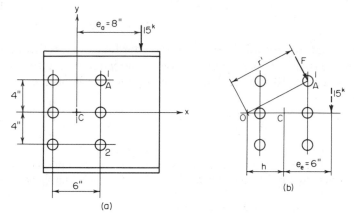

(a)

(b)

fig. 11-5

page 4-50 of the Manual. Refer to the symmetrical rivet group in Fig. 11-5a, and let

e_a = actual eccentricity of load
e_e = effective eccentricity
n = number of rivets in vertical row

Then
$$e_e = e_a - \left(\frac{1 + n}{2}\right) \tag{11-3}$$

An eccentrically loaded rivet group may be analyzed by two distinct methods. The first method entails superposing the effects of the equivalent concentric load and moment. With respect to a given rivet, let

f = force caused by moment
f' = force caused by concentric load
F = resultant force

The second method of solution entails locating the instantaneous center of rotation of the connected member under the eccentric load. Refer to Fig. 11-5*b*, where *O* is the center of rotation, and let

h = distance from center of rotation to centroid of rivet group
r' = distance from center of rotation to center of rivet
N = total number of rivets

$$h = \frac{J}{e_e N} \tag{11-4}$$

$$F = \frac{Mr'}{J} \tag{11-5}$$

The action line of this force is normal to the radius from center of rotation to center of rivet.

Example 11-5 With reference to the connection in Fig. 11-5*a*, calculate the maximum force exerted on a rivet.

Solution

$$e_e = 8 - \frac{1+3}{2} = 6 \text{ in.}$$

$$J = \Sigma(x^2 + y^2) = 6 \times 3^2 + 4 \times 4^2 = 118 \text{ sq in.}$$

$$P = 15{,}000 \text{ lb} \qquad M = 15{,}000 \times 6 = 90{,}000 \text{ in.-lb}$$

METHOD 1. As the calculations will disclose, rivets 1 and 2 receive the greatest thrust. For these rivets,

$$x = 3 \text{ in.} \qquad y = 4 \text{ in.}$$

$$f_x = \frac{90{,}000 \times 4}{118} = 3050 \text{ lb}$$

$$f_y = \frac{90{,}000 \times 3}{118} = 2290 \text{ lb}$$

$$f_y' = \frac{15{,}000}{6} = 2500 \text{ lb}$$

$$F_x = f_x = 3050 \text{ lb}$$

$$F_y = f_y + f_y' = 2290 + 2500 = 4790 \text{ lb}$$

$$F = \sqrt{3050^2 + 4790^2} = \textbf{5680 lb}$$

METHOD 2

$$h = \frac{118}{6 \times 6} = 3.28 \text{ in.}$$

For rivets 1 and 2, $r' = \sqrt{6.28^2 + 4^2} = 7.45 \text{ in.}$

$$F = \frac{90{,}000 \times 7.45}{118} = 5680 \text{ lb}$$

11-3   Welded Connections   In the following material, it is to be understood that the connections are made with fillet welds of A233 Class E60 series electrodes. The weld profile is con-

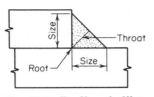

sidered to be an isosceles triangle, as shown in Fig. 11-6. It is assumed that failure would occur by shearing along the throat of weld, and the allowable shearing stress as prescribed in Sec. 1.5.3.1 of the AISC Specification is 13,600 psi.

fig. 11-6 Profile of fillet weld.

Let n denote the number of sixteenths included in the weld size. (For example, for a $\frac{3}{8}$-in. weld, $n = 6$.) Then

$$\text{Weld size} = \frac{n}{16}$$

$$\text{Throat area per lin. in. of weld} = \frac{0.707n}{16}$$

$$= 0.0442n \qquad \text{sq in.}$$

$$\text{Capacity of weld} = 13,600 \times 0.0442n = 600n \qquad \text{pli}$$

Consider that a structural member in the form of an angle is to be welded to its support on three sides, as shown in Fig. 11-7, the weld at

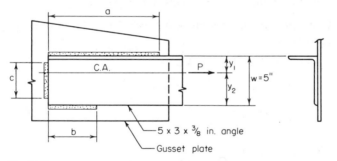

fig. 11-7

the end being centered about the angle leg. Assume that the member will sustain repeated variation in stress. Section 1.15.3 of the AISC Specification requires that the weld be so disposed as to place its centroidal axis in vertical alignment with that of the angle.

Let L denote the total length of weld. The required disposition of weld is as follows:

$$a = \frac{Ly_2}{w} - \frac{c}{2} \qquad b = \frac{Ly_1}{w} - \frac{c}{2} \tag{11-6}$$

where the notational system is that shown in Fig. 11-7.

Example 11-6   The 5-in. leg of a $5 \times 3 \times \frac{3}{8}$ in. angle is to be welded to a gusset plate in the manner shown in Fig. 11-7.   The member will be subjected to repeated variation in stress.   Design a suitable joint.

Solution.   We shall design the connection for the capacity P of the member. The properties of the section are recorded on page 1-31 of the AISC Manual.

$$A = 2.86 \text{ sq in.} \qquad P = 2.86 \times 22,000 = 62,920 \text{ lb}$$
$$y_1 = 1.70 \text{ in.} \qquad y_2 = 5.00 - 1.70 = 3.30 \text{ in.}$$

Section 1.17.5 restricts the weld size to $\frac{5}{16}$ in.; this has a capacity of 3000 pli.

$$L = \frac{62,920}{3000} = 20.97 \text{ in.} \qquad \text{Set } c = 5 \text{ in.}$$

$$a = \frac{20.97 \times 3.30}{5} - \frac{5}{2} = 11.34 \text{ in.}$$

$$b = \frac{20.97 \times 1.70}{5} - \frac{5}{2} = 4.63 \text{ in.}$$

Make $a = 11.5$ in. and $b = 5$ in.

In Art. 11-2, we analyzed an eccentrically loaded rivet group by two alternative methods.   These methods are valid with respect to a weld group as well.   In this analysis, the weld may be considered as concentrated along the edge of the supported member.

Example 11-7   The bracket in Fig. 11-8 is connected to its support with a $\frac{1}{4}$-in. fillet weld.   Compute the maximum stress in the weld.

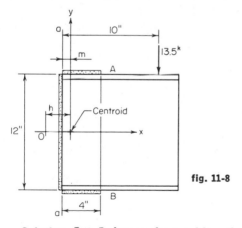

fig. 11-8

Solution.   Let L denote the total length of the weld group and s the maximum stress.   Taking moments of the weld group with respect to line aa, we obtain

$$m = \frac{2 \times 4 \times 2}{12 + 2 \times 4} = 0.8 \text{ in.}$$

$$M = 13,500(10 - 0.8) = 124,200 \text{ in.-lb}$$

The properties of the weld group are as follows:

$$I_x = \frac{1}{12} \times 12^3 + 2 \times 4 \times 6^2 = 432 \text{ in.}^3$$
$$I_y = 12 \times 0.8^2 + 2 \times \frac{1}{12} \times 4^3 + 2 \times 4(2 - 0.8)^2 = 29.9 \text{ in.}^3$$
$$J = I_x + I_y = 432 + 29.9 = 461.9 \text{ in.}^3$$

We shall apply the center-of-rotation method. Let O denote the center of rotation. Equation (11-4), when adapted to a weld group, becomes

$$h = \frac{J}{eL} = \frac{461.9}{9.2 \times 20} = 2.51 \text{ in.}$$

The maximum stress occurs at A and B. At these points,

$$x = 4 - 0.8 = 3.2 \text{ in.} \qquad x + h = 5.71 \text{ in.}$$
$$r' = \sqrt{5.71^2 + 6^2} = 8.28 \text{ in.}$$

Applying Eq. (11-5),

$$F = \frac{124,200 \times 8.28}{461.9} = 2230 \text{ pli}$$

$$s = \frac{2230}{0.707 \times 0.25} = \textbf{12,600 psi}$$

TWELVE

Design of Steel Beams

12-1 Introduction The design of steel members in flexure will be executed in accordance with the Specification of the American Institute of Steel Construction, adopted 1963. The Appendix to the Specification presents the numerical values of the allowable stresses associated with each grade of steel, and it includes tables that facilitate beam design.

The present analysis of steel beams is based upon elastic (or working-stress) design. However, many provisions of the Specification for elastic design implicitly recognize the postelastic behavior of the members. In the absence of an express statement to the contrary, it is to be understood that the structural members are made of ASTM A36 steel, which has a yield-point stress of 36,000 psi.

The notational system for the design of steel beams conforms with that adopted in Chap. 5 but is augmented to include the following:

A_f = area of flange
A_w = area of web
b_f = width of flange
d = depth of section
d_w = depth of web

t_f = thickness of flange
t_w = thickness of web
L' = unbraced length of compression flange
f_y = yield-point stress
W = total uniform load on beam

12-2   Design of Rolled Sections   The design of a rolled section to support a given load system is usually governed by the allowable bending stress rather than the allowable shearing stress.   However, if the ratio of maximum vertical shear to maximum bending moment is extraordinarily large, as in the case of a heavily loaded short-span beam or a beam that carries a large concentrated load near its support, the shearing strength of the member may be the determining criterion.   Since the variation in shearing stress across the web of a rolled section is relatively small, we use a nominal shearing stress v computed in the following manner:

$$v = \frac{V}{dt_w} \tag{12-1}$$

The compression flange tends to deflect laterally, and its postelastic behavior is influenced by its shape.   Consequently, the allowable bending stress in this flange is governed by the restraint against lateral deflection and the width-thickness ratio of the flange.

Example 12-1   A beam on a simple span of 30 ft carries a uniform superimposed load of 1640 plf.   The compression flange has continuous lateral support. Select the most economical rolled section.
   Solution. Assume that the beam weighs 60 plf and satisfies the requirements of a compact section as set forth in Sec. 1.5.1.4.1 of the AISC Specification.

$$M = \tfrac{1}{8}wL^2 = \tfrac{1}{8} \times 1700 \times 30^2 \times 12 = 2{,}295{,}000 \text{ in.-lb}$$

Refer to page 5-67 of the AISC Manual.   In accordance with Sec. 1.5.1.4.1, the allowable bending stress is 24,000 psi.

$$S = \frac{M}{f} = \frac{2{,}295{,}000}{24{,}000} = 95.6 \text{ in.}^3$$

The rolled sections are listed on pages 2-4 and 2-5 of the Manual in descending order with respect to their section moduli.

Use **18WF55:** $S = 98.2$ in.^{3} section compact

For the sake of completeness, we shall calculate the shearing stress, although it is manifestly not critical in the present instance.   Section 1.5.1.2 provides an allowable shearing stress of 14,500 psi.   The properties of this section are recorded on pages 1-10 and 1-11 of the Manual.

$$d = 18.12 \text{ in.} \qquad t_w = 0.390 \text{ in.}$$
$$V = \tfrac{1}{2} \times 1695 \times 30 = 25{,}430 \text{ lb}$$
$$v = \frac{25{,}430}{18.12 \times 0.390} = 3600 \text{ psi} \qquad \text{OK}$$

Alternatively, the member may be designed by consulting the tables of allowable uniform loads commencing on page 2-14 of the AISC Manual.   The total load on the beam is 50,900 lb.   As shown on page 2-22, the capacity of an 18WF55 beam on a 30-ft span is 52,000 lb.

Assume that the compression flange of a beam has only intermittent lateral support.   After a trial section has been selected, it is necessary to compare the unbraced length L' with the properties L_c and L_u of that section in order to establish the allowable bending stress.   These properties are defined in the following manner:

L_c = maximum allowable unbraced length of compression flange if allowable bending stress is to equal $0.66f_y$

L_u = maximum allowable unbraced length of compression flange if allowable bending stress is to equal $0.60f_y$

The values of L_c and L_u associated with each rolled section made of the indicated grade of steel are recorded in the allowable–uniform-load tables of the AISC Manual.   The former value is established by applying the definition of a "laterally supported" member as presented in Sec. 1.5.1.4.1 of the Specification; the latter value is established by applying Formula (4) or (5) of Sec. 1.5.1.4.5, whichever controls.

There are four conditions relating to the allowable stress, as follows:

Condition	*Allowable stress*
Compact section; $L' \leq L_c$	$0.66f_y$
Compact section; $L_c < L' \leq L_u$	$0.60f_y$
Noncompact section; $L' \leq L_u$	$0.60f_y$
$L' > L_u$	Apply Formula (4) or (5); use greater value.

The values of allowable uniform load recorded in the AISC tables apply to beams of A36 steel satisfying the first or third condition, depending on whether the section is compact or noncompact, respectively.

Example 12-2   A beam on a simple span of 25 ft carries a uniformly distributed load, including its estimated weight, of 45 kips.   The member is laterally supported at 5-ft intervals.   Select the most economical member (*a*) using A36 steel and (*b*) using A242 steel.

Solution

PART *a*. Refer to page 2-23 of the AISC Manual.   Use **16WF45**.

$$W_{allow} = 46 \text{ kips}$$
$$L_c = 7.6 > 5 \text{ ft} \qquad \text{OK}$$

PART *b*. As noted on page 5-91 of the Manual, the yield-point stress of A242 steel is 50,000 psi when the thickness of metal is ¾ in. or less.   Although the allowable–uniform-load tables pertain directly to beams of A36 steel, they may be applied indirectly in the present instance by the following method: Assume that the shape selected will be compact.   The true load for an A242 member is transformed to an equivalent load for an A36 member by applying the conversion factor 1.38, this being the ratio of allowable stresses.   The conversion factors are recorded at the bottom of the allowable–uniform-load tables.

$$\text{Equivalent load} = \frac{45}{1.38} = 32.6 \text{ kips}$$

The lightest adequate section appears to be the 16WF36, which has a capacity of 36 kips on a simple span of 25 ft.   However, as noted at the bottom of the table, the section is noncompact in A242 steel, and the proper conversion factor is therefore 1.25.

$$\text{Equivalent load} = \frac{45}{1.25} = 36 \text{ kips}$$
$$L_u = 6.3 > 5 \text{ ft} \qquad \therefore \text{ use } \mathbf{16WF36}$$

We shall verify the design by calculating the bending stress in the member. From page 1-11 or 2-23 of the Manual, $S = 56.3$ in.³

$$M = \tfrac{1}{8}WL = \tfrac{1}{8} \times 45,000 \times 25 \times 12 = 1,688,000 \text{ in.-lb}$$
$$f = \frac{M}{S} = \frac{1,688,000}{56.3} = 30,000 \text{ psi}$$
$$f_{allow} = 0.6 \times 50,000 = 30,000 \text{ psi} \qquad \text{OK}$$

Where the unbraced length L' exceeds L_u, the allowable bending stress is found by applying the provisions of Sec. 1.5.1.4.5 of the AISC Specification.   For A36 steel, Formula (4) reduces to the following form:

$$f_1 = 22,000 - \frac{0.679(L'/r)^2}{C_b} \qquad \text{psi} \tag{12-2}$$

By Formula (5),

$$f_2 = \frac{12,000,000}{L'd/A_f} \qquad \text{psi} \tag{12-3}$$

The allowable stress is taken as the larger of the two values.

Where deflection is a criterion, the beam size must satisfy Sec. 1.13 of the Specification.

Example 12-3 The compression flange of the beam in Fig. 12-1a will be braced only at points A, B, C, D, and E. By consulting the chart on page 2-52 of the AISC Manual, the designer has selected a 21WF55 section. Verify the design.

Solution. The shear and bending-moment diagrams are shown in Fig. 12-1b and c, respectively. The relevant properties of the 21WF55, which are presented on pages 1-9 and 2-20 of the AISC Manual, are as follows:

$$S = 109.7 \text{ in.}^3 \qquad I_y = 44.0 \text{ in.}^4$$
$$b_f = 8.215 \text{ in.} \qquad t_f = 0.522 \text{ in.}$$
$$d = 20.80 \text{ in.} \qquad t_w = 0.375 \text{ in.}$$

$$\frac{d}{A_f} = 4.85 \text{ per in.}$$

$$L_c = 8.9 \text{ ft} \qquad L_u = 9.4 \text{ ft}$$

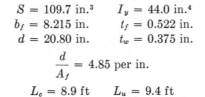

(a) Force diagram

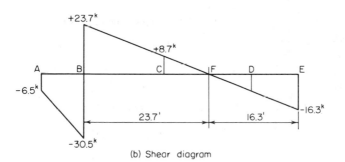

(b) Shear diagram

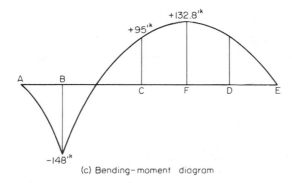

(c) Bending-moment diagram

fig. 12-1

Since $L' > L_u$ between B and D, the allowable bending stress is below 22,000 psi in this region.   Refer to Fig. 12-2.   The moment of inertia of the T section is found in this manner:

$$A_f = 8.215 \times 0.522 = 4.29 \text{ sq in.}$$
$$\tfrac{1}{6}A_w = \tfrac{1}{6} \times 19.76 \times 0.375 = \underline{1.24}$$
$$A_T = 5.53 \text{ sq in.}$$
$$I_T = \tfrac{1}{2} \times I_y \text{ of section} = 22.0 \text{ in.}^4$$
$$r = \sqrt{\frac{22.0}{5.53}} = 1.99 \text{ in.}$$

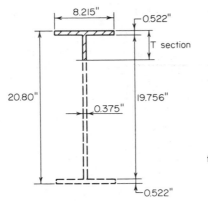

fig. 12-2   Dimensions of 21WF55.

INTERVAL AB

$$L' = 8 \text{ ft} < L_c \qquad \therefore f_{\text{allow}} = 24,000 \text{ psi}$$
$$f_{\max} = \frac{148,000 \times 12}{109.7} = 16,200 \text{ psi} \qquad \text{OK}$$

INTERVAL BC

$$\frac{L'}{r} = \frac{15 \times 12}{1.99} = 90.5 \qquad \frac{M_1}{M_2} = \frac{95}{-148} = -0.642$$
$$C_b = 1.75 - 1.05(-0.642) + 0.3(-0.642)^2 = 2.55$$

Therefore, setting $C_b = 2.3$,

$$f_1 = 22,000 - \frac{0.679 \times 90.5^2}{2.3} = 19,600 \text{ psi}$$
$$f_2 = \frac{12,000,000}{15 \times 12 \times 4.85} = 13,700 \text{ psi}$$
$$f_{\max} = 16,200 < 19,600 \text{ psi} \qquad \text{OK}$$

INTERVAL CD. Since the maximum moment occurs within the interval rather than at a boundary section, $C_b = 1$.

$$\frac{L'}{r} = \frac{16.5 \times 12}{1.99} = 99.5$$

$$f_1 = 22,000 - 0.679 \times 99.5^2 = 15,300 \text{ psi}$$

$$f_2 = \frac{12,000,000}{16.5 \times 12 \times 4.85} = 12,500 \text{ psi}$$

$$f_{\max} = \frac{132,800 \times 12}{109.7} = 14,500 < 15,300 \text{ psi} \qquad \text{OK}$$

INTERVAL DE. The allowable stress is 24,000 psi, and the actual stress is considerably below this value.

The 21WF55 is therefore satisfactory.

12-3   Cover-plated Beams   The flexural strength of a rolled beam may be augmented by supplementing the member with cover plates attached to the flanges.   These reinforcing plates must span the region where the bending moment exceeds the capacity of the rolled section alone.   The following approximation is helpful in securing a trial size of cover plate:

$$A = \frac{1.05(S - S_r)}{d_r} \tag{12-4}$$

where A = area of one cover plate
S = section modulus required
S_r = section modulus of rolled section
d_r = depth of rolled section

Example 12-4   Following the fabrication of an 18WF60 beam, a revision was made in the architectural plans, and the member is now required to support the loads shown in Fig. 12-3a.   Cover plates are to be welded to both flanges to develop the required strength.   Design these plates and their connection to the WF shape, using fillet welds of A233 Class E60 series electrodes.   The member has continuous lateral support.

Solution. The shear and bending-moment diagrams are shown in Fig. 12-3b and c, respectively.   Assume that the built-up section will be compact.

$$S = \frac{M}{f} = \frac{340.3 \times 12}{24} = 170.2 \text{ in.}^3$$

The properties of the 18WF60 as recorded on page 1-11 of the AISC Manual are as follows:

$$d = 18.25 \text{ in.} \qquad b_f = 7.56 \text{ in.} \qquad t_f = 0.695 \text{ in.}$$
$$I = 984 \text{ in.}^4 \qquad S = 107.8 \text{ in.}^3$$

By Eq. (12-4),

$$A = \frac{1.05(170.2 - 107.8)}{18.25} = 3.59 \text{ sq in.}$$

Try $10 \times \frac{3}{8}$ in. plates.

$$A = 3.75 \text{ sq in.}$$

Since the beam flange is $7\frac{1}{2}$ in. wide, ample space is provided to accommodate the welds. However, the cover plates must satisfy Secs. 1.5.1.4.1 and 1.9.1 of the AISC Specification.

Sec. 1.5.1.4.1: $\dfrac{7.56}{0.375} = 20.2 < 32$ OK

Sec. 1.9.1: $\dfrac{\frac{1}{2}(10 - 7.56)}{0.375} = 3.25 < 16$ OK

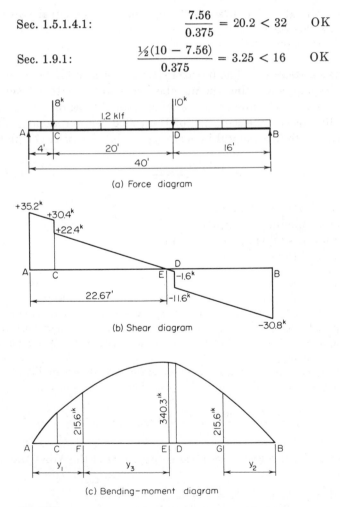

(a) Force diagram

(b) Shear diagram

(c) Bending-moment diagram

fig. 12-3

We shall test the adequacy of the trial section, which is shown in Fig. 12-4a. By Eq. (2-11),

$$I = 984 + 2 \times 3.75 \times 9.31^2 = 1634 \text{ in.}^4$$

$$S = \frac{I}{c} = \frac{1634}{9.5} = 172.0 \text{ in.}^3 \quad \text{OK}$$

We shall now establish the length of cover plates and design their connection to the WF section. In Fig. 12-3c, let F and G denote the sections at which the bending moment equals the capacity of the WF section alone. This moment is

$$M = fS = \frac{24 \times 107.8}{12} = 215.6 \text{ ft-kips}$$

$$M_F = 35.2y_1 - 8(y_1 - 4) - \tfrac{1}{2} \times 1.2y_1^2 = 215.6$$

$$M_G = 30.8y_2 - \tfrac{1}{2} \times 1.2y_2^2 = 215.6$$

Solving, $y_1 = 8.25 \text{ ft}$ $y_2 = 8.36 \text{ ft}$

For symmetry, the cover plates will be centered about midspan. The theoretical cutoff points therefore lie 8 ft 3 in. from each support. However, the plates must be extended beyond these points in order that the axial force in each plate at its end may be transmitted to the WF shape. Let P denote this force

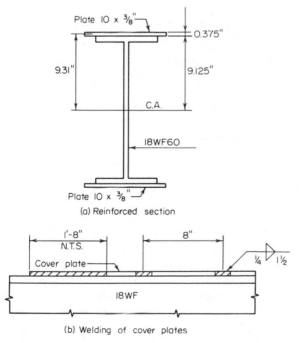

(a) Reinforced section

(b) Welding of cover plates

fig. 12-4

and L the length of weld required for its transmission.   The mean bending stress in the cover plate at F is

$$f_{\text{mean}} = \frac{My}{I} = \frac{215,600 \times 12 \times 9.31}{1634} = 14,740 \text{ psi}$$

Then $P = Af_{\text{mean}} = 3.75 \times 14,740 = 55,280 \text{ lb}$

Use a $\frac{1}{4}$-in. fillet weld, which satisfies the requirements of Secs. 1.17.4 and 1.17.5.

$$\text{Capacity of weld} = 4 \times 600 = 2400 \text{ pli}$$
$$L = \frac{55,280}{2400} = 23.0 \text{ in.}$$

In accordance with Sec. 1.10.4, we shall extend the cover plates 20 in. beyond the theoretical cutoff point at each end and supply a continuous $\frac{1}{4}$-in. fillet weld along both edges in this extension.   Thus, there will be 40 in. of weld as compared with the 23 in. needed to develop the plate.

The intermittent weld must resist the longitudinal shear at the inner surface of the cover plate.   Refer to Eq. (5-8).

$$V_F = 35.2 - 8 - 1.2 \times 8.25 = 17.3 \text{ kips}$$
$$V_G = -30.8 + 1.2 \times 8.36 = -20.8 \text{ kips}$$
$$q = \frac{VQ}{I} = \frac{20,800 \times 3.75 \times 9.31}{1634} = 444 \text{ pli}$$

Section 1.17.7 requires a minimum weld length of $1\frac{1}{2}$ in.   Let s denote the center-to-center spacing as governed by shear.

$$s = \frac{2 \times 1.5 \times 2400}{444} = 16.2 \text{ in.}$$

However, Secs. 1.18.2.3 and 1.18.3 impose additional restrictions on the weld spacing.   To preclude the possibility of error in fabrication, we shall provide an identical spacing at top and bottom.

$$s_{\text{max}} = 21 \times 0.375 = 7.9 \text{ in.}$$

Therefore, use a $\frac{1}{4}$-in. fillet weld, $1\frac{1}{2}$ in. long, 8 in. on centers, as shown in Fig. 12-4*b*.

12-4   Continuous Beams   Elastic theory alone does not afford a reliable means of evaluating the capacity of a beam that is continuous over several spans, as Example 14-7 will demonstrate.   For this reason, Sec. 1.5.1.4.1 of the AISC Specification stipulates that the maximum positive and negative moments in a continuous beam as evaluated on the basis of elastic theory shall be modified in the prescribed manner.

Example 12-5   The beam in Fig. 12-5*a* is continuous from A to D and is laterally supported at 5-ft intervals.   Design the member.

Solution. The bending moments at the interior supports may be found by moment distribution, and the reactions are then evaluated. The shear and bending-moment diagrams are shown in Fig. 12-5*b* and *c*, respectively.

The maximum moments as obtained by elastic theory are as follows:

$$+101.7 \text{ ft-kips} \quad \text{and} \quad -130.2 \text{ ft-kips}$$

The modified maximum moments as obtained in accordance with Sec. 1.5.1.4 are as follows:

$$+101.7 + 0.1 \times \tfrac{1}{2}(115.9 + 130.2) = +114.0 \text{ ft-kips}$$
$$0.9(-130.2) = -117.2 \text{ ft-kips}$$

The design moment is therefore 117.2 ft-kips.

$$S = \frac{M}{f} = \frac{117.2 \times 12}{24} = 58.6 \text{ in.}^3$$

Use **16WF40:** $S = 64.4$ in.^{3} $L_c = 7.6$ ft

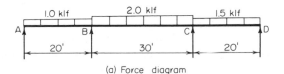

(a) Force diagram

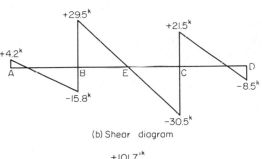

(b) Shear diagram

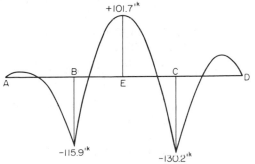

(c) Bending-moment diagram

fig. 12-5

12-5 Plate Girders   When the bending moment imposed on a member surpasses the flexural capacity of the heaviest rolled section, recourse may be had to a plate girder.   This is a beam formed by the assemblage of simpler shapes.   As illustrated in Fig. 12-6, a riveted girder comprises a web plate and four flange angles, with the longer legs outstanding.   The flange angles project $\frac{1}{4}$ in. beyond the edges of the web plate.   In welded

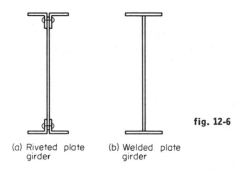

fig. 12-6

(a) Riveted plate   (b) Welded plate
    girder   girder

construction, horizontal plates are joined to the web plate at its top and bottom to form the flanges.   Cover plates may be employed to supply up to 70 percent of the flange area of a plate girder.

Example 12-6   A welded plate girder is composed of a $66 \times \frac{3}{8}$ in. web plate and two $20 \times \frac{3}{4}$ in. flange plates.   The unbraced length of the compression flange is 18 ft.   If C_b in Eq. (12-2) is 1, what bending moment can this member resist?
Solution. The properties of the section are as follows:

$$A_f = 15 \text{ sq in.} \qquad A_w = 24.75 \text{ sq in.}$$
$$I = 42{,}400 \text{ in.}^4 \qquad S = 1256 \text{ in.}^3$$

(The tables on pages 2-66 to 2-72 of the AISC Manual are useful in the calculation of moment of inertia.)

The properties of the T section comprising the flange and one-sixth the web are as follows:

$$A = 15 + \tfrac{1}{6} \times 24.75 = 19.13 \text{ sq in.}$$
$$I = \tfrac{1}{12} \times 0.75 \times 20^3 = 500 \text{ in.}^4$$
$$r = \sqrt{\frac{500}{19.13}} = 5.11 \text{ in.} \qquad \frac{L'}{r} = \frac{18 \times 12}{5.11} = 42.3$$

We must ascertain whether the member satisfies Secs. 1.9.1 and 1.10.2 of the AISC Specification.   Let h denote the clear distance between flanges.

Flange:
$$\frac{\frac{1}{2} \times 20}{0.75} = 13.3 < 16 \qquad \text{OK}$$

Web:
$$\frac{h}{t_w} = \frac{66}{0.375} = 176 < 320 \qquad \text{OK}$$

The allowable bending stress is found by applying Eqs. (12-2) and (12-3) and Formula (11) in Sec. 1.10.6 of the Specification.

$$f_1 = 22,000 - 0.679 \times 42.3^2 = 20,800 \text{ psi}$$
$$f_2 = \frac{12,000,000 \times 15}{18 \times 12 \times 67.5} = 12,300 \text{ psi}$$

Therefore, set $F_b = 20,800$ psi in Formula (11).

$$f_3 = 20,800 \left[1 - 0.0005 \times \frac{24.75}{15} \left(176 - \frac{24,000}{\sqrt{20,800}} \right) \right]$$
$$= 20,600 \text{ psi}$$

Then
$$M = f_3 S = \frac{20.6 \times 1256}{12} = \textbf{2156 ft-kips}$$

In computing the capacity of a riveted girder, Sec. 1.10.1 of the AISC Specification permits us to disregard the impairment of section caused by the rivet holes if the area of these holes does not exceed 15 percent of the gross flange area. Moreover, in the remaining cases, only the excess above 15 percent need be taken into account.

Example 12-7 A riveted plate girder is composed of the following material:

One web plate $48 \times \frac{3}{8}$ in.
Four flange angles $6 \times 4 \times \frac{3}{4}$ in.
Two cover plates $14 \times \frac{1}{2}$ in.

The flange angles are set 48.5 in. back to back with their 6-in. legs outstanding; they are connected to the web plate by $\frac{7}{8}$-in. rivets. If the member has continuous lateral support, what bending moment may be applied? What spacing of flange-to-web rivets is required in a panel where the vertical shear is 180 kips?

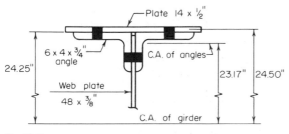

fig. 12-7

Solution. Refer to Fig. 12-7. The properties of the angles are recorded on page 1-31 of the AISC Manual. For two flange angles,

$$A = 13.88 \text{ sq in.} \qquad I_o = 17.4 \text{ in.}^4$$
$$y = 24.25 - 1.08 = 23.17 \text{ in.}$$

The cover plates must comply with Secs. 1.9.1, 1.9.2, and 1.10.3 of the AISC Specification.

$$\text{Gross flange area} = 13.88 + 7.00 = 20.88 \text{ sq in.}$$
$$\text{Area of holes} = 2 \times \tfrac{1}{2} \times 1 + 4 \times \tfrac{3}{4} \times 1 = 4.00 \text{ sq in.}$$
$$\text{Allowable area of holes} = 0.15 \times 20.88 = \underline{3.13}$$
$$\text{Excess} = \overline{0.87} \text{ sq in.}$$

We shall consider this excess area to be extracted from the outstanding legs of the flange angles.   The y distance is therefore 23.88 in.

I OF SECTION

One web plate, I_o. . . . .   3,456 in.[4]
Four flange angles, I_o.   35
$\quad Ay^2 = 2 \times 13.88 \times 23.17^2$. 14,900
Two cover plates:
$\quad Ay^2 = 2 \times 7.00 \times 24.50^2$. . . . . $\underline{8,400}$
I of gross section. 26,791
Deduct $2 \times 0.87 \times 23.88^2$. . . . . $\underline{991}$
I of net section. . . . . 25,800 in.[4]

With respect to Sec. 1.10.6 of the AISC Specification, we have

$$\frac{h}{t_w} = \frac{48.5 - 8}{0.375} < \frac{24,000}{\sqrt{22,000}}$$

Therefore, the allowable stress is 22,000 psi.

Then
$$M = \frac{fI}{c} = \frac{22 \times 25,800}{24.75 \times 12} = \mathbf{1911 \ ft\text{-}kips}$$

The flange-to-web rivets must resist the longitudinal shear as given by Eq. (5-8).   From page 4-5 of the AISC Manual, the capacity of each rivet is 15,900 lb. Let s denote the rivet spacing.

$$Q \text{ of flange} = 13.88 \times 23.17 + 7.0 \times 24.50$$
$$- 0.87 \times 23.88 = 472 \text{ in.}^3$$
$$q = \frac{VQ}{I} = \frac{180,000 \times 472}{25,800} = 3290 \text{ pli}$$
$$s = \frac{15,900}{3290} = 4.8 \text{ in.}$$

Therefore, use a **4¾-in.** pitch.   This satisfies the requirements of Secs. 1.18.2 and 1.18.3 of the Specification.

When a plate girder is to be designed, a trial section may be secured by applying the following approximation:

$$A_f = \frac{Mc}{2fy^2} - \frac{A_w}{6} \tag{12-5}$$

where y = distance from neutral axis to centroidal axis of flange

c = distance from neutral axis to extreme fiber

f = bending stress at extreme fiber

Example 12-8   A welded plate girder is to carry the loads shown in Fig. 12-8a. The uniformly distributed load includes the estimated weight of member and a load of 2.8 klf that bears directly on the top flange, thereby providing continuous lateral support.   The girder will rest on masonry buttresses at its ends.   Architectural requirements limit the total depth to approximately 70 in.

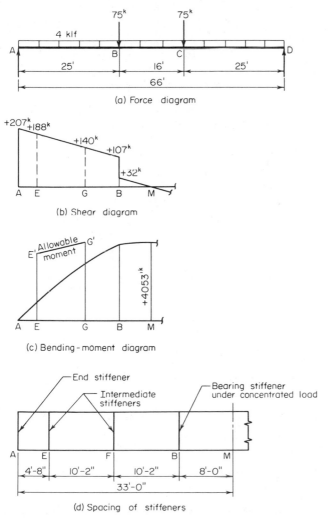

(a) Force diagram

(b) Shear diagram

(c) Bending - moment diagram

(d) Spacing of stiffeners

fig. 12-8

Design a cross section without cover plates, establish the spacing of the transverse stiffeners, and design both the intermediate stiffeners and the bearing stiffeners at the supports.

Solution. The shear and bending-moment diagrams for half-span are shown in Fig. 12-8b and c, respectively. The maximum shear is 207 kips and the maximum moment is 4053 ft-kips.

We shall use a 68-in. web plate. Section 1.10.2 of the AISC Specification limits the slenderness ratio h/t_w to 320. However, if an allowable bending stress of 22,000 psi is to be maintained, Sec. 1.10.6 imposes the following upper limit:

$$\frac{24,000}{\sqrt{22,000}} = 162$$

Then
$$t_w = \frac{h}{162} = \frac{68}{162} = 0.42 \text{ in.}$$

Use a $\frac{7}{16}$-in. plate.

$$A_w = 68 \times \frac{7}{16} = 29.75 \text{ sq in.}$$

Assume tentatively that the flange plates will be 1 in. thick. The required flange area is approximated by applying Eq. (12-5).

$$c = 34 + 1 = 35 \text{ in.} \qquad y = 34 + 0.5 = 34.5 \text{ in.}$$

$$
\begin{aligned}
A_f &= \frac{Mc}{2fy^2} - \frac{A_w}{6} \\
&= \frac{4053 \times 12 \times 35}{2 \times 22 \times 34.5^2} - \frac{29.75}{6} = 27.54 \text{ sq in.}
\end{aligned}
$$

Try $22 \times 1\frac{1}{4}$ in. plates.

$$A_f = 27.5 \text{ sq in.}$$

Section 1.9.1 of the Specification limits the width-thickness ratio of the projecting flange to

$$\frac{3000}{\sqrt{36,000}} = 16$$

In the present instance, the ratio is $11/1.25 = 8.8$.

TRIAL SECTION. One web plate is $68 \times \frac{7}{16}$ in. Two flange plates are $22 \times 1\frac{1}{4}$ in.

$$I = \frac{1}{12} \times 0.438 \times 68^3 + 2 \times 27.5 \times 34.63^2 = 77,440 \text{ in.}^3$$

$$f = \frac{Mc}{I} = \frac{4053 \times 12 \times 35.25}{77,440} = 22.1 \text{ ksi}$$

$$v = \frac{V}{A_w} = \frac{207}{29.75} = 6.96 \text{ ksi}$$

Since the excess bending stress is negligible and the allowable shearing stress is 14.5 ksi, the trial section is satisfactory.

The spacing of transverse stiffeners is recorded in Fig. 12-8d. We must first establish the length of the end panel AE. Section 1.10.5.3 stipulates that the smaller dimension of this panel shall not exceed the following value:

$$\frac{11,000 \times 0.438}{\sqrt{6960}} = 57.8 < 68 \text{ in.}$$

Stiffeners will therefore be placed 56 in. from the ends.

We shall now determine whether intermediate stiffeners are required within the interval EB by applying the criteria of Secs. 1.10.5.2 and 1.10.5.3. Stiffeners are not required when $h/t_w < 260$ and the shearing stress within the panel is below the value given by Formula (8) or (9), whichever applies.

$$EB = 396 - (56 + 96) = 244 \text{ in.}$$
$$\frac{h}{t_w} = \frac{68}{0.438} = 155 < 260 \qquad \text{OK}$$
$$\frac{a}{h} = \frac{244}{68} = 3.59$$

In lieu of solving Formula (8) or (9) directly, we may refer to Table 3-36 on page 5-70 of the AISC Manual. Entering the table with $a/h > 3$ and $h/t_w = 155$, we obtain

$$v_{\text{allow}} = 3.45 \text{ ksi}$$

At E,
$$V = 207 - 4.67 \times 4 = 188 \text{ kips}$$
$$v = \frac{188}{29.75} = 6.32 > 3.45 \text{ ksi}$$

It is therefore necessary to provide intermediate stiffeners for the interval EB. We shall consider whether placing stiffeners at the center F will satisfy Sec. 1.10.5.3.

$$\left(\frac{260}{h/t_w}\right)^2 = \left(\frac{260}{155}\right)^2 = 2.81$$
$$\frac{a}{h} = \frac{122}{68} = 1.79 < 2.81 \qquad \text{OK}$$

Entering Table 3-36 with $a/h = 1.79$ and $h/t_w = 155$, we obtain

$$v_{\text{allow}} = 7.85 > 6.32 \text{ ksi} \qquad \text{OK}$$

Before concluding that the stiffener spacing is satisfactory, we must investigate the combined shearing and bending stress and the bearing stress in interval EB. Formula (12) in Sec. 1.10.7 in effect reduces the allowable moment wherever $V > 0.6V_{\text{allow}}$, as indicated in the Commentary.

$$V_{\text{allow}} = v_{\text{allow}}A_w = 7.85 \times 29.75 = 234 \text{ kips}$$
$$0.6 \times 234 = 140 \text{ kips}$$

In Fig. 12-8b, let G denote the section where $V = 140$ kips. The allowable moment must be reduced to the left of G.

$$AG = \frac{207 - 140}{4} = 16.75 \text{ ft}$$

$$M_G = \tfrac{1}{2} \times 16.75(207 + 140) = 2906 \text{ ft-kips}$$
$$M_E = \tfrac{1}{2} \times 4.67(207 + 188) = 922 \text{ ft-kips}$$

At G, $\qquad\qquad\qquad M_{\text{allow}} = 4053$ ft-kips

The allowable bending stress at E as given by Formula (12) is

$$f_{\text{allow}} = (0.825 - 0.375 \times {}^{188}\!/_{234}) \times 36 = 18.9 \text{ ksi}$$
$$M_{\text{allow}} = \frac{f_{\text{allow}} I}{c} = \frac{18.9 \times 77,440}{35.25 \times 12} = 3460 \text{ ft-kips}$$

Plotting points E' and G' in Fig. 12-8c to represent the allowable moments at the respective sections and connecting these points with a straight line, we find that in all instances $M < M_{\text{allow}}$.

The allowable bearing stress in interval EB as given by Sec. 1.10.10.2 is

$$f_{b,\text{allow}} = \left[5.5 + \frac{4}{(a/h)^2} \right] \frac{10,000}{(h/t_w)^2} \quad \text{ksi}$$
$$= \left(5.5 + \frac{4}{1.79^2} \right) \frac{10,000}{155^2} = 2.81 \text{ ksi}$$

The actual bearing stress is

$$f_b = \frac{2.8}{12 \times 0.438} = 0.53 \text{ ksi} \qquad \text{OK}$$

The stiffener spacing in interval EB is therefore satisfactory in all respects. We shall now investigate the need for transverse stiffeners in interval BC.

$$V = 32 \text{ kips} \qquad v = \frac{32}{29.75} = 1.08 \text{ ksi}$$
$$\frac{a}{h} = \frac{192}{68} = 2.82 \simeq \left(\frac{260}{h/t_w} \right)^2$$

By Table 3-36, $v_{\text{allow}} > 1.08$ ksi.

$$f_{b,\text{allow}} = \left(5.5 + \frac{4}{2.82^2} \right) \frac{10,000}{155^2} = 2.49 > 0.53 \text{ ksi} \qquad \text{OK}$$

Since all requirements are satisfied, stiffeners are not needed in interval BC.

The intermediate stiffeners are designed in accordance with Sec. 1.10.5.4. For the interval EB, we have the following values from the preceding calculations:

$$v = 6.32 \text{ ksi} \qquad v_{\text{allow}} = 7.85 \text{ ksi}$$

In lieu of solving Formula (10) directly, we may refer to Table 3-36. Entering the table with $a/h = 1.79$ and $h/t_w = 155$, we obtain 7.45 as the percentage of web area.

$$A_{st} \text{ required} = 0.0745 \times 29.75 \times \frac{6.32}{7.85} = 1.78 \text{ sq in.}$$

Try two $4 \times \frac{1}{4}$ in. plates.

$$A_{st} = 2.0 \text{ sq in.}$$

$$\text{Width-thickness ratio} = \frac{4}{0.25} = 16 \qquad \text{OK}$$

$$\left(\frac{h}{50}\right)^4 = \left(\frac{68}{50}\right)^4 = 3.42 \text{ in.}^4$$

The moment of inertia of a pair of stiffeners with respect to the center of web is

$$I = \frac{1}{12} \times 0.25 \times 8.44^3 = 12.52 > 3.42 \text{ in.}^4 \qquad \text{OK}$$

The stiffeners must be in intimate contact with the compression flange, but they may terminate $1\frac{3}{4}$ in. from the tension flange. The connection of the stiffeners to the web must transmit the vertical shear specified in Sec. 1.10.5.4.

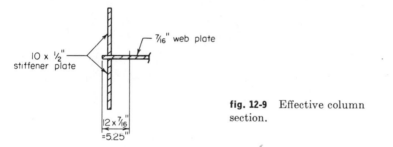

$\frac{7}{16}''$ web plate

$10 \times \frac{1}{2}''$ stiffener plate

$12 \times \frac{7}{16}''$
$= 5.25''$

fig. 12-9 Effective column section.

The bearing stiffeners at the supports are designed in the manner prescribed in Sec. 1.10.5.1. The stiffeners are considered to act in conjunction with the tributary portion of the web to form a column section, as shown in Fig. 12-9.

$$\text{Area of web} = 5.25 \times 0.438 = 2.30 \text{ sq in.}$$

Assume an allowable stress of 20 ksi.

$$\text{Plate area required} = {}^{20}\!\frac{7}{2}{}_{0} - 2.30 = 8.05 \text{ sq in.}$$

We shall try two plates $10 \times \frac{1}{2}$ in. and compute the column capacity.

$$A = 2 \times 10 \times 0.5 + 2.30 = 12.30 \text{ sq in.}$$
$$I = \frac{1}{12} \times 0.5 \times 20.44^3 = 356 \text{ in.}^4$$
$$r = \sqrt{\frac{356}{12.30}} = 5.38 \text{ sq in.} \qquad \frac{L}{r} = \frac{0.75 \times 68}{5.38} = 9.5$$

Entering Table 1-36 on page 5-68 of the AISC Manual with this slenderness ratio, we obtain an allowable axial stress of 21.2 ksi. The actual stress is

$$f = \frac{207}{12.30} = 16.8 < 21.2 \text{ ksi} \qquad \text{OK}$$

In computing the bearing stress in the stiffeners, assume that each stiffener will be clipped 1 in. to clear the flange-to-web welding.

$$f = \frac{207}{2 \times 9 \times 0.5} = 23 \text{ ksi}$$

Section 1.5.1.5.1 provides an allowable stress of 33 ksi.

The 10 × ½ in. stiffeners at the supports are therefore satisfactory with respect to both column action and bearing.

THIRTEEN

Steel Columns and Tension Members

In the following material, we shall comply with the Specification of the American Institute of Steel Construction, adopted 1963. In the absence of an express statement to the contrary, it is to be understood that the members are made of ASTM A36 steel, which has a yield-point stress of 36,000 psi.

13-1 Analysis of Columns A *column* is an axially loaded compression member having a length that is very large in relation to its lateral dimensions. Assume that a column is loaded until it buckles, as shown in Fig. 13-1. The distance between two adjacent points of inflection on the elastic curve or on the imaginary extension of the elastic curve is termed the *effective* length of column. The actual length of column is denoted by L and the effective length by KL. Recommended design values of K corresponding to various end conditions are recorded in the table on page 5-117 of the AISC Manual.

Assume that a column is free to buckle in one direction only. The Euler equation for the minimum load that will induce buckling is

$$P = \frac{A\pi^2 E}{(KL/r)^2} \tag{13-1}$$

117

where P = load at incipient buckling
   A = cross-sectional area
   E = modulus of elasticity of material
   r = radius of gyration of cross-sectional area with respect to its axis of rotation

This equation discloses that:

1. If restraint conditions are identical in all directions, the column tends to buckle about the axis for which r is minimum, i.e., about its minor centroidal axis.

2. The capacity of the member is inversely proportional to the square of KL/r, which is termed the *slenderness ratio.*

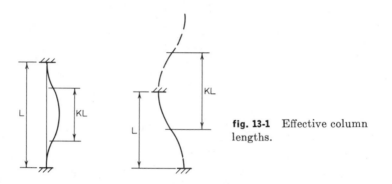

fig. 13-1   Effective column lengths.

The Euler equation is derived by assuming that the stress at incipient buckling is below the proportional limit, but this assumption is valid only with respect to members having relatively high slenderness ratios.   Consequently, the AISC Specification provides two equations for the capacity of a main compression member: One for slender members, and one for intermediate-length members.   These equations appear in Sec. 1.5.1.3.

To appraise the capacity of a given column, it is first necessary to identify the minor centroidal axis of its cross section.   Since an axis of symmetry is a principal axis, as demonstrated in Art. 2-3, this preliminary problem is easily solved.   (It is recommended that the reader review Chap. 2 if he deems such a review necessary.)

Example 13-1   A compression member consists of two 15-in. 40-lb channels laced together and spaced 10 in. back to back with flanges outstanding, as shown in Fig. 13-2.   What axial load may this member carry if its effective length is 22 ft?

Solution. Since x and y are axes of symmetry, they are the principal axes. However, it is not readily apparent which of these is the minor axis, and it is therefore necessary to calculate both r_x and r_y.   The symbol r, without a subscript, will be used to denote the minimum radius of gyration.

The properties of the individual channel as recorded on page 1-27 of the AISC Manual are as follows:

$$A = 11.70 \text{ in.} \qquad h = 0.78 \text{ in.}$$
$$r_1 = 5.44 \text{ in.} \qquad r_2 = 0.89 \text{ in.}$$

The radii of gyration of the built-up section are as follows:

$$r_x = 5.44 \text{ in.} \qquad r_y = \sqrt{r_2{}^2 + 5.78^2} > 5.78 \text{ in.}$$
$$\therefore r = 5.44 \text{ in.} \qquad \frac{KL}{r} = \frac{22 \times 12}{5.44} = 48.5$$

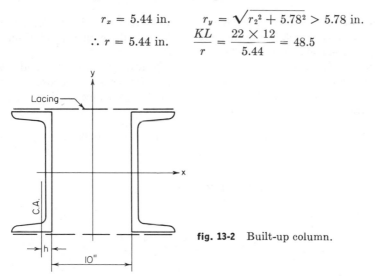

fig. 13-2 Built-up column.

Entering the table on page 5-68 of the Manual with a slenderness ratio of 48.5, we find that the allowable stress f is 18.48 ksi. Then

$$P = Af = 2 \times 11.70 \times 18.48 = \textbf{432 kips}$$

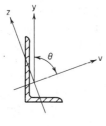

(a) Centroidal axes of angle section

(b) Star strut

fig. 13-3

Figure 13-3a is the cross section of an angle member. Let v and z denote the major and minor centroidal axes, respectively, and y the axis parallel to the long leg. The radii of gyration r_y and r_z are given in the AISC Manual. The radius of gyration r_v may be computed by applying the following equation:

$$r_v{}^2 = r_y{}^2 \sec^2 \theta - r_z{}^2 \tan^2 \theta \qquad (13\text{-}2)$$

For an equal-leg angle, $\theta = 45°$, and this equation reduces to

$$r_v{}^2 = 2r_y{}^2 - r_z{}^2 \qquad (13\text{-}2a)$$

Example 13-2 A star strut is composed of two $5 \times 5 \times \frac{3}{8}$ in. angles intermittently connected by $\frac{3}{8}$-in. batten plates in both directions. Determine the capacity of the member for an effective length of 12 ft.

  Solution. Refer to Fig. 13-3b. Since they are axes of symmetry, p and q are the principal axes, and p is manifestly the minor axis because the area lies closer to p than to q. The properties of the individual angle as recorded on page 1-28 of the AISC Manual are as follows:

$$A = 3.61 \text{ sq in.} \qquad r_y = 1.56 \text{ in.} \qquad r_z = 0.99 \text{ in.}$$

Equation (13-2a) yields

$$r_v = \sqrt{2 \times 1.56^2 - 0.99^2} = 1.97 \text{ in.}$$

For the built-up section,

$$r = r_p = 1.97 \text{ in.} \qquad \frac{KL}{r} = \frac{12 \times 12}{1.97} = 73$$

  Entering the table on page 5-68 of the Manual with a slenderness ratio of 73, we find that the allowable stress is 16.12 ksi. Then

$$P = Af = 2 \times 3.61 \times 16.12 = \textbf{116 kips}$$

  The AISC Manual presents tables of allowable column loads for the various rolled sections; these tables start on page 3-13. The allowable loads are calculated on the premise that the column tends to buckle about the minor centroidal axis. However, it frequently occurs that as a result of framing conditions the column has two effective lengths: one with respect to buckling about the minor axis, and one with respect to buckling about the major axis. In this situation, the assumption underlying the AISC column-load tables is not necessarily valid. To expedite the design, it is advantageous to introduce the concept of a *uniform-strength column*, this being one that is as likely to buckle about one principal axis as about the other.

  Let x and y denote the major and minor centroidal axes of the section, respectively, and K_xL and K_yL denote the effective lengths with respect to these axes. For a uniform-strength column,

$$\frac{K_xL}{r_x} = \frac{K_yL}{r_y} \qquad \text{or} \qquad K_xL = K_yL\frac{r_x}{r_y}$$

Values of r_x/r_y for the rolled sections are recorded at the bottom of the column-load tables. They enable us to identify the true axis of buckling associated with a given section.

Example 13-3 A column that is 30 ft long is to carry a load of 200 kips. The member will be braced about both principal axes at top and bottom and braced about its minor axis at midheight. Architectural details restrict the member to a nominal depth of 8 in. Select a section of A242 steel by consulting the allowable-load tables in the AISC Manual, and then verify the design.

Solution. Refer to Fig. 13-4. The effective length with respect to the minor axis may be taken as 15 ft. Then

$$K_xL = 30 \text{ ft} \quad \text{and} \quad K_yL = 15 \text{ ft}$$

Assume that the member will tend to buckle about the minor axis. Referring to page 3-39 of the Manual, we find by linear interpolation that an 8WF40 column

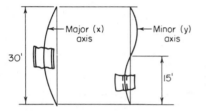

fig. 13-4 Effective column lengths.

has a capacity of 200 kips when $K_yL = 15.3$ ft; at the bottom of the page, we find that $r_x/r_y = 1.73$. If the column is to have uniform strength,

$$K_xL = 1.73 \times 15.3 = 26.5 < 30 \text{ ft}$$

The section is therefore inadequate. Proceeding to an 8WF48, we find that this column has a capacity of 200 kips when $K_yL = 17.7$ ft and that $r_x/r_y = 1.74$. For uniform strength,

$$K_xL = 1.74 \times 17.7 = 30.8 > 30 \text{ ft}$$

The 8WF48 therefore appears to be satisfactory, and we shall verify the design. The properties are as follows:

$$A = 14.11 \text{ sq in.} \quad r_x = 3.61 \text{ in.} \quad r_y = 2.08 \text{ in.}$$
$$\frac{K_xL}{r_x} = \frac{30 \times 12}{3.61} = 100 \quad \frac{K_yL}{r_y} = \frac{15 \times 12}{2.08} = 87$$

For this grade of steel and thickness of member, the yield-point stress is 50 ksi, as noted on page 3-39 of the Manual. Entering Table 1-50 on page 5-92 with a slenderness ratio of 100, we obtain $f = 14.71$ ksi. Then

$$P = 14.11 \times 14.71 = 208 \text{ kips} \quad \text{OK}$$

Therefore, use **8WF48**.

Where beams are framed to a column by means of rigid connections, the effective column length may be established by a simplified, approximate method presented in the AISC Manual.   The method is explained on pages 5-116 to 5-119.

Example 13-4   The beams shown in Fig. 13-5a are rigidly connected to a 14WF95 column of 28-ft height that is pinned at its foundation.   The column is held at its upper end by cross bracing lying in a plane normal to the web.   Compute the axial stress that would be permitted in the column in the absence of flexure.

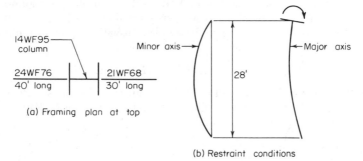

14WF95 column

24WF76 40' long

21WF68 30' long

Minor axis →

Major axis

28'

(a) Framing plan at top

(b) Restraint conditions

fig. 13-5

Solution. Figure 13-5b indicates the restraint conditions associated with buckling about the principal axes.   The cross bracing prevents sidesway at the top solely with respect to the minor axis, and the rigid beam-to-column connections afford partial fixity with respect to the major axis.   The I_x values of the members at the joint are as follows:

Section	I_x
14WF95	1064 in.[4]
24WF76	2096
21WF68	1478

For the column,

$$\frac{I_c}{L_c} = \frac{1064}{28} = 38.0$$

At top,

$$\sum \frac{I_g}{L_g} = \frac{2096}{40} + \frac{1478}{30} = 101.7$$

$$G_{\text{top}} = \frac{38.0}{101.7} = 0.37$$

In accordance with the instructions accompanying Fig. Cl.8.3 on page 5-118 of the AISC Manual, set $G_{\text{bot}} = 10$.

By placing a straightedge at the points in the alignment chart that represent the foregoing values, we obtain $K_x = 1.77$.

$$\frac{K_x L}{r_x} = \frac{1.77 \times 28 \times 12}{6.17} = 96.4$$

$$\frac{K_y L}{r_y} = \frac{28 \times 12}{3.71} = 90.6$$

Entering the table on page 5-68 with the greater value, we obtain

$$f = 13.43 \text{ ksi}$$

The elements of a built-up column must be connected to one another by means of lacing bars and tie plates in order to preserve the integrity of the member and prevent local failure. The lacing system must conform with Sec. 1.18.2 of the AISC Specification.

Example 13-5   Design the lacing bars and tie plates for the member analyzed in Example 13-1.   The lacing bars will be connected to the channel flanges with ½-in. rivets.

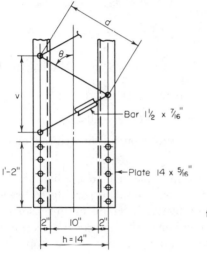

Bar 1½ x ⁷⁄₁₆"

Plate 14 x ⁵⁄₁₆"

1'-2"

2"   10"   2"

h = 14"

fig. 13-6   Lacing and tie plates.

Solution. Refer to Fig. 13-6.   Standard gage in 15-in. channel = 2 in. (Manual, p. 1-26); $h = 14 < 15$ in.; therefore, use single lacing.   Try $\theta = 60°$.

$$v = 2 \times 14 \cot 60° = 16.16 \text{ in.}$$

Set $v = 16$ in.: $\therefore d = 16.1$ in.

For built-up section, $\dfrac{KL}{r} = 48.5$

For single channel, $\dfrac{KL}{r} = \dfrac{16}{0.89} < 48.5$ OK

The spacing of bars is therefore satisfactory.

   The lacing system must be capable of transmitting an assumed transverse shear equal to 2 percent of the axial load.   This shear is carried by two bars, one on each side of the column.   Assume that the column will be loaded to its capacity of 432 kips.

$$\text{Force per bar} = \tfrac{1}{2} \times 0.02 \times 432 \times \frac{16.1}{14} = 5.0 \text{ kips}$$

A lacing bar is classified as a secondary member, and its slenderness ratio is limited to 140.   Then

$$r = \frac{d}{140} = \frac{16.1}{140} = 0.115 \text{ in.}$$

For a rectangular section of thickness t,

$$r = 0.289t \qquad \therefore t = \frac{0.115}{0.289} = 0.40 \text{ in.}$$

Set $t = \frac{7}{16}$ in.

$$r = 0.127 \text{ in.} \qquad \frac{KL}{r} = \frac{16.1}{0.127} = 127 \qquad f_{\text{allow}} = 9.59 \text{ ksi}$$

$$\text{Area} = \frac{5.0}{9.59} = 0.52 \text{ sq in.}$$

Minimum bar width required for $\frac{1}{2}$-in. rivets = $1\frac{1}{2}$ in.   (Manual, p. 5-37). Therefore, use flat bar **$1\frac{1}{2} \times \frac{7}{16}$ in.**, with $A = 0.66$ sq in.

The end tie plates are designed in accordance with Sec. 1.18.2.5.

$$\text{Minimum length} = 14 \text{ in.} \qquad t = \frac{14}{50} = 0.28 \text{ in.}$$

Therefore, use tie plates **$14 \times \frac{5}{16}$ in.**   The rivet pitch is limited to 6 diameters, or 3 in.

In many instances, a column sustains both a load applied at the top and one applied at an intermediate level, the latter serving to brace the column in one direction only.   Manifestly, it would be unreasonable to equate the effective length of the member in the unbraced direction to its height, since only part of the total load is applied at the top.   If the intermediate load is applied approximately at midheight, a rational value of the effective length of the member may be obtained by the following procedure: Let

$$m = \frac{\text{load at intermediate level}}{\text{total load}}$$

Replace the factor K with a factor K' defined by the equation

$$K' = K\sqrt{1 - \frac{m}{2}} \tag{13-3}$$

Example 13-6   A column of 30-ft length carries a load of 130 kips applied at the top and one of 56 kips applied to the web at midheight.   The member will be pinned at top and bottom, and the intermediate load will provide restraint against buckling about the minor axis.   Select an 8-in. column of A242 steel.

Solution

$$m = \frac{56}{186} = 0.30 \qquad K_x'L = 30\sqrt{1 - 0.15} = 27.6 \text{ ft}$$
$$K_yL = \frac{1}{2} \times 30 = 15 \text{ ft}$$

We shall select a trial section on the basis of the K_yL value. From page 3-39 of the AISC Manual, for an 8WF40,

$$\text{Capacity} = 186 \text{ kips} \qquad \text{when } K_yL = 16.2 \text{ ft}$$

and

$$\frac{r_x}{r_y} = 1.73$$

For a uniform-strength column,

$$K_xL = 1.73 \times 16.2 = 28.0 > 27.6 \text{ ft}$$

Therefore, use **8WF40**.

13-2 Analysis of Beam-Columns A member that is subjected simultaneously to axial compressive loads and flexure is termed a *beam-column*. The design of this type of member is regulated by Sec. 1.6.1 of the AISC Specification. The notational system is as follows:

C_m = moment coefficient computed in manner described in Sec. 1.6.1
R = slenderness ratio of member with respect to plane of bending
f_a = axial stress
f_b = maximum bending stress
f_y = yield-point stress
F_a = axial stress that would be permitted in absence of bending
F_b = bending stress that would be permitted in absence of axial loads
$F'_e = 149{,}000{,}000/R^2$, psi
S = section modulus

If the ratio f_a/F_a exceeds 15 percent, it is necessary that the simultaneous set of values of f_a and f_b satisfy the following requirements:

$$\frac{f_a}{F_a} + \frac{C_m}{1 - f_a/F'_e}\frac{f_b}{F_b} \leq 1 \tag{13-4}$$

$$\frac{f_a}{0.6f_y} + \frac{f_b}{F_b} \leq 1 \tag{13-5}$$

Example 13-7 A 12WF53 column with an effective length of 20 ft is to carry an axial load of 160 kips and the end moments indicated in Fig. 13-7. The member will be secured against sidesway in both directions. Is the section adequate?
Solution. The properties of the section are as follows:

$$A = 15.59 \text{ sq in.} \qquad S_x = 70.7 \text{ in.}^3$$
$$r_x = 5.23 \text{ in.} \qquad r_y = 2.48 \text{ in.}$$

From page 2-26 or 3-21 of the Manual,

$$L_c = 10.8 \text{ ft} \qquad L_u = 21.7 \text{ ft}$$

Considering the member as a column, we obtain the following values:

$$f_a = \frac{160}{15.59} = 10.26 \text{ ksi}$$

$$\frac{KL}{r} = \frac{240}{2.48} = 96.8 \qquad \therefore F_a = 13.38 \text{ ksi}$$

$$\frac{f_a}{F_a} = \frac{10.26}{13.38} = 0.767 > 0.15$$

Equations (13-4) and (13-5) therefore apply to this member.

Considering the member as a beam, we obtain the following values:

$$f_b = \frac{31.5 \times 12}{70.7} = 5.35 \text{ ksi}$$

$$L_u < KL < L_c \qquad \therefore F_b = 22 \text{ ksi}$$

(Although this consideration is irrelevant in the present instance, it is to be observed that Sec. 1.5.1.4 establishes two maximum d/t ratios for a compact section. One applies to a beam, the other to a beam-column.)

In calculating C_m, the ratio M_1/M_2 is considered positive because the algebraic sign of the bending moment remains unchanged across the member.

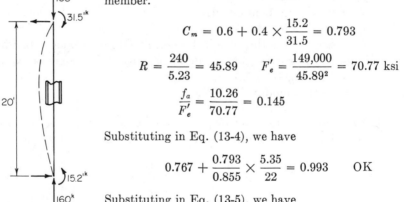

$$C_m = 0.6 + 0.4 \times \frac{15.2}{31.5} = 0.793$$

$$R = \frac{240}{5.23} = 45.89 \qquad F'_e = \frac{149,000}{45.89^2} = 70.77 \text{ ksi}$$

$$\frac{f_a}{F'_e} = \frac{10.26}{70.77} = 0.145$$

Substituting in Eq. (13-4), we have

$$0.767 + \frac{0.793}{0.855} \times \frac{5.35}{22} = 0.993 \qquad \text{OK}$$

Substituting in Eq. (13-5), we have

fig. 13-7
Beam-column.

$$\frac{10.26}{22} + \frac{5.35}{22} = 0.709 \qquad \text{OK}$$

The section is therefore adequate.

To reduce the labor entailed in analyzing a given section as a beam-column, the AISC Manual introduces the design factors B and a, which are defined by the following equations:

$$B = \frac{A}{S} \text{ per in.}$$

$$a = 0.149 \times 10^6 I \qquad \text{in.}^4$$

To apply these factors, let

P = axial load, kips
P' = axial load that would be permitted in absence of bending, kips
M = maximum bending moment, in.-kips

Equations (13-4) and (13-5) may be transformed to the following:

$$P + BMC_m \frac{F_a}{F_b} \frac{a}{a - P(KL)^2} \leq P' \qquad (13\text{-}6)$$

$$P \frac{F_a}{0.6f_y} + BM \frac{F_a}{F_b} \leq P' \qquad (13\text{-}7)$$

where KL, B, and a are evaluated with respect to the plane of bending.

Example 13-8   With reference to Example 13-7, investigate the adequacy of the 12WF53 section by applying the values of the beam-column factors recorded in the AISC Manual.

Solution. The basic values are as follows:

$$P = 160 \text{ kips} \qquad M = 378 \text{ in.-kips}$$
$$F_b = 22 \text{ ksi} \qquad C_m = 0.793$$

Referring to page 3-21 of the Manual, we obtain the following properties of the 12WF53:

$$A = 15.59 \text{ sq in.} \qquad B_x = 0.221 \text{ per in.}$$
$$a_x = 63.5 \times 10^6 \text{ in.}^4$$

When $KL = 20$ ft,

$$P' = 209 \text{ kips} \qquad F_a = \frac{P'}{A} = \frac{209}{15.59} = 13.41 \text{ ksi}$$

$$P(KL)^2 = 160 \times 240^2 = 9.22 \times 10^6 \text{ kip-in.}^2$$

$$\frac{a_x}{a_x - P(KL)^2} = \frac{63.5}{63.5 - 9.22} = 1.17$$

Substituting in Eq. (13-6), we have

$$160 + 0.221 \times 378 \times 0.793 \times \frac{13.41}{22} \times 1.17 = 207 < 209 \text{ kips} \qquad \text{OK}$$

Substituting in Eq. (13-7), we have

$$160 \times \frac{13.41}{22} + 0.221 \times 378 \times \frac{13.41}{22} = 148 < 209 \text{ kips} \qquad \text{OK}$$

The section is therefore satisfactory.

13-3   Design of Tension Members   Consider that a tension member is to be loaded to failure.   If the member is connected to its support with rivets arranged in a single transverse row, failure will occur on the transverse section through the center of rivets.   On the other hand, if the rivets are staggered, failure may occur along an irregular path through rivet centers.   It therefore becomes necessary to identify the path of failure before the tensile capacity of the member may be evaluated.

With reference to any set of adjacent rivets, let

g = transverse spacing, or gage
s = longitudinal spacing, or pitch

Section 1.14.3 of the AISC Specification prescribes that the net width of the member along a path of potential rupture be computed by the following formula: From the gross width, deduct the sum of the diameters of all holes lying on the path, and add the sum of the quantities $s^2/4g$ for all sets of adjacent holes.   The path of failure is the one that yields the minimum net width.   However, in no case is the net width to be taken as more than 85 percent of the gross width.

Example 13-9   The 7 × ¼ in. plate in Fig. 13-8 carries a tensile force of 18,000 lb and is connected to its support with three ¾-in. rivets in the manner shown. Compute the maximum tensile stress in the member.

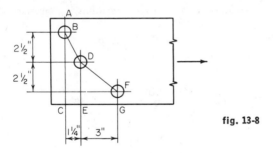

fig. 13-8

Solution. The values associated with the sets of adjacent holes are as follows:

For B and D: $s = 1.25$ in. $g = 2.5$ in. $\dfrac{s^2}{4g} = 0.156$ in.

For D and F: $s = 3$ in. $g = 2.5$ in. $\dfrac{s^2}{4g} = 0.900$ in.

The effective diameter of holes is ⅞ in.   The net widths at the indicated paths are as follows:

$$w_{AC} = 7 - 0.875 = 6.125 \text{ in.}$$
$$w_{ABDE} = 7 - 2 \times 0.875 + 0.156 = 5.406 \text{ in.}$$
$$w_{ABDFG} = 7 - 3 \times 0.875 + 0.156 + 0.900 = 5.431 \text{ in.}$$

Applying the 85 percent limit, we have

$$w_{\max} = 0.85 \times 7 = 5.95 \text{ in.}$$

The critical path is therefore $ABDE$, and the tensile stress along this path is

$$f = \frac{18,000}{5.406 \times 0.25} = \textbf{13,300 psi}$$

Example 13-10 The bottom chord of a roof truss sustains a tensile force of 141 kips. The member will be spliced with $\frac{3}{4}$-in. rivets in the manner shown in Fig. 13-9a. Design a double-angle member and specify the minimum rivet pitch.

Solution. It is convenient to visualize each angle in its "developed" form, i.e., as it would appear if the outstanding leg were cut and made coplanar with the other one, as shown in Fig. 13-9b. The gross width of the angle is the width of the equivalent plate thus formed, and it equals the sum of the two legs of the angle less the thickness.

To select the angle size, assume tentatively that the net width will equal the gross width less 2.5 times the effective diameter of holes. Let w_g and t denote the gross width and thickness of the angle, respectively.

Net area required = $\frac{141}{22}$ = 6.40 sq in.

Then $\quad 2t(w_g - 2.5 \times 0.875) = 6.40$

$$w_g = \frac{3.20}{t} + 2.19$$

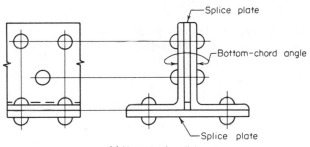

(a) Method of splicing

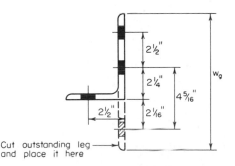

(b) Development of angle for net section

fig. 13-9

By assigning trial values to t and solving for w_g, we obtain the values recorded in the accompanying table. The angle size must be such that the sum of the two legs equals or exceeds $w_g + t$. We shall use two angles **6 × 4 × 7/16 in.** as being the most economical.

t, in.	w_g, in.	$w_g + t$, in.	Available size	Area, sq in.
1/2	8.59	9.09	6 × 3½ × ½	4.50
7/16	9.50	9.94	6 × 4 × 7/16	4.18
3/8	10.72	11.10	None	

Figure 13-9*b* shows the standard rivet gages for this member, as given on page 4-82 of the AISC Manual. Let s denote the stagger.

$$\text{Net width required} = \frac{\frac{1}{2} \times 6.40}{\frac{7}{16}} = 7.31 \text{ in.}$$

$$\text{Gross width} = 6 + 4 - 0.44 = 9.56 \text{ in.}$$

$$9.56 - 3 \times 0.875 + \frac{s^2}{4 \times 2.5} + \frac{s^2}{4 \times 4.31} = 7.31$$

Solving, $s = 1.55$ in.

For convenience, we may use the standard longitudinal spacing of **3 in.** This results in a net width of 7.29 in.; the deficiency is negligible.

FOURTEEN
Plastic Design of Steel Structures

The method of structural design that is based upon an appraisal of the load that will induce failure of a structure is designated as *plastic design* when applied to steel structures and *ultimate-strength design* when applied to reinforced-concrete structures. An alternative expression is *limit design*.

In the following material, it is to be understood that the members are made of ASTM A36 steel, which has a yield-point stress of 36,000 psi.

14-1 Basic Concepts of Plastic Design   When a bar of structural steel is subjected to a gradually increasing longitudinal load, a point is reached at which the member undergoes a very large deformation without any increase in load. This behavior is referred to as *yielding*, and the stress at which yielding commences is termed the *yield-point stress*. If the member is deformed beyond the yield point, it does not revert to its original length when the load is removed; instead, it retains a *permanent set*. The deformation that occurs prior to yielding is therefore described as *elastic*, and that which occurs subsequently is described as *plastic*. The yield-point stress is denoted by f_y.

131

Consider that a structure is subjected to a gradually increasing load until it collapses. When the yield-point stress first appears, the structure is said to be in a state of *initial yielding*. The load that exists when failure impends is termed the *ultimate load*.

Elastic design considers that a structure has been loaded to capacity when it attains initial yielding, on the theory that plastic deformation would annul the utility of the structure. Plastic design, on the other hand, recognizes that a structure may be loaded beyond initial yielding if those parts of the structure that remain in the elastic-stress range are capable of supporting this incremental load and of preventing plastic deformation of the other parts. The ultimate load is reached when these conditions cease to exist and the structure therefore collapses.

Thus, elastic design is concerned with an allowable *stress*, which equals the yield-point stress divided by an appropriate factor of safety. In contrast, plastic design is concerned with an allowable *load*, which equals the ultimate load divided by an appropriate factor called the *load factor*. In reality, however, the distinction between elastic and plastic design has become blurred because specifications that ostensibly pertain to elastic design make covert concessions to plastic behavior. Several of these concessions will be underscored in the material that follows.

Example 14-1   A load is applied to a rigid bar that is symmetrically supported by three steel rods in the manner shown in Fig. 14-1. The cross-sectional areas are as follows: Rods A and C, 1.2 sq in.; rod B, 1.0 sq in. Determine the maximum load that may be applied (*a*) using elastic design with an allowable stress of 22,000 psi and (*b*) using plastic design with a load factor of 1.85.

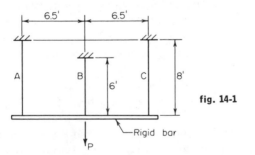

fig. 14-1

Solution. As a result of the symmetrical disposition, the bar deflects vertically without rotating, thereby elongating the three rods by an identical amount.

PART *a*. Consider that the load is gradually increased from zero to its allowable value. We must identify the rod in which the allowable stress first appears. Applying Eq. (3-2), we have

$$\Delta L = \frac{s_A L_A}{E} = \frac{s_B L_B}{E} = \frac{s_C L_C}{E}$$

$$\therefore \ s_A = s_C \quad \text{and} \quad s_A = s_B \frac{L_B}{L_A} = 0.75 s_B$$

Since s_B is maximum, the allowable stress first appears in rod B. At this instant,

$$s_B = 22,000 \text{ psi} \qquad s_A = 0.75 \times 22,000 = 16,500 \text{ psi}$$
$$P_{\text{allow}} = 2 \times 16,500 \times 1.2 + 22,000 \times 1.0 = \textbf{61,600 lb}$$

PART b. Consider that the load is gradually increased from zero to its ultimate value. When rod B attains its yield-point stress, its tendency to deform plastically is inhibited by rods A and C, since the rigidity of the bar constrains the three rods to elongate uniformly. The structure therefore remains stable as the load is increased beyond the elastic range until rods A and C also attain their yield-point stress. The ultimate load P_u therefore has the following value:

$$P_u = 36,000(2 \times 1.2 + 1.0) = 122,400 \text{ lb}$$

Then
$$P_{\text{allow}} = \frac{122,400}{1.85} = \textbf{66,200 lb}$$

The notational system pertaining to a beam is as follows:

M_y = yield moment
M_p = plastic moment
y = distance from neutral axis to given fiber, *in absolute value*
y_m = mean value of y for entire section
Z = plastic modulus
SF = shape factor

In the plastic analysis of flexural members, the following simplifying assumptions are made:

1. As the loading is gradually increased, a state is eventually reached at which all fibers at the section of maximum moment are stressed to the yield point, either in tension or in compression. The section is then said to be in a state of *plastification*.

2. While plastification is proceeding at one section, the adjacent sections retain their linear stress distribution.

The foregoing assumptions are untrue, but they simplify the analysis enormously without introducing any appreciable error.

When plastification is completed at a given section, each fiber has reached its limiting bending stress f_y, and the section is thus rendered incapable of resisting any additional bending moment. As an incremental load is applied, the beam behaves as if it had been constructed with a hinge at the given section. Consequently, the beam is said to have developed a *plastic hinge* (in contradistinction to a true hinge) at the plastified section.

The *yield moment* of a beam section is the bending moment associated with initial yielding. The *plastic moment* is the bending moment associated with plastification.

The *plastic modulus* of a beam section, which is analogous to the section modulus S used in elastic design, is defined by the equation

$$Z = \frac{M_p}{f_y}$$

Figure 14-2 shows the conditions at a section where M_p exists. We may write

$$M_p = f_y \int y \, dA = A f_y y_m$$

Then

$$Z = A y_m \tag{14-1}$$

Where the section is symmetrical about the neutral axis, y_m equals the distance from the neutral axis to the centroidal axis of the half-section.

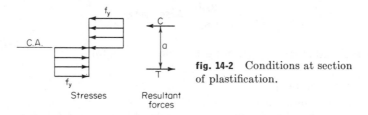

fig. 14-2 Conditions at section of plastification.

The *shape factor* is the ratio of M_p to M_y, being so named because its value depends on the shape of the section. It affords an index of the postelastic strength of the section. Then

$$\mathrm{SF} = \frac{M_p}{M_y} = \frac{f_y Z}{f_y S} = \frac{Z}{S}$$

Example 14-2 Without applying the equations and numerical values of the plastic modulus presented in the AISC Manual, determine the shape factor associated with the following shapes: a rectangle, a circle, and a 16WF40.

Solution

RECTANGLE. Let b and d denote the width and depth, respectively.

$$A = bd \qquad y_m = \frac{d}{4} \qquad \therefore Z = \frac{bd^2}{4}$$

$$S = \frac{bd^2}{6}$$

$$\mathrm{SF} = \frac{bd^2/4}{bd^2/6} = 1.5$$

CIRCLE. Let R denote the radius. The properties of the circle and half-circle are presented on page 6-25 of the AISC Manual.

$$A = \pi R^2 \qquad y_m = \frac{4R}{3\pi} \qquad \therefore Z = \frac{4R^3}{3}$$

$$S = \frac{\pi R^3}{4}$$

$$SF = \frac{4R^3/3}{\pi R^3/4} = \frac{16}{3\pi} = 1.70$$

16WF40

$$A = 11.77 \text{ sq in.} \qquad S = 64.4 \text{ in.}^3$$

Referring to page 1-40 of the AISC Manual for the properties of the ST8WF20, we obtain

$$y_m = 8.00 - 1.82 = 6.18 \text{ in.} \qquad Z = 11.77 \times 6.18 = 72.7 \text{ in.}^3$$

$$SF = \frac{72.7}{64.4} = 1.13$$

The fact that the shape factor of the circle far exceeds that of the WF shape may be readily explained by considering the contribution made by a given fiber to the moments M_p and M_y. Let dA denote the area of the fiber.

At plastification: $\qquad dM_p = f_y y \, dA$

At initial yielding: $\qquad f = f_y \dfrac{y}{c}$

$$dM_y = f_y \frac{y^2}{c} \, dA$$

$$\frac{dM_p}{dM_y} = \frac{c}{y}$$

If we compare a circle and a hypothetical WF section that have the same area and depth, we find that the circle has a higher shape factor because of its relatively low values of y.

As the preceding analysis demonstrates, the process of plastification mitigates the detriment that accrues from placing area near the neutral axis because the stress at plastification is independent of the position of the fiber. Consequently, a section that is relatively inefficient with respect to flexure from an elastic point of view has a compensatingly high shape factor.

The AISC Specification for elastic design implicitly recognizes the value of the shape factor by assigning an allowable bending stress of $0.75f_y$ to rectangular bearing plates and $0.90f_y$ to pins.

The following example is intended to illuminate the postelastic behavior of a statically indeterminate beam.

Example 14-3   The 18WF45 beam in Fig. 14-3*a* is simply supported at *A* and fixed at *C*.   Disregarding the beam weight, calculate the ultimate load that may be applied at *B* by analyzing the behavior of the beam during its two phases.

   Solution.   As the load is gradually increased from zero to its ultimate value, the beam passes through two phases.   During phase 1 (the elastic phase), the member is restrained against rotation at *C*.   This phase terminates when a plastic hinge forms at that support.   During phase 2 (the postelastic, or plastic, phase), the member functions as a simply supported beam.   This phase terminates when a plastic hinge forms at *B*, since the member then becomes unstable.

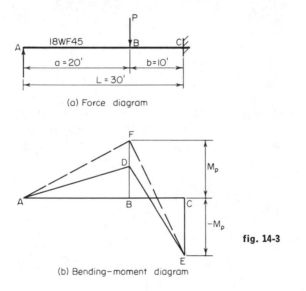

(a) Force diagram

fig. 14-3

(b) Bending–moment diagram

   Let P_1 denote the load applied at *B* during phase 1 and P_2 denote the incremental load applied during phase 2.   In Fig. 14-3*b*, *ADE* and *AFE* are the bending-moment diagrams at completion of phases 1 and 2, respectively.   The plastic moduli of the rolled sections are recorded on pages 2-7 to 2-9 of the AISC Manual.

$$Z = 89.6 \text{ in.}^3$$

$$M_p = f_y Z = \frac{36 \times 89.6}{12} = 268.8 \text{ ft-kips}$$

   The bending moments at completion of phase 1 may be found by applying the equations for Case 14 on page 2-124 of the AISC Manual.   In Fig. 14-3*b*,

$$CE = -\frac{ab(a + L)}{2L^2} P_1 = -\frac{20 \times 10 \times 50}{2 \times 900} P_1 = -268.8$$

$$P_1 = 48.38 \text{ kips}$$

$$BD = \frac{ab^2(a + 2L)}{2L^3} P_1 = \frac{20 \times 100 \times 80}{2 \times 27{,}000} \times 48.38$$

$$= 143.3 \text{ ft-kips}$$

By considering the beam as simply supported during phase 2, we obtain the following results:

$$DF = \frac{ab}{L}P_2 = \frac{20 \times 10}{30}P_2 = 6.67P_2$$

But $\qquad DF = BF - BD = 268.8 - 143.3 = 125.5$

Solving, $\qquad P_2 = 18.82$ kips

Then $\qquad P_u = 48.38 + 18.82 = \mathbf{67.20}$ **kips**

14-2 Analysis of Beams by Statical and Mechanism Methods

The ultimate-load capacity of a beam may be assessed by two alternative methods: the statical method and the mechanism method.

The *statical* method requires that we identify the sections at which plastic hinges form before collapse occurs and then calculate the ultimate load accordingly. *The sequence in which these plastic hinges formed at their respective sections is immaterial.*

Example 14-4 Solve Example 14-3 by applying the statical method.

Solution. The following considerations are crucial: The bending-moment diagram always has vertices at B and C, and formation of two plastic hinges will cause failure of the member. Consequently, the plastic moment exists at B and at C when failure impends.

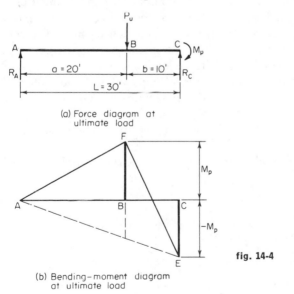

(a) Force diagram at ultimate load

(b) Bending-moment diagram at ultimate load

fig. 14-4

Figure 14-4 shows the force and bending-moment diagrams corresponding to ultimate load. From Example 14-3, we have $M_p = 268.8$ ft-kips. Then

$$BF = 20R_A = 268.8 \qquad \therefore R_A = 13.44 \text{ kips}$$
$$CE = 30R_A - 10P_u = 30 \times 13.44 - 10P_u = -268.8$$
$$P_u = 67.20 \text{ kips}$$

The following is an alternative method of solution:

$$BF = \frac{ab}{L} P_u - \frac{a}{L} M_p = M_p$$

$$\frac{20 \times 10}{30} P_u = \frac{50}{30} M_p$$

$$P_u = \frac{50}{200} \times 268.8 = 67.20 \text{ kips}$$

The *mechanism* method of computing ultimate-load capacity is based upon the following analysis: As Example 14-3 illustrates, a statically indeterminate beam passes through several phases as the load is gradually increased from zero to its ultimate value. We shall add a final phase. Consider that when the ultimate load is reached the member is subjected to an incremental deflection. This will of course result in collapse, but we may study the behavior of the member during a virtual (infinitesimally small) deflection from its stable position.

Since this virtual deflection occurs without the application of any additional load, there are no changes in bending stress, and rotation therefore occurs solely at the real and plastic hinges. Thus, during the virtual deflection, the member behaves as a mechanism (a constrained chain of pin-connected rigid bodies, or links). By equating the external work performed upon the beam during the virtual deflection to the internal work (or increase in strain energy of the beam), we secure an equation that permits evaluation of the ultimate load.

The work performed by a force equals the product of the force and the displacement of its point of application in the direction of the force. The work performed by a moment equals the product of the moment and the angular displacement of its section of application in the direction of the moment.

The mechanism method is also referred to as the *virtual-work* or *kinematic* method.

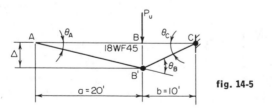

fig. 14-5

Example 14-5 Solve Example 14-3 by applying the mechanism method.

Solution. Figure 14-5 indicates in hyperbolic manner the virtual displacement of the member from its initial position ABC to a subsequent position $AB'C$. (The initial position may be represented by a straight line for simplicity because we are concerned solely with the deformation that occurs *during* the virtual deflection.)   Dots are used to represent plastic hinges.

It is necessary to express the linear displacement under the load and the angular displacement at every plastic hinge in terms of some convenient unit.   We shall use θ_A for this purpose.

$$\Delta = a\theta_A = b\theta_C \qquad \therefore \theta_C = \frac{a}{b}\theta_A = 2\theta_A$$

$$\theta_B = \theta_A + \theta_C = 3\theta_A$$

Let W_E and W_I denote, respectively, the external and internal work associated with the virtual displacement.   These quantities are equal to one another.

$$W_E = P_u\Delta = P_u a\theta_A = 20P_u\theta_A$$
$$W_I = M_p(\theta_B + \theta_C) = 5M_p\theta_A$$
$$20P_u\theta_A = 5M_p\theta_A$$
$$P_u = \tfrac{5}{20} \times 268.8 = 67.20 \text{ kips}$$

The preceding examples illustrate the following important characteristics of plastic design:

1. Plastic design is far simpler than elastic design.

2. Plastic design yields results that are considerably more reliable than those secured through elastic design.   For example, assume that the support at C in Fig. 14-3a does not completely inhibit rotation at that end.   This departure from design conditions will invalidate the elastic analysis but will have no bearing on the plastic analysis.

Example 14-6   If the beam in Fig. 14-3a is fixed at A as well as at C, what is the ultimate load that may be applied at B?

Solution.   Failure impends when hinges exist at A, B, and C.   This problem lends itself to solution by the mechanism method.   Refer to Example 14-5.

$$W_E = 20P_u\theta_A$$
$$W_I = M_p(\theta_A + \theta_B + \theta_C) = 6M_p\theta_A$$
$$20P_u\theta_A = 6M_p\theta_A$$
$$P_u = \tfrac{6}{20} \times 268.8 = \textbf{80.64 kips}$$

Example 14-7   The continuous 18WF45 beam in Fig. 14-6 carries two equal concentrated loads having the locations indicated.   Disregarding the weight of

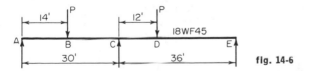

fig. 14-6

beam, compute the ultimate value of these loads, applying both the statical and the mechanism method.

Solution.   The continuous beam becomes unstable when a plastic hinge exists at C and at another section.   The bending-moment diagram has vertices at

B and *D*, but it is not readily apparent at which of these sections the second hinge will form. The answer is found by assuming a plastic hinge at *B* and at *D* in turn, computing the corresponding value of P_u, and selecting the lesser value as the correct result.

STATICAL METHOD. First assume a plastic hinge at *C* and at *B*. Figure 14-7*a* and *b* shows the force and bending-moment diagrams, respectively, for span *AC* associated with this assumed condition. An alternative form of the moment diagram appears in Fig. 14-7*c*, where *ACH* represents the moments that would exist in the absence of restraint at *C*, and *ACJ* represents, in absolute value, the moments induced by this restraint. From Example 14-3, we have

$$M_p = 268.8 \text{ ft-kips}$$
$$M_B = \frac{14 \times 16}{30} P_u - {}^{14}\!/_{30} M_p = M_p$$
$$P_u = {}^{44}\!/_{224} \times 268.8 = 52.8 \text{ kips}$$

Now assume a plastic hinge at *C* and at *D*. Figure 14-7*d* and *e* shows the force and bending-moment diagrams, respectively, for span *CE* associated with this assumed condition.

$$M_D = \frac{12 \times 24}{36} P_u - {}^{24}\!/_{36} M_p = M_p$$
$$P_u = {}^{60}\!/_{288} \times 268.8 = 56.0 \text{ kips}$$

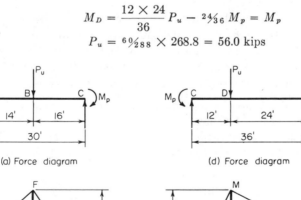

(a) Force diagram

(d) Force diagram

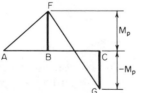

(b) Moment diagram

(e) Moment diagram

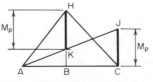

(c) Moment diagram by parts

fig. 14-7

The correct value of P_u is the lesser of these alternative results, namely, **52.8 kips.** When this load is reached, plastic hinges exist at B and C but not at D.

MECHANISM METHOD. First assume a plastic hinge at C and at B, and refer to Fig. 14-8.

$$\theta_C = {}^{14}\!/_{16}\theta_A \qquad \theta_B = {}^{30}\!/_{16}\theta_A \qquad \Delta = 14\theta_A$$
$$W_E = P_u\Delta = 14P_u\theta_A$$
$$W_I = M_p(\theta_B + \theta_C) = 2.75M_p\theta_A$$
$$14P_u\theta_A = 2.75M_p\theta_A \qquad P_u = 52.8 \text{ kips}$$

By assuming a plastic hinge at C and at D and repeating the foregoing procedure, we obtain the value $P_u = 56.0$ kips, which we discard.

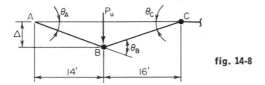

fig. 14-8

Example 14-8 Using a load factor of 1.70, design a continuous beam to carry the working loads (with estimated beam weight included) shown in Fig. 14-9a. The maximum length that may be transported is 60 ft.

Solution. Since the member must be spliced, it will be economical to adopt the following design:

1. Use the particular beam size required for each portion of the member, considering that the two portions will fail simultaneously at ultimate load. Therefore, three plastic hinges will exist at failure: one at the interior support and one in the interior of each span.

2. Extend one portion beyond the interior support, splicing the member at the point of contraflexure in the adjacent span. Since the maximum simple-span moment is greater for AB than for BC, it is plausible to assume that for economy the left portion rather than the right one should overhang the support.

The working loads must be multiplied by the load factor to obtain the ultimate load for which the structure is to be designed.

$$w = 1.2 \text{ klf} \qquad w_u = 1.70 \times 1.2 = 2.04 \text{ klf}$$
$$P = 10 \text{ kips} \qquad P_u = 1.70 \times 10 = 17 \text{ kips}$$

Figure 14-9 presents the ultimate-load diagram and the corresponding bending-moment diagram for each span. The maximum positive bending moment M_D in span AB and the negative bending moment M_B are set equal to one another in absolute value to find the plastic moment. An indirect but simple method of solution consists of assigning a series of trial values to M_B and calculating the corresponding value of M_D, continuing this process until the required equality is established. A direct but more cumbersome method comprises the following calculations:

$$M_B = 40R_A - 2.04 \times 40 \times 20 - 17 \times 12$$

$$R_A = 45.9 + \frac{M_B}{40} \qquad x = \frac{R_A}{2.04}$$

$$M_D = \frac{R_A x}{2} = \frac{R_A{}^2}{4.08} = -M_B$$

Substituting the value of R_A and solving, we obtain

$$M_D = 342 \text{ ft-kips}$$

For the left portion of the member,

$$Z = \frac{M_D}{f_y} = \frac{342 \times 12}{36} = 114 \text{ in.}^3$$

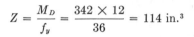

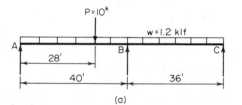

(a)

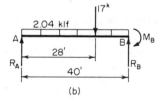

(b)

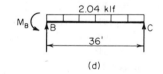

(d)

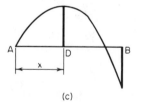

(c)

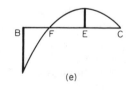

(e)

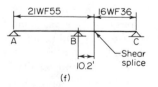

(f)

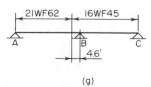

(g)

fig. 14-9

The rolled sections are listed on pages 2-7 to 2-9 of the AISC Manual in descending order with respect to their plastic moduli.

Use 21WF55: $Z = 125.4$ in.[3]

In designing the right portion of the member, we shall equate M_B to the true plastic-moment capacity of the 21WF55 and evaluate the maximum positive moment M_E accordingly.

$$M_B = -\frac{36 \times 125.4}{12} = -376.2 \text{ ft-kips}$$

$$R_C = 36.72 - \frac{376.2}{36} = 26.27 \text{ kips}$$

$$EC = \frac{26.27}{2.04} = 12.88 \text{ ft}$$

$$M_E = \frac{1}{2} \times 2.04 \times 12.88^2 = 169 \text{ ft-kips}$$

$$Z = \frac{169 \times 12}{36} = 56.3 \text{ in.}^3$$

Use 16WF36: $Z = 63.9$ in.[3]

The point of contraflexure F is at the following location:

$$BF = 36 - 2(EC) = 10.2 \text{ ft}$$

The design is summarized in Fig. 14-9f. By inserting a hinge at F, we destroy the continuity of the member and thereby modify its behavior under gradually increasing load. However, the ultimate-load conditions, which constitute the only valid design criterion, are not affected.

An alternative design, in which the right portion overhangs the support, is summarized in Fig. 14-9g. The total beam weight associated with each scheme is as follows:

Design 1		*Design* 2	
$55 \times 50.2 =$	2761 lb	$62 \times 35.4 =$	2195 lb
$36 \times 25.8 =$	929	$45 \times 40.6 =$	1827
Total	3690 lb	Total	4022 lb

For completeness, the column sizes associated with the two schemes should also be compared.

14-3 Frame Analysis   The statical and mechanism methods of assessing the ultimate load are applicable to frames as well as beams. We shall define the bending moment at a given section as the algebraic sum of the moments of all forces between the left support and the given section with respect to that section, considering a clockwise moment as positive.

Example 14-9 The prismatic frame in Fig. 14-10a carries the indicated working loads. Calculate the plastic moment and the reactions at the supports at ultimate load, using a load factor of 1.85. Apply the mechanism method.

Solution. There are three potential modes of failure to be considered:

1. Failure of the beam *BD* through the formation of plastic hinges at *B*, *C*, and *D* (Fig. 14-10*b*).

2. Failure by sidesway through the formation of plastic hinges at *B* and *D* (Fig. 14-10*c*).

3. A composite of the foregoing modes of failure, characterized by the formation of plastic hinges at *C* and *D* (Fig. 14-10*d*).

Since the true mode of failure is not readily discernible, it is necessary to investigate each of the foregoing modes.   The true mode of failure is the one that yields the highest value of the plastic moment, and the frame must be designed to sustain this moment.

Although the work quantities are always positive, it is advantageous to supply each angular displacement with an algebraic sign.   A rotation is considered positive if the angle on the interior side of the frame increases.   Manifestly, the algebraic sum of the angular displacements must equal zero.

$$P_u = 1.85 \times 40 = 74 \text{ kips} \qquad Q_u = 1.85 \times 12 = 22.2 \text{ kips}$$

Assume the mode of failure represented in Fig. 14-10*b*.

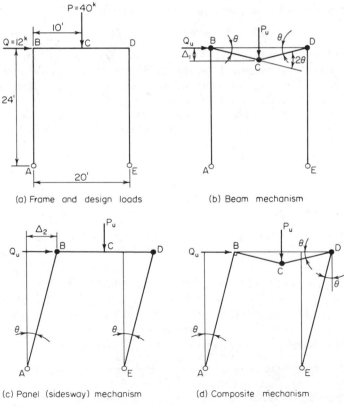

(a) Frame and design loads

(b) Beam mechanism

(c) Panel (sidesway) mechanism

(d) Composite mechanism

fig. 14-10

$$\Delta_1 = 10\theta \qquad W_E = 74 \times 10\theta = 740\theta$$

The calculations for internal work are recorded in the accompanying table, where the bending moments are shown in absolute value only.

Section	Angular displacement	Moment	W_I
A			
B	$-\theta$	M_p	$M_p\theta$
C	$+2\theta$	M_p	$2M_p\theta$
D	$-\theta$	M_p	$M_p\theta$
E			
Total.......	...	...	$4M_p\theta$

Equating the external and internal work, we have

$$4M_p\theta = 740\theta \qquad M_p = 185 \text{ ft-kips}$$

Assume the mode of failure represented in Fig. 14-10c.

$$\Delta_2 = 24\theta \qquad W_E = 22.2 \times 24\theta = 532.8\theta$$

Section	Angular displacement	Moment	W_I
A	$-\theta$		
B	$+\theta$	M_p	$M_p\theta$
C			
D	$-\theta$	M_p	$M_p\theta$
E	$+\theta$		
Total.......	...	...	$2M_p\theta$

$$2M_p\theta = 532.8\theta \qquad M_p = 266.4 \text{ ft-kips}$$

Assume the mode of failure represented in Fig. 14-10d.   Since this results from superposition of the two preceding modes, the angular displacements and external work may be obtained by adding the algebraic values previously found.

$$W_E = 740\theta + 532.8\theta = 1272.8\theta$$

Section	Angular displacement	Moment	W_I
A	$-\theta$		
B			
C	$+2\theta$	M_p	$2M_p\theta$
D	-2θ	M_p	$2M_p\theta$
E	$+\theta$		
Total.......	...	...	$4M_p\theta$

$$4M_p\theta = 1272.8\theta \qquad M_p = 318.2 \text{ ft-kips}$$

The true plastic moment is the highest value obtained, namely, **318.2 ft-kips.** The structure fails through the formation of plastic hinges at C and D. That a hinge should appear at D rather than at B is plausible when we consider that the bending moments induced by the two loads are of like sign at D but of opposite sign at B.

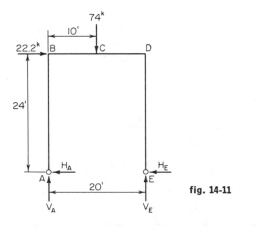

fig. 14-11

Figure 14-11 is the free-body diagram of the frame at ultimate load.

$$\Sigma M_E = 20V_A + 22.2 \times 24 - 74 \times 10 = 0$$
$$\therefore V_A = \textbf{10.36 kips} \qquad V_E = 74 - 10.36 = \textbf{63.64 kips}$$
$$M_C = 10V_A + 24H_A = 103.6 + 24H_A = 318.2$$
$$\therefore H_A = \textbf{8.94 kips} \qquad H_E = 22.2 - 8.94 = \textbf{13.26 kips}$$
$$M_D = -24H_E = -24 \times 13.26 = -318.2 \text{ ft-kips} \qquad \text{OK}$$

Example 14-10   With reference to the frame in Fig. 14-10a, calculate the plastic moment by applying the statical method.

Solution.   In accordance with our sign convention, the bending moment at a given section in this frame is positive if the fibers on the interior side of the neutral plane are in tension.   Consequently, as the mechanisms in Fig. 14-10 reveal, the algebraic sign of the plastic moment at a given section agrees with that of its angular displacement during collapse.

We must determine the relative values of the bending moments at B, C, and D. Refer to Fig. 14-11.   The vertical reactions were previously determined by statics.

$$V_A = 10.36 \text{ kips} \qquad M_B = 24H_A$$
$$M_C = 24H_A + 10V_A$$
$$\therefore M_C = M_B + 103.6 \qquad\qquad\qquad (a)$$
$$M_D = 24H_A + 20V_A - 74 \times 10$$
$$\therefore M_D = M_B - 532.8 \qquad\qquad\qquad (b)$$

or
$$M_D = M_C - 636.4 \qquad\qquad\qquad (c)$$

Assume the mode of failure represented in Fig. 14-10b.   This requires that

$$M_B = M_D = -M_p$$

This relationship is incompatible with Eq. (*b*), and the assumed mode of failure is therefore incorrect.

Assume the mode of failure represented in Fig. 14-10*c*.   This requires that

$$M_B = M_p \quad \text{and} \quad M_C < M_p$$
$$\therefore M_C < M_B$$

This relationship is incompatible with Eq. (*a*), and the assumed mode of failure is therefore incorrect.

By a process of elimination, we have ascertained that the frame will fail in the manner represented in Fig. 14-10*d*.   Then

$$M_C = M_p \qquad M_D = -M_p$$

Substituting these values in Eq. (*c*), we obtain

$$-M_p = M_p - 636.4 \qquad M_p = 318.2 \text{ ft-kips}$$

We shall now establish a criterion that enables us to determine when a composite mechanism is significant; i.e., under what conditions it may yield a value of M_p greater than that associated with the basic mechanisms.

The external and internal work associated with a given mechanism may be expressed as

$$W_E = e\theta \qquad \text{and} \qquad W_I = iM_p\theta$$

where the coefficients e and i are obtained by applying the mechanism method.   Then

$$M_p = \frac{e}{i}$$

Assume that there are two basic mechanisms to be investigated.   Let the subscripts 1 and 2 refer to these mechanisms and the subscript 3 to their composite mechanism.

$$M_{p1} = \frac{e_1}{i_1} \qquad M_{p2} = \frac{e_2}{i_2}$$

When the basic mechanisms are superposed, the values of W_E are additive.   If the two mechanisms do not produce rotations of opposite sign at any section, the values of W_I are also additive, and we have

$$M_{p3} = \frac{e_3}{i_3} = \frac{e_1 + e_2}{i_1 + i_2}$$

This value is intermediate between M_{p1} and M_{p2}, and the composite mechanism therefore lacks significance.   On the other hand, if the basic mechanisms produce rotations of opposite sign at any section whatsoever, M_{p3} *may* exceed both M_{p1} and M_{p2}.   In summary:

A composite mechanism is significant only if the two basic mechanisms of which it is composed produce rotations of opposite sign at any section.

This theorem, which establishes a condition that is necessary but not sufficient, simplifies the analysis of a complex frame by enabling us to discard the nonsignificant composite mechanisms at the outset.

Example 14-11   The frame in Fig. 14-12a sustains the ultimate loads indicated. Applying the mechanism method, compute the plastic moment and ultimate-load reactions.

Solution. The basic mechanisms are shown in Fig. 14-12b. We shall apply the theorem of composite mechanisms to identify those that are significant.

Mechanisms 1 *and* 2: The rotations at B are of opposite sign; the composite mechanism therefore warrants investigation.

Mechanisms 1 *and* 3: There are no rotations of opposite sign; the composite mechanism therefore fails the test.

Mechanisms 2 *and* 3: The rotations at B are of opposite sign; the composite mechanism therefore warrants investigation.

The composite mechanisms are shown in Fig. 14-12c. The values of the external work associated with the various mechanisms are as follows:

Mechanism	W_E
1	$80\Delta_1 = 80 \times 10\theta = 800\theta$
2	$20\Delta_2 = 20 \times 15\theta = 300\theta$
3	300θ
4	1100θ
5	600θ

The accompanying table indicates the sections at which plastic hinges form and the angular displacement of each hinge.

Mechanism	Section			
	B	C	D	F
1	$-\theta$	$+2\theta$	$-\theta$	
2	$+\theta$	....	-1.25θ	
3	-1.5θ	....	....	$+2.5\theta$
4	......	$+2\theta$	-2.25θ	
5	-0.5θ	....	-1.25θ	$+2.5\theta$

By equating the external and internal work associated with each mechanism, we obtain the following results:

$$M_{p1} = \frac{800}{4} = 200 \qquad M_{p2} = \frac{300}{2.25} = 133.3$$

$$M_{p3} = \frac{300}{4} = 75 \qquad M_{p4} = \frac{1100}{4.25} = 258.8$$

$$M_{p5} = \frac{600}{4.25} = 141.2$$

Then $M_p = \textbf{258.8 ft-kips}$

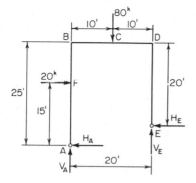

(a) Frame and ultimate loads

Mechanism I

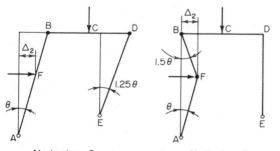

Mechanism 2   Mechanism 3
(b) Basic mechanisms

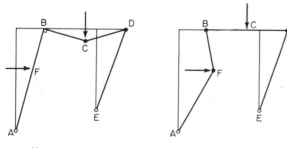

Mechanism 4   Mechanism 5
Composite of I and 2   Composite of 2 and 3
(c) Composite mechanisms

fig. 14-12

The frame therefore fails through the formation of plastic hinges at C and D. The reactions at the supports are found by applying the computed value of M_p.

$$M_D = -20H_E = -258.8 \qquad \therefore H_E = \textbf{12.94 kips}$$
$$M_C = M_D + 10V_E = 258.8 \qquad \therefore V_E = \textbf{51.76 kips}$$
$$H_A = 20 - 12.94 = \textbf{7.06 kips}$$
$$V_A = 80 - 51.76 = \textbf{28.24 kips}$$
$$\Sigma M_E = 20V_A + 5H_A + 20 \times 10 - 80 \times 10 = 0 \qquad \text{OK}$$

The value of M_p may be verified by ascertaining that the moments at B and F are less than M_p in absolute value.

$$M_B = 25H_A - 20 \times 10 = -23.5 \text{ ft-kips} \qquad \text{OK}$$
$$M_F = 15H_A = 105.9 \text{ ft-kips} \qquad \text{OK}$$

Example 14-12 The prismatic frame in Fig. 14-13a carries the ultimate loads indicated. Determine the plastic moment developed in the frame by applying the statical method.

Solution. The vertical reactions are statically determinate, but the horizontal reactions are indeterminate.

$$\Sigma M_G = 40V_A + 4 \times 25 - 34 \times 30 - 25 \times 20 - 22 \times 10 = 0$$
$$V_A = 41 \text{ kips} \qquad \text{and} \qquad V_G = 40 \text{ kips}$$

Assume that H_A is directed to the right. The bending moments at the significant sections are as follows:

$$M_B = -25H_A$$
$$M_C = 41 \times 10 - 4 \times 6 - 31H_A = 386 - 31H_A$$
$$M_D = 41 \times 20 - 4 \times 12 - 34 \times 10 - 37H_A = 432 - 37H_A$$
$$M_E = 276 - 31H_A \qquad M_F = -100 - 25H_A$$

In analyzing a gable frame, it is helpful to use a *projected* bending-moment diagram. This is constructed in the following manner: Consider the rafter BD to be projected on the plane of column AB, and the rafter FD to be projected on the plane of column GF. Juxtapose the halves, as shown in Fig. 14-13b.

The bending moment at a given section may be resolved into its determinate and indeterminate elements. The former is the moment caused by the loads and the reaction V_A; the latter is the moment caused by the reaction H_A. The diagrams representing these moments are shown in Fig. 14-13b, both being drawn above the base line. Since the indeterminate moment is negative across the entire frame, the true moment at a given section is represented by the difference between the ordinates of the two diagrams.

Failure of the frame will result from the formation of two plastic hinges. It is evident by inspection of the bending-moment diagram that these hinges form at D and F, since the moments at these sections will exceed in absolute value the moment at B, C, and E. We therefore have the following:

$$M_D = M_p \qquad \text{and} \qquad M_F = -M_p$$

Then
$$M_p = 432 - 37H_A = -(-100 - 25H_A)$$

Solving,
$$H_A = 5.35 \text{ kips} \qquad \text{and} \qquad M_p = \textbf{234 ft-kips}$$

To verify this result, we shall compute the bending moment at the remaining sections.

$$M_B = -5.35 \times 25 = -133.8 \text{ ft-kips}$$
$$M_C = 386 - 5.35 \times 31 = 220.2 \text{ ft-kips}$$
$$M_E = 276 - 5.35 \times 31 = 110.2 \text{ ft-kips}$$

These results are all below the plastic moment of 234 ft-kips in absolute value.

The analysis of a gable frame by the mechanism method involves an application of the theorem of virtual displacements, which we shall now develop.

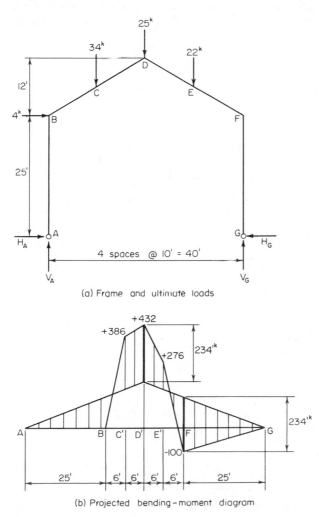

(a) Frame and ultimate loads

(b) Projected bending-moment diagram

fig. 14-13

In Fig. 14-14*a*, point P is displaced along a virtual (infinitesimally small) circular arc PP' centered at O and having a central angle θ. We wish to evaluate the horizontal and vertical displacement of P. Refer to Fig. 14-14*b*, and let

r_h = length of OP as projected on horizontal line
r_v = length of OP as projected on vertical line
Δ_h = horizontal displacement of P
Δ_v = vertical displacement of P

Since PP' is infinitesimally small, we may replace this circular arc with the straight line PP'' that is tangent to the arc at P and therefore normal

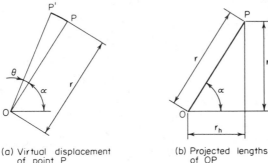

(a) Virtual displacement   (b) Projected lengths
    of point P   of OP

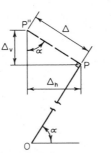

(c) Displacement diagram

fig. 14-14

to radius OP, where P'' lies on the radius through P'. Line PP'' is shown in Fig. 14-14*c*. Since θ is infinitesimally small, we may set

$$PP'' = r\theta$$
$$\Delta_h = PP'' \sin \alpha = r\theta \sin \alpha$$
$$\Delta_v = PP'' \cos \alpha = r\theta \cos \alpha$$

But $\qquad\qquad r \sin \alpha = r_v \qquad$ and $\qquad r \cos \alpha = r_h$

$$\therefore \ \Delta_h = r_v \theta \qquad \text{and} \qquad \Delta_v = r_h \theta \tag{14-2}$$

These results may be combined and expressed verbally in the following manner:

If a point is displaced along a virtual circular arc, its displacement as projected on the u axis equals the displacement angle times the length of the radius as projected on an axis normal to u.

Example 14-13 With reference to the frame in Fig. 14-13*a*, assume that plastic hinges form at D and F. Calculate the plastic moment associated with this assumed mode of failure by applying the mechanism method.

Solution. During collapse, the frame consists of three rigid bodies: ABD, DF, and GF. To evaluate the external and internal work performed during a virtual displacement, it is necessary to locate the instantaneous center of rotation of each body.

In Fig. 14-15, the dash lines represent the configuration of the frame following a virtual displacement that brings D to D' and F to F'. Line AD is drawn, intersecting GF prolonged at H.

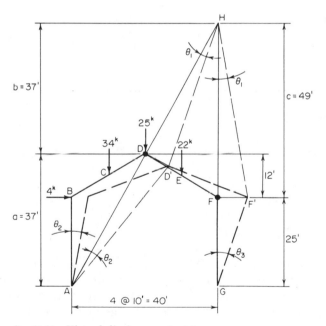

fig. 14-15 Virtual displacement of frame.

Since A is the center of rotation of ABD, DD' is normal to AD and HD; since G is the center of rotation of GF, FF' is normal to GF and HF. It therefore follows that H is the instantaneous center of rotation of DF. We shall express the angular displacement at D and F and the internal work in terms of θ_1, using absolute values.

$$\frac{\theta_2}{\theta_1} = \frac{HD}{AD} \qquad \therefore \ \theta_2 = \theta_1$$

$$\frac{\theta_3}{\theta_1} = \frac{HF}{GF} = \frac{49}{25} \qquad \therefore \ \theta_3 = 1.96\theta_1$$

$$\theta_D = \theta_1 + \theta_2 = 2\theta_1$$
$$\theta_F = \theta_1 + \theta_3 = 2.96\theta_1$$
$$W_I = M_p(\theta_D + \theta_F) = 4.96M_p\theta_1$$

To evaluate the external work, it is necessary to find the displacement of each load in the direction of the load.   This is done by applying the theorem of virtual displacements.   The calculations for the external work are recorded in the accompanying table.

Section	Load, kips	Displacement in direction of load, ft	External work, ft-kips
B	4	$\Delta_h = 25\theta_2 = 25\theta_1$	$100\theta_1$
C	34	$\Delta_v = 10\theta_2 = 10\theta_1$	$340\theta_1$
D	25	$\Delta_v = 20\theta_1$	$500\theta_1$
E	22	$\Delta_v = 10\theta_1$	$220\theta_1$
Total......	...	....	$1160\theta_1$

Equating the external and internal work, we obtain

$$4.96M_p\theta_1 = 1160\theta_1 \qquad M_p = 234 \text{ ft-kips}$$

Other modes of failure may be assumed and the corresponding value of M_p computed in a similar manner.   It will be found that the failure mechanism analyzed in this example (plastic hinges at D and F) yields the highest value of M_p and is therefore the true mechanism.

14-4   Analysis of Beam-Columns   The presence of an axial force reduces the plastic-moment capacity of a member, and it is therefore necessary to establish the manner in which these quantities are related.   Figure 14-16a is the stress diagram at plastification of a member subjected to an axial compressive force and bending moment.   The resultant compressive and tensile forces on the cross section are represented by C and T, respectively.   For simplicity, we may resolve this stress diagram into the two parts shown at the right.   This procedure is tantamount to assuming that the axial force is resisted by a central core and the moment is resisted by the outer segments of the section, although in reality they are jointly resisted by the integral action of the entire section.

The notational system is as follows:

d = depth of section

d_w = depth of web

t_f = thickness of flange

t_w = thickness of web

P = axial force

P_y = axial force that would induce plastification if this acted alone = Af_y

M'_p = plastic-moment capacity of section in combination with P

Z_c = plastic modulus of core

Z_r = plastic modulus of remainder of section

Example 14-14 A 10WF45 beam-column is subjected to an axial force of 84 kips at ultimate load. Applying the exact method, calculate the plastic-moment capacity of this section with respect to the major axis.

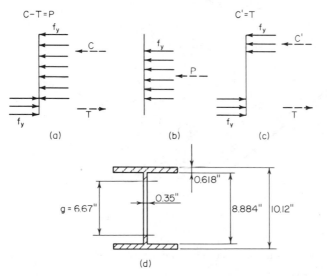

fig. 14-16

Solution. Refer to Fig. 14-16d. The properties of the section are as follows:

$$A = 13.24 \text{ sq in.} \qquad d = 10.12 \text{ in.}$$
$$t_f = 0.618 \text{ in.} \qquad t_w = 0.350 \text{ in.}$$
$$d_w = 10.12 - 2 \times 0.618 = 8.884 \text{ in.}$$
$$Z = 55.0 \text{ in.}^3 \qquad \text{(Manual, p. 2-8)}$$

Assume that the core that resists the 84-kip load is encompassed within the web. The depth g of this core is

$$g = \frac{84}{0.35 \times 36} = 6.67 < 8.884 \text{ in.} \qquad \text{OK}$$

The equation for the plastic modulus of a rectangular section was derived in Example 14-2 and is presented on page 6-22 of the AISC Manual.

$$Z_c = \tfrac{1}{4}t_w g^2 = \tfrac{1}{4} \times 0.35 \times 6.67^2 = 3.9 \text{ in.}^3$$
$$Z_r = 55.0 - 3.9 = 51.1 \text{ in.}^3$$
$$M'_p = \frac{51.1 \times 36}{12} = \textbf{153.3 ft-kips}$$

An *interaction diagram* for a beam-column is one that represents simultaneous sets of values of P and M'_p. By assigning a series of values to the parameter g and computing the corresponding sets of values of P and M'_p for the 10WF45, we obtain the interaction diagram shown in Fig. 14-17. This comprises the parabolic curves CB and BA, where the points A, B, and C correspond to the conditions $g = 0$, $g = d_w$, and $g = d$, respectively.

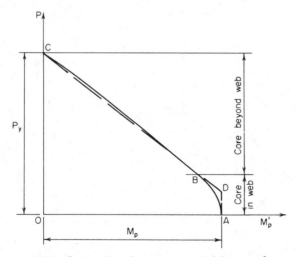

fig. 14-17   Interaction diagram for axial force and moment.

The interaction diagram may be readily analyzed by applying the following relationships, in which t denotes the thickness of the section at a given point:

$$\frac{dP}{dg} = f_y t \qquad \frac{dM'_p}{dg} = -\tfrac{1}{2}f_y tg$$
$$\therefore \frac{dP}{dM'_p} = -\frac{2}{g}$$

Since the variation in the value of g between points B and C is small, it follows that the change in slope along CB is slight, and the curvature of arc CB is therefore negligible.

To facilitate the design of a beam-column, the true interaction diagram is replaced with a diagram that comprises two straight lines. In the present instance, these are the vertical line AD of length $0.15P_y$, and line CD. The equation of CD is found in this manner:

$$\text{Slope of } CD = -\frac{0.85P_y}{M_p}$$

$$\therefore P = P_y - \frac{0.85P_y}{M_p} M_p'$$

or
$$M_p' = 1.18\left(1 - \frac{P}{P_y}\right) M_p \qquad (14\text{-}3)$$

The provisions of Sec. 2.3 of the AISC Specification are based upon the linear interaction diagram.

Example 14-15 Applying the data of Example 14-14, calculate the plastic-moment capacity by use of the approximate method.

Solution. We must ascertain whether the point representing $P = 84$ kips lies on line AD or CD in Fig. 14-17. If it lies on CD, Eq. (14-3) is valid.

$$P_y = Af_y = 13.24 \times 36 = 476.6 \text{ kips}$$

$$\frac{P}{P_y} = \frac{84}{476.6} = 0.176 \qquad \therefore \text{ Eq. (14-3) applies}$$

$$M_p = \frac{55.0 \times 36}{12} = 165 \text{ ft-kips}$$

$$M_p' = 1.18(1 - 0.176) \times 165 = \mathbf{160.4 \text{ ft-kips}}$$

This approximate value differs from the true value by 4.6 percent.

FIFTEEN
Timber Design

15-1 Introduction For the design of timber members, we shall refer to the following sources:

"Wood Handbook" (Handbook No. 72, 1955 ed.), published by the Forest Products Laboratory of the U.S. Department of Agriculture.

"National Design Specification for Stress-grade Lumber and Its Fastenings" (1962 ed.), published by the National Lumber Manufacturers Association.

The properties of the standard timber sections are presented in the table at the back of the National Design Specification. The average weight of timber is 40 pcf. We shall assume in all instances that the members will be continuously dry and subject to normal loading conditions.

15-2 Flexural Members The notational system applied in the following material conforms with that adopted in Art. 5-3. In addition, we shall denote the width and depth of a rectangular section by b and d, respectively.

In computing the capacity of a timber beam, it is usually necessary to investigate its strength in flexure and in shear and to ascertain that its deflection is below the imposed limit. As explained in the section titled

Depth Factor on page 204 of the Wood Handbook, an increase in the depth of a beam is accompanied by a decrease in the modulus of rupture. The allowable bending stress for a given species of wood applies to a *shallow* beam, this being defined as one having a depth of 16 in. or less. The allowable bending stress in a deep beam equals that in a shallow beam multiplied by a *depth factor F*, which has the following value:

$$F = 0.81 \frac{d^2 + 143}{d^2 + 88} \tag{15-1}$$

Example 15-1   A floor is supported by 3 × 8 in. wood joists spaced 16 in. on centers on an effective span of 10 ft.   The total floor load transmitted to the joists is 107 psf.   Compute the maximum bending stress and initial deflection, using $E = 1,760,000$ psi.

Solution. The beam properties are as follows:

$$A = 19.7 \text{ sq in.} \qquad I = 92.3 \text{ in.}^4 \qquad S = 24.6 \text{ in.}^3$$

$$\text{Beam weight} = \frac{19.7}{144} \times 40 = 5 \text{ plf}$$

$$w = 107 \times 1.33 + 5 = 148 \text{ plf}$$
$$M = \tfrac{1}{8}wL^2 = \tfrac{1}{8} \times 148 \times 10^2 \times 12 = 22,200 \text{ in.-lb}$$

Applying Eq. (5-5), we have

$$f = \frac{M}{S} = \frac{22,200}{24.6} = 902 \text{ psi}$$

The equation for the midspan deflection of a uniformly loaded beam appears on page 2-120 of the AISC Manual.

$$\Delta = \frac{5}{384} \frac{wL^4}{EI} = \frac{5 \times 148 \times 10^4 \times 1728}{384 \times 1,760,000 \times 92.3} = 0.205 \text{ in.}$$

Example 15-2   If the allowable bending stress in a shallow beam is 1500 psi, what is the moment capacity of a 12 × 20 in. beam?

Solution. The true depth of the section is 19½ in.   Since this is a deep beam, we must introduce the depth factor as given by Eq. (15-1).

$$F = 0.81 \times \frac{19.5^2 + 143}{19.5^2 + 88} = 0.905$$

$$f_{\text{allow}} = 0.905 \times 1500 = 1358 \text{ psi} \qquad S = 728.8 \text{ in.}^3$$

$$M = \frac{1.358 \times 728.8}{12} = 82.48 \text{ ft-kips}$$

In accordance with Eq. (5-9), the shearing stress in a solid rectangular section varies parabolically with the depth and has a maximum value equal to 1.5 times the average stress.   However, the cross section of a timber beam is discontinuous rather than solid as a result of its physical characteristics.   An analysis of the shearing strength of timber beams is presented in the section titled Shear in Checked Beams on page 206 of the Wood Handbook.

Checks are sometimes present near the neutral axis of a beam, and their detrimental effect is taken into account in establishing the allowable shearing stress.   However, these checks also have a salutary effect, for they modify the stress distribution across the section and thereby reduce the maximum stress.   The amount of this reduction depends upon the position of the load.   The maximum shearing stress induced by a stationary concentrated load is considered to be the following:

$$v = \frac{10}{9} \frac{(a/d)^2}{2 + (a/d)^2} v' \tag{15-2}$$

where v = assumed maximum shearing stress

v' = nominal maximum shearing stress as computed by Eq. (5-9)

a = distance from load to adjacent support

The maximum shearing stress induced by a distributed load is computed in the following manner: Set the maximum vertical shear equal to the reaction at the support, less the load that lies within a distance d of the support.   Find the shearing stress by applying Eq. (5-9).

Example 15-3   A 3 × 10 in. beam on a span of 12 ft carries a concentrated load of 2730 lb located 2 ft from the support.   If the allowable shearing stress is 120 psi, determine whether this load is excessive.   Neglect the beam weight.

Solution. The maximum vertical shear equals the reaction at the adjacent support.

$$d = 9.5 \text{ in.} \quad A = 24.9 \text{ sq in.}$$

$$V = 2730 \times \frac{12 - 2}{12} = 2275 \text{ lb}$$

$$v' = \frac{1.5V}{A} = \frac{1.5 \times 2275}{24.9} = 137 \text{ psi}$$

$$\left(\frac{a}{d}\right)^2 = \left(\frac{24}{9.5}\right)^2 = 6.38$$

Applying Eq. (15-2), we have

$$v = \frac{10 \times 6.38 \times 137}{9 \times 8.38} = 116 < 120 \text{ psi}$$

The load is therefore not excessive.

A transient concentrated load rolling across a beam induces the absolute maximum shearing stress when it lies at a certain critical distance from the support rather than directly above it.   This condition arises from the fact that as the load recedes from the support the reaction decreases but the shear-redistribution effect becomes less pronounced.   For simplicity, the shearing stress is computed by placing the load at a distance of $3d$ or $\frac{1}{4}L$ from the support, whichever is less, and applying Eq. (5-9).

Example 15-4 A 4 × 12 in. beam on a span of 10 ft carries a total uniform load of 150 plf and a moving concentrated load. If the allowable shearing stress is 130 psi, what is the allowable value of the moving load as governed by shear?

Solution. Let P denote the load.

$$d = 11.5 \text{ in.} = 0.96 \text{ ft} \qquad A = 41.7 \text{ sq in.}$$
$$3d = 2.9 \text{ ft} \qquad \tfrac{1}{4}L = 2.5 \text{ ft} \qquad \text{(governs)}$$
$$V = 150(5 - 0.96) + 0.75P = 610 + 0.75P$$
$$v = \frac{1.5V}{A} \qquad 130 = \frac{1.5(610 + 0.75P)}{41.7}$$

Solving,
$$P = \textbf{4000 lb}$$

15-3 Wood-Plywood Girders   Since a beam of rectangular cross section is relatively inefficient, timber girders are often constructed as built-up members having a cross section in the shape of a box, an I, or a double I. These girders consist of a plywood web and either solid or laminated flanges, the web and flanges being glued to one another. An analysis of members of this type is presented in the section titled Design of Wood-Plywood Beams and Girders on pages 263 to 272 of the Wood Handbook.

We shall adopt the following notational system:

A_f = area of flange
a = distance between resultant forces in flanges
d = depth of member
d_f = depth of flange
I_f = moment of inertia of flanges with respect to neutral axis
I_o = moment of inertia of single flange with respect to its own centroidal axis
I_w = moment of inertia of web with respect to neutral axis
n = number of webs
Q_f = statical moment of flange area with respect to neutral axis
t_w = thickness of web
v_1 = shearing stress at surface of contact of flange and web
v_2 = shearing stress in web normal to plane of plies
Δ = deflection of girder

To simplify the calculations, the following assumptions are made: Bending is resisted solely by the flanges, and the shearing stress v_1 is constant across the depth of flange. The latter assumption causes Eq. (5-9) to assume the following form for a box girder:

$$v_1 = \frac{VQ_f}{nId_f} \tag{15-3}$$

The conventional methods of calculating the deflection of a beam assume that deflection is caused solely by flexure, the deflection caused by shear being considered negligible.   However, in the case of a timber girder having a thin plywood web, the shear in the web contributes materially to the total deflection.   The deflection due to web shear depends upon the orientation of the grain relative to the longitudinal axis. Since a precise calculation of deflection is not possible, the practice in design is to multiply the deflection caused by flexure by some specified factor.

Example 15-5   A girder having a 36-ft span is to carry a uniform load of 550 plf, which includes its estimated weight.   Design a box-type member of glued construction, using the allowable stresses recorded in the accompanying table. Architectural details limit the depth to 40 in., and the ratio of deflection to span cannot exceed $\frac{1}{360}$.   The modulus of elasticity of both materials is 1,760,000 psi. Assume that the total deflection will be 1.5 times that caused by flexure alone.

	Lumber	Plywood
Tension........................	1500 psi	2000 psi
Compression parallel to grain......	1350	1460
Compression normal to grain......	390	405
Shear parallel to plane of plies.....	....	72*
Shear normal to plane of plies.....	....	192

* Use 36 psi at contact surface of flange and web to allow for stress concentration.

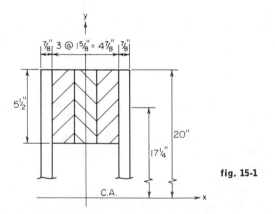

fig. 15-1

Solution.   Refer to Fig. 15-1.   To preclude the possibility of field error, the tension and compression flanges will be made identical.

We shall assume that the member precisely satisfies the requirements for flexure and deflection and determine the depth associated with this balanced condition. By Eq. (5-5),

$$M = \frac{fI}{c} = \frac{2fI}{d} = \frac{2700I}{d} \qquad (a)$$

Multiplying the midspan deflection due to flexure by 1.5, we obtain

$$\Delta = \frac{7.5}{384} \frac{wL^4}{EI} = \frac{7.5}{48} \frac{wL^2}{8} \frac{L^2}{EI}$$

or

$$\Delta = \frac{7.5}{48} \frac{L^2}{EI} M = \frac{L}{360} \qquad (b)$$

By substituting in Eq. (b) the value of M as given by Eq. (a), we arrive at the value $d = 37.3$ in. We shall therefore use the permissible depth of 40 in. As a result of this increase in depth, a section that satisfies the requirement for flexure will satisfy the requirement for deflection as well.

Assume tentatively that the flanges will be $5\frac{1}{2}$ in. deep. The average bending stress is

$$f_{\mathrm{av}} = 1350 \times \frac{17.25}{20} = 1165 \text{ psi}$$

Applying Eq. (2-14), we obtain the following value for the lever arm of the resultant forces in the flanges:

$$a = 40 - 2\left[\frac{5.5}{3}\left(\frac{20 + 2 \times 14.5}{20 + 14.5} \right) \right] = 34.8 \text{ in.}$$
$$M = \frac{1}{8} \times 550 \times 36^2 \times 12 = 1{,}070{,}000 \text{ in.-lb}$$
$$A_f = \frac{M/a}{f_{\mathrm{av}}} = \frac{1{,}070{,}000}{1165 \times 34.8} = 26.4 \text{ sq in.}$$

Use three 2×6 in. sections with glued vertical laminations for both the tension and compression flanges.

$$A_f = 3 \times 8.93 = 26.79 \text{ sq in.}$$
$$I_o = 3 \times 22.5 = 67.5 \text{ in.}^4$$

The web thickness will be tentatively established by assuming that the maximum shearing stress is 1.25 times the average stress, with the total web area included.

$$V = \frac{1}{2} \times 550 \times 36 = 9900 \text{ lb}$$
$$t_w = \frac{1.25V}{dv_2} = \frac{1.25 \times 9900}{40 \times 192} = 1.61 \text{ in.}$$

Try two $\frac{7}{8}$-in. thick plywood webs. A catalog of plywood properties reveals that the $\frac{7}{8}$-in. member consists of seven plies and that the parallel plies have an aggregate thickness of 0.5 in.

TRIAL SECTION

Depth: 40 in.
Webs: Two $\frac{7}{8}$-in. sections
Each flange: Three 2×6 in. sections

We shall investigate the trial section.

$$I_f = 2(67.5 + 26.79 \times 17.25^2) = 16,080 \text{ in.}^4$$

$$f = \frac{Mc}{I} = \frac{1,070,000 \times 20}{16,080} = 1330 < 1350 \text{ psi} \qquad \text{OK}$$

$$Q_f = 26.79 \times 17.25 = 462 \text{ in.}^3$$

By Eq. (15-3),

$$v_1 = \frac{VQ_f}{nId_f} = \frac{9900 \times 462}{2 \times 16,080 \times 5.5} = 26 < 36 \text{ psi} \qquad \text{OK}$$

In computing the shearing stress in the webs, we shall evaluate Q and I by considering solely the web area furnished by the parallel plies.

$$Q = Q_f + Q_w = 462 + 2 \times 0.5 \times 20 \times 10 = 662 \text{ in.}^3$$

$$I = I_f + I_w = 16,080 + 2 \times \tfrac{1}{12} \times 0.5 \times 40^3 = 21,410 \text{ in.}^4$$

Applying Eq. (5-9), we have

$$v_2 = \frac{VQ}{It_w} = \frac{9900 \times 662}{21,410 \times 2 \times 0.875} = 175 < 192 \text{ psi} \qquad \text{OK}$$

$$\Delta = \frac{7.5 \, wL^4}{384 \, EI_f} = \frac{7.5 \times 550 \times 36^4 \times 1728}{384 \times 1,760,000 \times 16,080} = 1.10 \text{ in.}$$

$$\Delta_{\text{allow}} = \frac{L}{360} = \frac{36 \times 12}{360} = 1.20 \text{ in.} \qquad \text{OK}$$

The trial section is satisfactory in all respects.

The girder must be braced for lateral stability. The allowable distance between points of lateral support is a function of the ratio of the moments of inertia of the area with respect to its two principal axes.

$$I_y = 2 \times \tfrac{1}{12} \times 5.5 \times 4.875^3 + 2 \times 0.5 \times 40 \times 2.875^2$$
$$= 436 \text{ in.}^4$$

$$\frac{I_z}{I_y} = \frac{16,080}{436} = 36.9$$

For this ratio, the Wood Handbook stipulates that ". . . the beam should be restrained by bridging or other bracing at intervals of not more than 8 ft."

15-4 Design of Columns   The notational system pertaining to columns is as follows:

P = allowable load
A = sectional area
L = unbraced length
d = smaller dimension of rectangular section
E = modulus of elasticity
f_c = allowable compressive stress parallel to grain in short column of given species
f = allowable compressive stress parallel to grain in given column

The recommendations of the Forest Products Laboratory for the design of solid columns are presented on pages 216 to 220 of the Wood Handbook. Columns are divided into three categories, short, intermediate, and long. Let K denote a parameter defined by the equation

$$K = 0.64 \left(\frac{E}{f_c}\right)^{\frac{1}{2}}$$

The range of the slenderness ratio and the allowable stress assigned to each category are as follows:

Short column:

$$\frac{L}{d} \leq 11 \qquad f = f_c$$

Intermediate column:

$$11 < \frac{L}{d} \leq K \qquad f = f_c\left[1 - \frac{1}{3}\left(\frac{L/d}{K}\right)^4\right] \tag{15-4}$$

Long column:

$$\frac{L}{d} > K \qquad f = \frac{0.274E}{(L/d)^2} \tag{15-5}$$

The maximum L/d ratio is set at 50.

The National Design Specification covers the design of solid columns in Sec. 401-E. The allowable stress in a rectangular section is as follows:

$$f = \frac{0.30E}{(L/d)^2} \qquad \text{but} \qquad f \leq f_c \tag{15-6}$$

Example 15-6 An 8 × 10 in. column has an unbraced length of 10 ft 6 in. The allowable compressive stress is 1500 psi and $E = 1,760,000$ psi. Calculate the allowable load on this column (a) by applying the recommendations of the Wood Handbook, and (b) by applying the provisions of the National Design Specification.

Solution

$$A = 71.3 \text{ sq in.} \qquad \frac{L}{d} = \frac{126}{7.5} = 16.8$$

PART a

$$K = 0.64 \left(\frac{1,760,000}{1500}\right)^{\frac{1}{2}} = 21.9$$

This is therefore an intermediate column. Applying Eq. (15-4), we have

$$P = Af = 71.3 \times 1500 \left[1 - \frac{1}{3}\left(\frac{16.8}{21.9}\right)^4\right] = \textbf{94,600 lb}$$

PART b. Applying Eq. (15-6), we have

$$f = \frac{0.30 \times 1,760,000}{16.8^2} = 1870 \text{ psi}$$

Therefore, set $f = 1500$ psi.

$$P = 71.3 \times 1500 = \textbf{107,000 lb}$$

Example 15-7 A column 12 ft long supports a load of 98 kips. Design a solid section in accordance with the recommendations of the Wood Handbook, using $f_c = 1400$ psi and $E = 1,760,000$ psi.
  Solution. Assume that $d = 7\frac{1}{2}$ in.

$$\frac{L}{d} = \frac{144}{7.5} = 19.2 \qquad K = 0.64\left(\frac{1,760,000}{1400}\right)^{\frac{1}{2}} = 22.7$$

This is an intermediate column if the assumed dimension is correct.

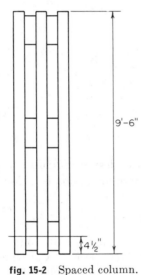

9'-6"

4½"

fig. 15-2 Spaced column.

$$f = 1400\left[1 - \frac{1}{3}\left(\frac{19.2}{22.7}\right)^4\right] = 1160 \text{ psi}$$

$$A = \frac{98,000}{1160} = 84.5 \text{ sq in.}$$

Use an **8 $\times$ 12 in.** section; $A = 86.3$ sq in.

A compression member in a wood truss is often designed as a *spaced column*. This is a built-up member whose elements are separated by spacer blocks, the elements being tied together by timber connectors passing through the blocks.

The design of spaced columns is covered on pages 223 to 225 of the Wood Handbook. In analyzing a spaced column, it is necessary to assess both the aggregate strength of the elements and the strength of the built-up section. The end spacer blocks partially restrain the elements against rotation and thereby enhance their capacity. This effect is taken into account by multiplying the modulus of elasticity by a *fixity factor F*. Values of F are presented in the first paragraph on page 225 of the Wood Handbook.

Example 15-8 The column in Fig. 15-2 is composed of three 3 $\times$ 8 in. sections. Determine the capacity of the member if $f_c = 1400$ psi and $E = 1,760,000$ psi.
  Solution. The fixity factor is 2.5. For the individual element, we have the following:

$$A = 19.7 \text{ sq in.} \qquad \frac{L}{d} = \frac{114}{2.625} = 43.4$$

$$K = 0.64\left(\frac{2.5 \times 1,760,000}{1400}\right)^{\frac{1}{2}} = 35.9 \qquad \therefore \text{ long column}$$

$$f = \frac{0.274 \times 2.5 \times 1,760,000}{43.4^2} = 640 \text{ psi}$$

The aggregate strength of the elements is

$$P = 3 \times 19.7 \times 640 = 37{,}800 \text{ lb}$$

For the built-up member, we have the following:

$$\frac{L}{d} = \frac{114}{7.5} = 15.2$$

From Example 15-7, $K = 22.7$, and the column is therefore intermediate. Applying Eq. (15-4), we have

$$f = 1400 \left[1 - \frac{1}{3} \left(\frac{15.2}{22.7} \right)^4 \right] = 1306 > 640 \text{ psi}$$

The column capacity is therefore limited by the elements, and its value is

$$P = \textbf{37,800 lb}$$

15-5 Compression on Oblique Plane Consider that a timber member sustains a compressive force whose action line makes an oblique angle with the grain. Let

P = allowable compressive stress parallel to grain
Q = allowable compressive stress normal to grain
N = allowable compressive stress inclined to grain
θ = angle between direction of stress N and direction of grain

By Hankinson's equation,

$$N = \frac{PQ}{P \sin^2 \theta + Q \cos^2 \theta} \tag{15-7}$$

Example 15-9 Determine whether the joint in Fig. 15-3 is satisfactory with

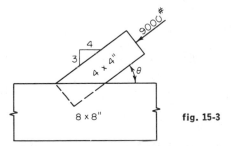

fig. 15-3

respect to bearing if the allowable compressive stresses are 1400 and 400 psi parallel and normal to the grain, respectively.

Solution

$$P = 1400 \text{ psi} \qquad Q = 400 \text{ psi} \qquad f = \frac{9000}{3.625^2} = 685 \text{ psi}$$

$$\sin^2 \theta = (\tfrac{3}{5})^2 = 0.36 \qquad \cos^2 \theta = (\tfrac{4}{5})^2 = 0.64$$

Equation (15-7) yields

$$N = \frac{1400 \times 400}{1400 \times 0.36 + 400 \times 0.64} = 737 > 685 \text{ psi}$$

Therefore, the joint is satisfactory.

Alternatively, the value of N may be obtained by computing θ and consulting the Scholten nomograph on page 181 of the Wood Handbook.

In Fig. 15-4, member M_1 must be notched at the joint to avoid removing an excessive area from member M_2. If the member is cut in such a

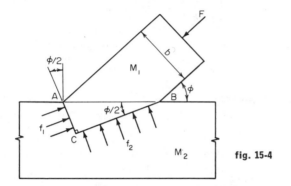

fig. 15-4

manner that AC and BC make an angle of $\phi/2$ with vertical and horizontal planes, respectively, the allowable bearing pressures at these faces are identical for the two members. Let

A = sectional area of member M_1
f_1 = pressure at AC
f_2 = pressure at BC

It may be readily shown that

$$AC = b\,\frac{\sin\,(\phi/2)}{\sin\,\phi} \qquad BC = b\,\frac{\cos\,(\phi/2)}{\sin\,\phi} \qquad (15\text{-}8)$$

$$f_1 = \frac{F\,\sin\,\phi}{A\,\tan\,(\phi/2)} \qquad f_2 = \frac{F\,\sin\,\phi\,\tan\,(\phi/2)}{A} \qquad (15\text{-}9)$$

This type of joint is often used in wood trusses.

Example 15-10 With reference to Fig. 15-4, M_1 is a 4 $\times$ 4, $F = 5500$ lb, and $\phi = 30°$. The allowable compressive stresses are as follows: $P = 1200$ psi, $Q = 390$ psi. The projection of M_1 into M_2 is restricted to a vertical distance of $2\frac{1}{2}$ in. Design a suitable notch.

Solution. We shall try a half-angle notch.

$$\sin 30° = 0.500 \qquad \cos 15° = 0.966$$
$$\sin 15° = 0.259 \qquad \tan 15° = 0.268$$

The area of a 4×4 is 13.1 sq in.

$$f_1 = \frac{5500 \times 0.500}{13.1 \times 0.268} = 783 \text{ psi}$$

$$f_2 = \frac{5500 \times 0.500 \times 0.268}{13.1} = 56 \text{ psi}$$

$$N_1 = \frac{1200 \times 390}{1200 \times 0.259^2 + 390 \times 0.966^2} = 1053 \text{ psi} \qquad \text{OK}$$

$$N_2 = \frac{1200 \times 390}{1200 \times 0.966^2 + 390 \times 0.259^2} = 408 \text{ psi} \qquad \text{OK}$$

$$AC = 3.625 \times \frac{0.259}{0.500} = 1.9 \text{ in.}$$

$$BC = 3.625 \times \frac{0.966}{0.500} = 7.0 \text{ in.}$$

Make AC 2 in. and BC 7 in.

15-6 Design of Connections An outstanding feature of a timber structure is the ease with which its parts may be joined together. The criteria governing the design of timber connections are discussed in the section titled Timber Fastenings on pages 165 to 200 of the Wood Handbook.

We shall comply with the provisions of the National Design Specification. The timber species are classified under two schemes. The first scheme, which is used to determine the capacity of split-ring connectors, is presented in Table 7 on page 28 of the Specification. The other scheme, which is used to determine the capacity of nails, lag screws, and bolts, is presented in Table 13 on page 39.

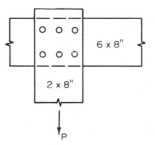

fig. 15-5

Example 15-11 The western hemlock members in Fig. 15-5 are connected with six 50d common nails. Calculate the load P that may be applied to this connection.

Solution. Western hemlock is classified in Group III. According to Table 17 on page 45 of the Specification, the lateral-load capacity of a 50d nail in Group III timber is 165 lb, provided that the penetration of the nail is at least 13 times its diameter. Where the penetration is less, the allowable load is reduced in the manner prescribed in Sec. 800-E-1. The dimensions of the nail are found in the table on page 43 of the Specification. In the present instance, we have the following:

$$\text{Length} = 5.5 \text{ in.} \qquad \text{diameter} = 0.244 \text{ in.}$$

$$\frac{\text{Penetration}}{\text{Diameter}} = \frac{5.5 - 1.63}{0.244} = 15.9 > 13$$

Then $P = 6 \times 165 = \textbf{990 lb}$

Example 15-12   The cottonwood members in Fig. 15-6 are connected with three
⅝-in. lag screws, 8 in. long.   Calculate the load P that may be applied to this
connection.

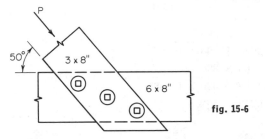

fig. 15-6

Solution. Cottonwood is classified in Group IV.   Entering Table 15a on page 41
of the Specification with the given data, we obtain the following values for each
screw:

Allowable load parallel to grain = 550 lb

Allowable load normal to grain = 330 lb

The capacity of each screw in this connection is found by applying Eq. (15-7) or
consulting the Scholten nomograph.

$$\text{Capacity} = \frac{550 \times 330}{550 \sin^2 50° + 330 \cos^2 50°} = 395 \text{ lb}$$
$$P = 3 \times 395 = \textbf{1185 lb}$$

Example 15-13   A 6 × 12 in. southern pine member that carries a tensile force of
56 kips parallel to the grain is to be spliced with steel side plates.   Design the
splice, using ⅞-in. bolts.

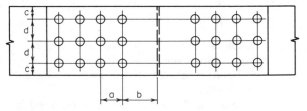

fig. 15-7

Solution. The bolt capacity as recorded in Table 12 on page 37 of the National
Design Specification is 3940 lb.   However, Sec. 600-J-3 of the Specification
authorizes an increase of 25 percent in the capacity in parallel-to-grain loading
when steel plates are used as side members.   The number of bolts required is

$$\frac{56,000}{3940 \times 1.25} = 11.4$$

We shall use 12 bolts having the trial pattern shown in Fig. 15-7.   Section
601-B-2 of the Specification imposes a lower limit on the ratio of the net area of

the cross section to the total area in bearing under the bolts. Consider the diameter of the holes to be $1\frac{5}{16}$ in.

$$\text{Gross area} = 63.25 \text{ sq in.}$$
$$\text{Net area} = 63.25 - 3 \times 0.94 \times 5.5 = 47.74 \text{ sq in.}$$

Bearing area under bolts $= 12 \times 0.875 \times 5.5 = 57.75$ sq in.

$$\frac{47.74}{57.75} = 0.83 > 0.80 \qquad \text{OK}$$

The joint is therefore satisfactory in this respect, and it merely remains to establish the bolt spacing. The longitudinal spacing is governed by Secs. 601-E-1 and 601-G-2.

$$a = 4 \times \frac{7}{8} = 3\frac{1}{2} \text{ in.} \qquad b_{\min} = 7 \times \frac{7}{8} = 6\frac{1}{8} \text{ in.}$$

The transverse spacing is governed by Sec. 601-H-2. (The requirement of Sec. 601-F-1 has already been satisfied.)

$$\frac{L}{D} = \frac{5.5}{\frac{7}{8}} = 6.3 > 6 \quad \therefore c_{\min} = \frac{1}{2}d$$

Set $c = 2$ in. and $d = 3\frac{3}{4}$ in.

Example 15-14   The members in Fig. 15-8*a* have the following sizes:

$$\text{Member } A : 4 \times 8 \text{ in.} \qquad \text{Member } B : 3 \times 8 \text{ in.}$$

They are connected by six 4-in. split-ring connectors, in the manner indicated. The species of lumber is dense structural redwood. Investigate the adequacy of this joint and establish the spacing of the connectors.

Solution. It is necessary to investigate both the capacity of the connectors and the capacity of the net section of member A.

Table 7 on page 28 of the National Design Specification classifies this species in Group C. According to Table 8, the value of a connector in parallel-to-grain loading for Group C timber is 4380 lb.

$$\text{Capacity of connectors} = 6 \times 4380 = 26,280 \text{ lb} \qquad \text{OK}$$

Table 8 also requires a minimum edge distance of $2\frac{3}{4}$ in.; the edge distance in the present instance is $3\frac{3}{4}$ in.

The gross area of member A is 27.19 sq in. The dimensions of the bolt hole and the groove for the ring are recorded in Appendix G of the Specification. Refer to Fig. 15-8*b*.

Outside diameter of groove $= 4.08 + 2 \times 0.21 = 4.50$ in.
Depth of groove $= 0.50$ in.
Bolt-hole diameter $= 1\frac{3}{16}$ in.
Projected area of groove and bolt hole $= 4.50 \times 1.00 + 0.813 \times 2.625$
$$= 6.63 \text{ sq in.}$$
Net area $= 27.19 - 6.63 = 20.56$ sq in.

The stress at the net section is

$$f = \frac{26,000}{20.56} = 1260 \text{ psi}$$

Table 1 on page 8 of the Specification provides a basic allowable stress of 1700 psi. However, this value is reduced for a member in the present type of connection. In accordance with Sec. 502-B-1,

$$f_{\text{allow}} = \text{⅞} \times 1700 = 1488 \text{ psi}$$

In accordance with Sec. 502-B-3 and Table 6,

$$f_{\text{allow}} = 1650 \text{ psi}$$

The joint is therefore satisfactory in all respects. The connectors are spaced in the manner required by Table 4a of the Specification. Since the connectors are stressed almost to capacity, we shall apply the recorded values without any reduction.

$$a = 7 \text{ in.} \qquad b = 9 \text{ in.}$$

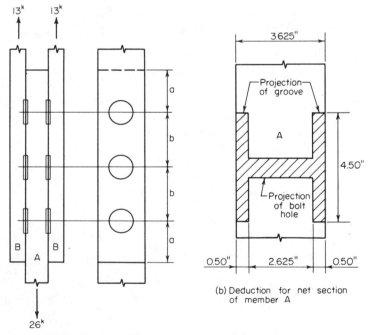

(a) Split–ring connection

(b) Deduction for net section of member A

fig. 15-8

SIXTEEN
Reinforced-concrete Beams:
Ultimate-strength Design

16-1 Introduction The design of reinforced-concrete members will be executed in accordance with the specification titled "Building Code Requirements for Reinforced Concrete" of the American Concrete Institute. This is presented in the publication designated as ACI 318-63, dated June, 1963. The ACI publication "Reinforced Concrete Design Handbook," designated as SP-3, contains many useful tables that serve to expedite design.

When concrete is deposited in a standard test cylinder under certain prescribed conditions of temperature and moisture, the maximum compressive stress which this concrete can withstand at the expiration of 28 days is termed its *ultimate strength*. This strength is used to identify the grade of concrete.

Since the tensile strength of concrete is relatively small, it is assumed for simplicity that the concrete can sustain only compressive bending stresses. Consequently, the effective beam section is considered to comprise the reinforcing steel and the concrete on the compression side of the neutral axis, the concrete between these component areas serving merely as the ligature of the member.

The spacing of steel reinforcing bars in a concrete member is subject to the restrictions imposed by Secs. 804 and 808 of the ACI Code.   With reference to the beam and slab shown in Fig. 16-1, the reinforcing steel is assumed for simplicity to be concentrated at its centroidal axis, and the effective depth of the flexural member is taken as the distance from the extreme compression fiber to this axis.   (The term *depth* will hereafter

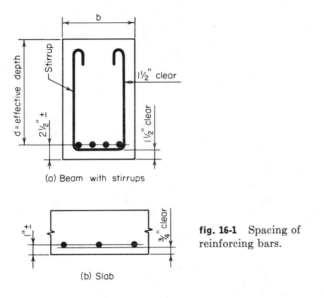

(a) Beam with stirrups

(b) Slab

fig. 16-1   Spacing of reinforcing bars.

refer to the effective rather than the overall depth of beam.)   To design a member, it is usually assumed that the distance from the exterior surface to the center of the first row of steel bars is $2\frac{1}{2}$ in. in a beam with web stirrups, 2 in. in a beam without stirrups, and 1 in. in a slab.   Where two rows of steel bars are provided, it is usually assumed that the distance from the exterior surface to the centroidal axis of the reinforcement is $3\frac{1}{2}$ in.   Table 6a of the Reinforced Concrete Design Handbook records the minimum beam widths that are needed to accommodate various combinations of bars in one row.

In a well-proportioned beam, the width-depth ratio lies between $\frac{1}{2}$ and $\frac{3}{4}$.   The width and overall depth are usually made an even number of inches.

The basic notational system pertaining to reinforced-concrete beams is as follows:

f'_c = ultimate compressive strength of concrete
f_c = maximum compressive stress in concrete
f_s = tensile stress in steel

f_y = yield-point stress of steel
ϵ_c = strain of extreme compression fiber
ϵ_s = strain of steel
b = width of beam
d = depth of beam
t = thickness of slab
A_s = area of tension reinforcement
A_t = area of reinforcement for temperature and shrinkage
p = tension-reinforcement ratio A_s/bd
q = tension-reinforcement index pf_y/f_c
n = ratio of modulus of elasticity of steel to that of concrete, E_s/E_c
C = resultant compressive force on transverse section
T = resultant tensile force on transverse section

Where the subscript b is appended to a given symbol, it signifies that the given quantity is evaluated at balanced-design conditions.

In the ultimate-strength analysis of a reinforced-concrete structure, as in the plastic analysis of a steel structure, the capacity of the structure is found by determining the minimum load that will cause failure and dividing this result by the prescribed load factor. The load at impending failure is termed the *ultimate load,* and the maximum bending moment associated with this load is called the *ultimate moment.* The ultimate load for which a structure is to be designed is computed by multiplying the working loads by the factors given in Sec. 1506 of the ACI Code.

The following notational system is applied in ultimate-strength design:

a = depth of compression block
c = distance from extreme compression fiber to neutral axis
ϕ = capacity-reduction factor

Where the subscript u is appended to a symbol, it signifies that the given quantity is evaluated at ultimate load.

Figure 16-2 indicates the conditions at plastification. For simplicity, it is assumed that when the ultimate moment is attained at a given section there is a uniform stress in the concrete extending across a depth a, and that

$$f_c = 0.85f_c' \quad \text{and} \quad a = k_1 c$$

where k_1 has the value stipulated in Sec. 1503(g) of the ACI Code. The modulus of elasticity of the steel is taken as 29,000,000 psi.

A reinforced-concrete beam has three potential modes of failure: crushing of the concrete, which is assumed to occur when ϵ_c reaches the value of 0.003; yielding of the steel, which begins when f_s reaches the value f_y; and the simultaneous crushing of the concrete and yielding of the steel.

A beam that tends to fail by the third mode is said to be in *balanced design*. If the value of p exceeds that corresponding to balanced design (i.e., if there is an excess of reinforcement), the beam tends to fail by crushing of the concrete. On the other hand, if the value of p is less than that corresponding to balanced design, the beam tends to fail by yielding of the steel.

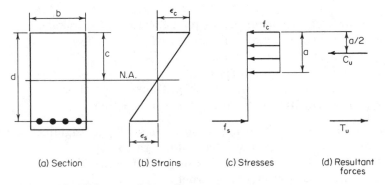

(a) Section   (b) Strains   (c) Stresses   (d) Resultant forces

fig. 16-2   Conditions at ultimate moment.

Failure of the beam by the first mode would occur precipitously and without warning, whereas failure by the second mode would occur gradually, offering visible evidence of progressive failure. Therefore, as a means of ensuring that yielding of the steel would precede failure of the concrete, Sec. 1601(b) of the ACI Code limits the value of p to $0.75p_b$.

To allow for imperfections of material, defects in workmanship, etc., the Code introduces the capacity-reduction factor ϕ. Section 1504(b) sets $\phi = 0.90$ with respect to flexure and $\phi = 0.85$ with respect to diagonal tension, bond, and anchorage.

16-2   Rectangular Beams   The basic equations for the ultimate-strength design of a rectangular beam reinforced solely in tension are as follows:

$$C_u = 0.85abf'_c \qquad T_u = A_s f_y \tag{16-1}$$

$$q = \frac{A_s}{bd} \frac{f_y}{f'_c} \tag{16-2}$$

$$a = 1.18qd \qquad c = \frac{1.18qd}{k_1} \tag{16-3}$$

$$M_u = \phi A_s f_y \left(d - \frac{a}{2} \right) \tag{16-4}$$

$$M_u = \phi A_s f_y d (1 - 0.59q) \tag{16-5}$$

$$M_u = \phi bd^2 f'_c q (1 - 0.59q) \tag{16-6}$$

$$A_s = \frac{bdf_c - \sqrt{(bdf_c)^2 - 2bf_c M_u/\phi}}{f_y} \tag{16-7}$$

$$p_b = 0.85k_1 \frac{f'_c}{f_y} \frac{87{,}000}{87{,}000 + f_y} \tag{16-8}$$

$$q_b = 0.85k_1 \frac{87{,}000}{87{,}000 + f_y} \tag{16-9}$$

In accordance with Sec. 1601(b) of the Code,

$$p_{\max} = 0.75p_b = 0.6375k_1 \frac{f'_c}{f_y} \frac{87{,}000}{87{,}000 + f_y} \tag{16-10}$$

$$q_{\max} = 0.75q_b = 0.6375k_1 \frac{87{,}000}{87{,}000 + f_y} \tag{16-11}$$

Figure 16-3 indicates the relationship between M_u and A_s for a beam of given size. As A_s increases, the internal forces C_u and T_u increase proportionately, but M_u increases by a smaller proportion because the

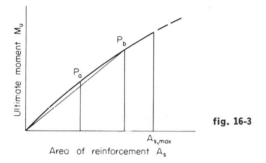

fig. 16-3

action line of C_u is depressed. The M_u-A_s diagram is parabolic, but its curvature is slight. Comparing the coordinates of two points P_a and P_b, we obtain the following relationship, in which the subscripts correspond with that of the given point:

$$\frac{M_{ua}}{A_{sa}} > \frac{M_{ub}}{A_{sb}} \qquad \text{if } A_{sa} < A_{sb} \tag{16-12}$$

Example 16-1 A rectangular beam having a width of 12 in. and effective depth of 19.5 in. is reinforced with steel bars having an area of 5.37 sq in. The beam is made of 2500-psi concrete and the steel has a yield-point stress of 40,000 psi. Compute the ultimate moment that this beam may resist (*a*) without referring to any design tables and without applying the basic equations of ultimate-strength design except those that are readily apparent and (*b*) by applying the basic equations.

Solution

PART *a*. Refer to Fig. 16-2. We shall test the member for compliance with Sec. 1601(b) of the ACI Code by evaluating the allowable area of reinforcement.

The following calculations pertain to balanced design.

$$\epsilon_s = \frac{f_y}{E_s} = \frac{40,000}{29,000,000} = 0.00138$$

$$\frac{c}{d} = \frac{\epsilon_c}{\epsilon_c + \epsilon_s} = \frac{0.003}{0.003 + 0.00138} = 0.685$$

$$c = 0.685 \times 19.5 = 13.36 \text{ in.}$$

By Sec. 1503(g),

$$k_1 = 0.85 \qquad a = k_1 c = 0.85 \times 13.36 = 11.36 \text{ in.}$$
$$T_u = C_u = ab \times 0.85 f'_c = 11.36 \times 12 \times 0.85 \times 2500 = 290,000 \text{ lb}$$
$$A_s = \frac{T_u}{f_y} = \frac{290,000}{40,000} = 7.25 \text{ sq in.}$$
$$0.75 \times 7.25 = 5.44 > 5.37 \text{ sq in.}$$

The area of reinforcement is therefore sufficiently low to ensure that failure would occur through yielding of the steel. The calculations for ultimate moment are as follows:

$$T_u = A_s f_y = 5.37 \times 40,000 = 215,000 \text{ lb}$$
$$C_u = ab \times 0.85 f'_c = 25,500a = 215,000 \text{ lb} \qquad a = 8.43 \text{ in.}$$
$$M_u = \phi T_u \left(d - \frac{a}{2} \right) = 0.90 \times 215,000 \left(19.5 - \frac{8.43}{2} \right)$$
$$= \textbf{2,960,000 in.-lb}$$

PART *b*. We shall test the member for compliance with Sec. 1601(b) by comparing the results of Eqs. (16-2) and (16-11).

$$q = \frac{5.37}{12 \times 19.5} \times \frac{40}{2.5} = 0.367$$
$$q_{max} = 0.6375 \times 0.85 \times {}^8\!\%_{27} = 0.371 \qquad \text{OK}$$

Equation (16-5) yields

$$M_u = 0.90 \times 5.37 \times 40,000 \times 19.5(1 - 0.59 \times 0.367)$$
$$= 2,960,000 \text{ in.-lb}$$

Example 16-2   A beam on a simple span of 20 ft is to carry a uniformly distributed live load of 1670 plf and dead load of 470 plf, which includes the estimated weight of beam. Architectural details restrict the beam width to 12 in. and require that the depth be made as small as possible. Design the section, using $f'_c = 3000$ psi and $f_y = 40,000$ psi.

Solution. The beam depth is minimized by providing the maximum amount of reinforcement permitted by the Code. From Example 16-1, $q_{max} = 0.371$.

Applying the load factors prescribed in Sec. 1506, we obtain the following:

$$w_u = 1.5 \times 470 + 1.8 \times 1670 = 3710 \text{ plf}$$
$$M_u = \tfrac{1}{8} \times 3710 \times 20^2 \times 12 = 2{,}230{,}000 \text{ in.-lb}$$

Applying Eq. (16-6),

$$d^2 = \frac{M_u}{\phi b f_c' q(1 - 0.59q)}$$

$$= \frac{2{,}230{,}000}{0.90 \times 12 \times 3000 \times 0.371 \times 0.781} \qquad d = 15.4 \text{ in.}$$

Set $d = 15.5$ in. The corresponding reduction in the value of q is negligible, and Eq. (16-2) may now be solved for the area of reinforcement.

$$A_s = qbd\,\frac{f_c'}{f_y} = 0.371 \times 12 \times 15.5 \times \tfrac{3}{40} = 5.18 \text{ sq in.}$$

Use four No. 9 and two No. 7 bars, for which $A_s = 5.20$ sq in. This group of bars must be placed in two rows, and the overall beam depth is therefore 19 in.

In summary, the design is as follows:

Beam size: 12×19 in.
Reinforcement: Four No. 9 and two No. 7 bars.

Example 16-3 A rectangular beam of 9-in. width and 13.5-in. effective depth is to sustain an ultimate moment of 95 ft-kips. Compute the area of reinforcement, using $f_c' = 3000$ psi and $f_y = 40{,}000$ psi.

Solution. We must first investigate the adequacy of the beam size. From Example 16-1, $q_{max} = 0.371$. By Eq. (16-6),

$$M_{u,max} = 0.90 \times 9 \times 13.5^2 \times 3 \times 0.371 \times 0.781 = 1280 \text{ in.-kips}$$
$$M_u = 95 \times 12 = 1140 \text{ in.-kips} \qquad \text{OK}$$

The area of reinforcement is found by applying Eq. (16-7).

$$f_c = 0.85 \times 3 = 2.55 \text{ ksi} \qquad bdf_c = 9 \times 13.5 \times 2.55 = 309.8 \text{ kips}$$

$$\frac{2bf_c M_u}{\phi} = \frac{2 \times 9 \times 2.55 \times 1140}{0.90} = 58{,}140 \text{ kips}^2$$

$$A_s = \frac{309.8 - \sqrt{309.8^2 - 58{,}140}}{40} = \textbf{2.88 sq in.}$$

16-3   T Beams   A reinforced-concrete girder is generally constructed integrally with the slab that it supports. It is therefore reasonable to consider that the beam itself and a portion of the tributary slab constitute a single structural entity in the form of a T-shaped beam.   The assignable width of flange is governed by Sec. 906 of the ACI Code.   Isolated T beams are also used when the depth is limited by architectural details.

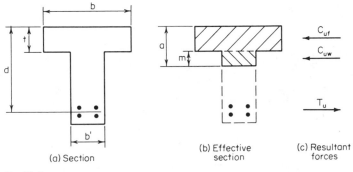

(a) Section   (b) Effective section   (c) Resultant forces

fig. 16-4

The notational system, part of which is illustrated in Fig. 16-4, is as follows:

b = width of flange
b' = width of web
a = depth of compression block
m = depth of compression block in web
C_{uf} = resultant compressive force in flange
C_{uw} = resultant compressive force in web
C_{u1} = resultant compressive force in overhanging portions of flange
C_{u2} = resultant compressive force in remainder of section
$A_{s1} = C_{u1}/f_y$
$A_{s2} = C_{u2}/f_y$
$p_2 = A_{s2}/b'd$
M_{u1} = bending moment associated with C_{u1}
M_{u2} = bending moment associated with C_{u2}

Section 1603(c) of the ACI Code restricts p_2 to the same value as p for a rectangular beam.

Example 16-4   Determine the ultimate moment that may be resisted by the T beam in Fig. 16-5, using f'_c = 3000 psi and f_y = 40,000 psi.
    Solution. Assume that the section satisfies Eq. (16-10).

$$T_u = 8.20 \times 40,000 = 328,000 \text{ lb} \qquad f_c = 0.85 \times 3000 = 2550 \text{ psi}$$
$$C_{uf} = 18 \times 6 \times 2550 = 275,400 \text{ lb}$$
$$C_{uw} = 328,000 - 275,400 = 52,600 \text{ lb}$$
$$m = \frac{52,600}{2550 \times 10} = 2.06 \text{ in.}$$

$$M_u = 0.90[275,400(20.5 - 3) + 52,600(20.5 - 6 - 1.03)]$$
$$= \textbf{4,975,000 in.-lb}$$

$$A_{s2} = \frac{8.06 \times 10 \times 2550}{40,000} = 5.14 \text{ sq in.} \qquad p_2 = \frac{5.14}{10 \times 20.5} = 0.025$$

Equation (16-10) yields

$$p_{2,\max} = 0.6375 \times 0.85 \times \tfrac{3}{40} \times {}^{87}\!/_{127}$$
$$= 0.0278 > 0.025 \qquad \text{OK}$$

Example 16-5 The T beam in Fig. 16-6 is made of 3000-psi concrete, and $f_y = 40,000$ psi. Determine the ultimate-moment capacity of this member if reinforced in tension only.

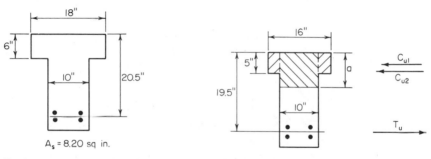

A_s = 8.20 sq in.

fig. 16-5   **fig. 16-6**

Solution. The beam must be supplied with the maximum amount of reinforcement permitted by the Code.

$$f_c = 2550 \text{ psi} \qquad C_{u1} = 2550 \times 5(16 - 10) = 76,500 \text{ lb}$$

From Example 16-4,

$$p_{2,\max} = 0.0278$$
$$A_{s2} = p_2 b' d = 0.0278 \times 10 \times 19.5 = 5.42 \text{ sq in.}$$
$$C_{u2} = 5.42 \times 40,000 = 216,800 \text{ lb} \qquad a = \frac{216,800}{10 \times 2550} = 8.50 \text{ in.}$$
$$M_u = 0.90[76,500(19.5 - 2.50) + 216,800(19.5 - 4.25)]$$
$$= 0.90(1,300,000 + 3,306,000) = \textbf{4,145,000 in.-lb}$$

Example 16-6 The T beam in Fig. 16-6 is to resist an ultimate moment of 3,960,000 in.-lb. Calculate the required area of reinforcement, using $f_c' = 3000$ psi and $f_y = 40,000$ psi. Verify the solution by computing the allowable ultimate moment of the section.
Solution. The bending moment is below the flexural capacity of the concrete area as computed in Example 16-5. To simplify the calculations, we shall divide

the given ultimate moment M_u by the capacity-reduction factor to secure a moment M'_u that is not subject to reduction.

$$M'_u = \frac{3,960,000}{0.9} = 4,400,000 \text{ in.-lb}$$

We must evaluate a.   From the calculations in Example 16-5, we have

$$M'_{u1} = 1,300,000 \text{ in.-lb}$$

Then $M'_{u2} = 4,400,000 - 1,300,000 = 3,100,000 \text{ in.-lb}$

But $M'_{u2} = 2550 \times 10a \left(19.5 - \frac{a}{2}\right)$

Solving, $a = 7.79 \text{ in.}$

The steel area is found by computing the resultant tensile force on the section. From Example 16-5,

$$C_{u1} = 76,500 \text{ lb}$$
$$C_{u2} = \frac{M'_{u2}}{d - \frac{1}{2}a} = \frac{3,100,000}{19.5 - 3.90} = 198,700 \text{ lb}$$
$$T_u = 76,500 + 198,700 = 275,200 \text{ lb}$$
$$A_s = \frac{275,200}{40,000} = \textbf{6.88 sq in.}$$

We shall verify the solution by computing the resultant compressive forces in the flange and web.

$$C_{uf} = 16 \times 5 \times 2550 = 204,000 \text{ lb}$$
$$C_{uw} = 275,200 - 204,000 = 71,200 \text{ lb}$$
$$m = \frac{71,200}{2550 \times 10} = 2.79 \text{ in.}$$
$$M_u = 0.90[204,000(19.5 - 2.5) + 71,200(19.5 - 5 - 1.40)]$$
$$= 3,960,000 \text{ in.-lb} \qquad \text{OK}$$

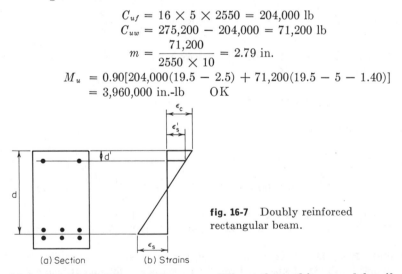

fig. 16-7   Doubly reinforced rectangular beam.

(a) Section   (b) Strains

16-4   Doubly Reinforced Beams   Where the architectural details restrict both the depth and width of a concrete beam, it is sometimes necessary to incorporate steel reinforcement in the compression as well as tension region of the member, as illustrated in Fig. 16-7.   For simplicity, we shall disregard the loss in concrete area caused by the presence of the compression reinforcement.

The notational system is as follows:

A_s = area of tension reinforcement
A'_s = area of compression reinforcement
d' = distance from compression face of concrete to centroid of compression reinforcement
f_s = stress in tension steel
f'_s = stress in compression steel
ϵ'_s = strain of compression steel
$p = A_s/bd$
$p' = A'_s/bd$
$q = pf_y/f'_c$
M_u = ultimate moment to be resisted by member
M_{u1} = ultimate-moment capacity of member if reinforced solely in tension
M_{u2} = increase in ultimate-moment capacity resulting from use of compression reinforcement

If $f'_s = f_y$, the tension reinforcement may be resolved into two parts having areas of $A_s - A'_s$ and A'_s. The first part, acting in combination with the concrete, develops the moment M_{u1}. The second part, acting in combination with the compression reinforcement, develops the moment M_{u2}.

To ensure that failure will result from yielding of the tension steel rather than crushing of the concrete, Sec. 1602(d) of the ACI Code limits $p - p'$ to a maximum value of $0.75p_b$, where p_b has the same significance as for a singly reinforced beam. Section 1602(b) in effect permits us to set $f'_s = f_y$ if inception of yielding in the compression steel will precede or coincide with failure of the concrete at balanced-design ultimate moment. This clause introduces an inconsistency, however, for the limit imposed on $p - p'$ precludes balanced design. It may be demonstrated that the requirement of Sec. 1602(b) is met if the following relationship holds:

$$p - p' \geq 0.85k_1 \frac{f'_c d'}{f_y d} \frac{87,000}{87,000 - f_y} \tag{16-13}$$

Where we may set $f'_s = f_y$, the following equations apply:

$$(A_s - A'_s)f_y = 0.85abf'_c \tag{16-14}$$

$$M_{u2} = \phi A'_s f_y (d - d') \tag{16-15}$$

$$M_u = \phi f_y \left[(A_s - A'_s)\left(d - \frac{a}{2}\right) + A'_s(d - d') \right] \tag{16-16}$$

Example 16-7 A beam that is to resist an ultimate moment of 690 ft-kips is restricted to a 14-in. width and 24-in. total depth. Using $f_c' = 5000$ psi and $f_y = 50,000$ psi, determine the area of reinforcement. Verify the design.

Solution. We shall calculate the value of M_{u1} to ascertain whether tension reinforcement alone will suffice. The value of k_1 for this grade of concrete is 0.80. Since two rows of tension bars are undoubtedly required,

$$d = 24 - 3.5 = 20.5 \text{ in.} \qquad M_u = 690,000 \times 12 = 8,280,000 \text{ in.-lb}$$

Applying Eq. (16-9), we obtain the following values for a singly reinforced beam:

$$q_b = 0.85 \times 0.80 \times {}^{87}\!/_{137} = 0.432$$
$$q_{max} = 0.75 \times 0.432 = 0.324$$

Applying Eq. (16-6), we obtain

$$M_{u1} = 0.90 \times 14 \times 20.5^2 \times 5000 \times 0.324 \times 0.809$$
$$= 6,940,000 \text{ in.-lb}$$

The member therefore requires compression reinforcement.

$$M_{u2} = 8,280,000 - 6,940,000 = 1,340,000 \text{ in.-lb}$$

We must investigate the strain in the compression reinforcement under the balanced-design ultimate moment. Equation (16-3) yields

$$c_b = \frac{1.18q_b d}{k_1} = \frac{1.18 \times 0.432 \times 20.5}{0.80} = 13.1 \text{ in.}$$
$$\frac{\epsilon_s'}{\epsilon_c} = \frac{13.1 - 2.5}{13.1} = 0.809$$
$$\epsilon_s' = 0.809 \times 0.003 = 0.00243$$

The strain at incipient yielding is

$$\epsilon_y = \frac{50}{29,000} = 0.0017 < \epsilon_s'$$

The compression reinforcement will therefore yield before the concrete fails This conclusion may also be arrived at by the following calculations:

$$d - c = 20.5 - 13.1 = 7.4 \text{ in.} \qquad c - d' = 10.6 \text{ in.}$$

Since the compression reinforcement is more remote from the neutral axis than is the tension reinforcement, the former reaches yield-point stress before the latter We may now set $f_s' = f_y$. By Eq. (16-15),

$$A_s' = \frac{1,340,000}{0.90 \times 50,000 \times 18.0} = \textbf{1.65 sq in.}$$

Equation (16-2) yields

$$A_s - A_s' = q_{max}bd\frac{f_c'}{f_y}$$
$$= 0.324 \times 14 \times 20.5 \times \tfrac{5}{50} = 9.30 \text{ sq in.}$$
$$A_s = 9.30 + 1.65 = \textbf{10.95 sq in.}$$

We shall verify the design.   The left-hand side of Eq. (16-13) has the following value:

$$\frac{9.30}{14 \times 20.5} = 0.0324$$

The right-hand side has the following value:

$$0.85 \times 0.80 \times \frac{5}{50} \times \frac{2.5}{20.5} \times \frac{87}{37} = 0.0195$$

Equation (16-13) is therefore satisfied.   Equation (16-14) yields the following:

$$a = \frac{(A_s - A_s')f_y}{0.85f_c'b} = \frac{9.30 \times 50{,}000}{0.85 \times 5000 \times 14} = 7.82 \text{ in.}$$

By Eq. (16-16),

$$M_u = 0.90 \times 50{,}000(9.30 \times 16.59 + 1.65 \times 18)$$
$$= 8{,}280{,}000 \text{ in.-lb}   \text{OK}$$

16-5   Web Reinforcement   The stress analysis in Art. 3-4 discloses that at every point in a reinforced-concrete beam between the compression zone and the longitudinal reinforcement there exists a tensile stress that is numerically equal to the shearing stress at that point and inclined at 45° with the longitudinal axis.   If this direct stress is excessive, steel reinforcement must be supplied to prevent failure by diagonal tension. This reinforcement usually consists of vertical stirrups looped about the longitudinal reinforcement and extended into the compression zone for anchorage.

The notational system is as follows:

v_u = nominal ultimate shearing stress
v_c = shearing stress resisted by concrete
v_u' = shearing stress resisted by web reinforcement
A_v = total cross-sectional area of stirrup
V_u = ultimate vertical shear at section
F = force carried by vertical stirrup
s = center-to-center spacing of stirrups

Section 1701 of the ACI Code provides two alternative methods of determining the allowable shearing stress on an unreinforced web. We shall apply the simpler method, which relates this stress solely to the ultimate strength of the concrete.

$$v_u = \frac{V_u}{bd} \tag{16-17}$$

$$v_c = 2\phi \sqrt{f_c'} \tag{16-18}$$

$$F = \phi A_v f_y = s v_u' b \tag{16-19}$$

The critical section for shear is taken at a distance d from the face of support. Sections 1705 and 1706 place restrictions on the beam size and stirrup spacing; Sec. 1504 sets $\phi = 0.85$ with respect to web reinforcement.

Example 16-8   A beam of 15-in. width and 22.5-in. effective depth carries a uniform ultimate load of 10.2 klf. The beam is simply supported, and the clear distance between supports is 18 ft. Using $f_c' = 3000$ psi and $f_y = 40,000$ psi, design web reinforcement in the form of vertical U stirrups.

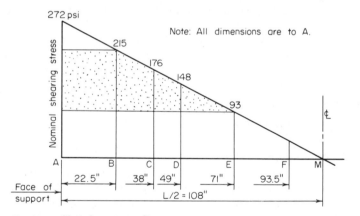

fig. 16-8   Shearing-stress diagram.

Solution. We shall check the beam size for compliance with Sec. 1705(b) of the ACI Code. Refer to Fig. 16-8. At the support,

$$V_u = 9 \times 10,200 = 91,800 \text{ lb} \qquad v_u = \frac{91,800}{15 \times 22.5} = 272 \text{ psi}$$

$$v_c = 2 \times 0.85 \sqrt{3000} = 93 \text{ psi}$$

Slope of diagram $= -272/108 = -2.52$ psi per in.

At distance d from face of support,

$$v_u = 272 - 22.5 \times 2.52 = 215 \text{ psi} \qquad v_u' = 215 - 93 = 122 \text{ psi}$$

$$v_{u,\text{max}} = 10\phi \sqrt{f_c'} = 466 > 215 \text{ psi} \qquad \text{OK}$$

We shall establish the interval AF in which web reinforcement is required. Section 1702(a) requires that the reinforcement be continued for a distance d

beyond the section where $v_u = v_c$. In the diagram,

$$AE = \frac{272 - 93}{2.52} = 71 \text{ in.} \qquad AF = 71 + 22.5 = 93.5 \text{ in.}$$

To select the stirrup size, we shall equate the spacing near the support to the minimum practical value, which is generally considered to be 4 in. Equation (16-19) yields

$$A_v = \frac{sv'_u b}{\phi f_y} = \frac{4 \times 122 \times 15}{0.85 \times 40{,}000} = 0.215 \text{ sq in.}$$

Since each stirrup is bent into the form of a U, the total cross-sectional area is twice that of a straight bar. We shall use No. 3 stirrups, for which

$$A_v = 2 \times 0.11 = 0.22 \text{ sq in.}$$

The upper limit for stirrup spacing as given by Sec. 1706 is as follows:

$$s_{\max} = \frac{d}{4} \qquad \text{if } v_u > 6\phi \sqrt{f'_c} \qquad 6\phi \sqrt{f'_c} = 279 \text{ psi}$$

$$s_{\max} = \frac{d}{2} \qquad \text{if } v_u \le 6\phi \sqrt{f'_c} \qquad \frac{d}{2} = 11.25 \text{ in.}$$

or $\qquad\qquad s_{\max} = \dfrac{A_v}{0.0015b} = \dfrac{0.22}{0.0015 \times 15} = 9.8 \text{ in.}$

We shall therefore limit the stirrup spacing to 9 in. Let C and D denote the sections at which the required spacing as given by Eq. (16-19) is 6 and 9 in., respectively.

At C: $\qquad v'_u = \dfrac{\phi A_v f_y}{sb} = \dfrac{0.85 \times 0.22 \times 40{,}000}{6 \times 15} = 83 \text{ psi}$

$$v_u = 83 + 93 = 176 \text{ psi} \qquad AC = \frac{272 - 176}{2.52} = 38 \text{ in.}$$

At D: $\qquad v'_u = 83 \times \tfrac{6}{9} = 55 \text{ psi}$

$$v_u = 55 + 93 = 148 \text{ psi} \qquad AD = \frac{272 - 148}{2.52} = 49 \text{ in.}$$

The stirrup spacing recorded in the accompanying table satisfies all requirements. This spacing requires 17 stirrups for each half of the span.

Quantity	Spacing, in.	Total, in.	Distance from last stirrup to face of support, in.
1	2	2	2
9	4	36	38
2	6	12	50
5	9	45	95

16-6 Bond Stresses   The adhesion of the concrete and steel must be sufficiently strong to resist the longitudinal shear flow.   The adhesive force on a unit area of contact is called the *bond stress*.   Let

u_u = ultimate bond stress
V_u = ultimate vertical shear
Σo = sum of perimeters of reinforcing bars
jd = distance between action lines of C_u and $T_u = d - a/2$

Equation (5-8) is not applicable in ultimate-strength design, since it is based upon an elastic distribution of stress.   In accordance with Eq. (16-4), the increase in T_u across a distance dx of the span is

$$dT_u = \frac{dM_u}{\phi jd}$$

Dividing dT_u by the area of contact of steel and concrete, we obtain

$$u_u = \frac{dT_u}{\Sigma o \, dx} = \frac{dM_u/dx}{\phi \Sigma ojd}$$

Then
$$u_u = \frac{V_u}{\phi \Sigma ojd} \tag{16-20}$$

The allowable bond stress is presented in Sec. 1801 of the ACI Code. Section 1504(b) sets $\phi = 0.85$ with respect to bond, and j is usually assigned the approximate value of 0.875 when investigating bond stress.

Example 16-9   A beam of 4000-psi concrete has an effective depth of 15 in. and is reinforced with four No. 7 bars.   Compute the ultimate bond stress at a section where the ultimate shear is 72 kips, and compare the result with the allowable stress.

Solution
$$\Sigma o = 4 \times 0.875\pi = 11.0 \text{ in.}$$

(This value may also be obtained from Table 5a of the Reinforced Concrete Design Handbook.)

$$u_u = \frac{72{,}000}{0.85 \times 11.0 \times 0.875 \times 15} = \textbf{587 psi}$$

The allowable stress as given by Sec. 1801 is

$$u_{u,\text{allow}} = \frac{9.5\sqrt{f_c'}}{D} \quad \text{but not above 800 psi}$$

$$u_{u,\text{allow}} = \frac{9.5\sqrt{4000}}{0.875} = \textbf{687 psi} \quad \text{OK}$$

16-7 Continuous Beams   Since concrete structures are usually built monolithically, reinforced-concrete beams are often continuous over several spans.   A precise evaluation of the maximum potential positive and negative bending moments in each span would be highly time-consuming and the ACI Code therefore permits the use of standard moment equations whenever the span and loading conditions satisfy the stipulated requirements.   These equations are presented in Sec. 904(c).   The notational system for the span is as follows:

$$L = \text{center-to-center spacing of supports}$$
$$L' = \text{clear span}$$

Example 16-10   A floor slab that is continuous over six spans carries a live load of 120 psf and dead load of 40 psf, exclusive of its own weight.   The clear spans are 16 ft.   Design the interior span, using $f'_c = 3000$ psi and $f_y = 50,000$ psi.

Solution. Refer to Fig. 16-9.   A slab is designed by considering a 1-ft strip as an individual beam, thus making $b = 12$ in.   Since the ratio of live load to dead load falls within the specified limit, the standard moment equations are applicable. In compliance with the ACI Code, we shall design the slab for a maximum positive moment of $\frac{1}{16}w_uL'^2$ at midspan, a maximum negative moment of $\frac{1}{11}w_uL'^2$ at the face of support, and a maximum shear of $\frac{1}{2}w_uL'$.   The steel reinforcement will

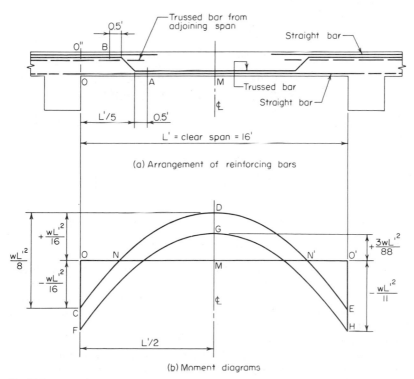

(a) Arrangement of reinforcing bars

(b) Moment diagrams

fig. 16-9

consist of both straight bars and trussed bars, the latter acting as reinforcement for positive moment in the central region and for negative moment near the supports.

Concrete tends to contract as it hardens, and its volume is also affected by temperature changes. Since the slab is not free to contract, tensile stresses are engendered in all directions, and the slab must therefore be reinforced transversely as well as longitudinally.

Section 909(b) of the Code imposes a lower limit on the slab thickness. Assume that $L = 17$ ft. Then

$$t_{min} = \frac{L}{35} = \frac{17 \times 12}{35} = 5.8 \text{ in.}$$

We shall therefore try a 6-in. slab. Since a slab is not reinforced for diagonal tension, it is necessary to consider both the bending and the shearing stress.

$$\text{Beam weight} = \tfrac{6}{12} \times 150 = 75 \text{ plf}$$
$$w_u = 1.5(40 + 75) + 1.8 \times 120 = 390 \text{ plf}$$
$$V_u = \tfrac{1}{2} \times 390 \times 16 = 3120 \text{ lb} \qquad d = 6 - 1 = 5 \text{ in.}$$
$$v_u = \frac{3120}{12 \times 5} = 52 \text{ psi} \qquad\qquad v_c = 93 \text{ psi} \qquad \text{OK}$$
$$M_{u,neg} = \tfrac{1}{11} \times 390 \times 16^2 \times 12 = 108{,}900 \text{ in.-lb}$$
$$M_{u,pos} = 108{,}900 \times \tfrac{11}{16} = 74{,}900 \text{ in.-lb}$$

The moment capacity of the slab is found by applying Eqs. (16-11) and (16-6).

$$q_{max} = 0.6375 \times 0.85 \times \tfrac{87}{137} = 0.344$$
$$M_{u,allow} = 0.90 \times 12 \times 5^2 \times 3000 \times 0.344 \times 0.797 = 222{,}000 \text{ in.-lb}$$

We shall therefore use a 6-in. slab. The area of reinforcement is found by applying Eq. (16-7).

$$bdf_c = 12 \times 5 \times 2.55 = 153.0 \text{ kips}$$
$$\frac{2bf_cM_{u,neg}}{\phi} = \frac{2 \times 12 \times 2.55 \times 108.9}{0.90} = 7405 \text{ kips}^2$$
$$A_{s,neg} = \frac{153.0 - \sqrt{153.0^2 - 7405}}{50} = 0.530 \text{ sq in.}$$

Similarly,
$$A_{s,pos} = 0.353 \text{ sq in.}$$

For positive reinforcement, use No. 4 trussed bars 13 in. on centers alternating with No. 4 straight bars 13 in. on centers, thus obtaining 0.362 sq in. For negative reinforcement, supplement the trussed bars over the support, which come from both spans, with No. 4 straight bars 13 in. on centers, thus obtaining 0.543 sq in.

The trussed bars are usually bent upward at the fifth points, as shown in Fig. 16-9. This practice satisfies Sec. 918(f) of the Code, which requires that "At least . . . one-fourth the positive moment reinforcement in continuous beams shall extend along the same face of the beam into the support at least 6 in."

We shall investigate the adequacy of the reinforcement beyond the bend points. In accordance with Secs. 911(b) and 807 of the Code,

$$A_{s,min} = A_t = 0.0020bt = 0.0020 \times 12 \times 6 = 0.144 \text{ sq in.}$$

Section 918(b) requires that the reinforcing bars be extended beyond the point at which they become superfluous with respect to flexure a distance equal to the effective depth or 12 bar diameters, whichever is greater. In the present instance,

$$\text{Extension} = 12 \times 0.5 = 6 \text{ in.}$$

Therefore, the trussed bars in effect terminate as positive reinforcement at section A.

$$\frac{L'}{5} = 3.2 \text{ ft} \qquad AM = 8 - 3.2 - 0.5 = 4.3 \text{ ft}$$

The conditions immediately to the left of A are as follows:

$$M_u = M_{u,pos} - \tfrac{1}{2}w_u(AM)^2$$
$$= 74,900 - \tfrac{1}{2} \times 390 \times 4.3^2 \times 12 = 31,630 \text{ in.-lb}$$

$$A_{s,pos} = 0.181 \text{ sq in.} \qquad q = \frac{0.181}{12 \times 5} \times \frac{50}{3} = 0.0503$$

By Eq. (16-5),

$$M_{u,allow} = 0.90 \times 0.181 \times 50,000 \times 5 \times 0.970$$
$$= 39,500 \text{ in.-lb} \qquad \text{OK}$$

Alternatively, we may apply Eq. (16-12) to obtain the following conservative approximation:

$$M_{u,allow} = 74,900 \times \frac{0.181}{0.353} = 38,400 \text{ in.-lb}$$

The trussed bars in effect terminate as negative reinforcement at B, where

$$0''B = 3.2 - 0.33 - 0.5 = 2.37 \text{ ft}$$

The conditions immediately to the right of B are as follows:

$$|M_u| = M_{u,neg} - 12(3120 \times 2.37 - \tfrac{1}{2} \times 390 \times 2.37^2)$$
$$= 108,900 - 75,600 = 33,300 \text{ in.-lb}$$
$$A_{s,neg} = 0.362 \text{ sq in.}$$

As a conservative approximation,

$$M_{u,allow} = 108,900 \times \frac{0.362}{0.530} = 74,400 \text{ in.-lb} \qquad \text{OK}$$

The points at which the top bars may theoretically be discontinued are found by equating the negative moment to its proper value.

We shall now investigate the bond stresses.   If CDE in Fig. 16-9b represents the true moment diagram, the bottom bars are subjected to bending stress in the interval NN'.   Manifestly, the maximum bond stress along the bottom occurs at the points of contraflexure N and N', where the shear is relatively high and the straight bars alone are present.

$$\left(\frac{MN}{L'/2}\right)^2 = \frac{1}{2} \qquad MN = 0.354L'$$

At N: $$V_u = 0.354 \times 16 \times 390 = 2210 \text{ lb}$$

Applying Eq. (16-20), we have

$$u_u = \frac{2210}{0.85 \times 1.45 \times 0.875 \times 5} = 410 \text{ psi}$$

It is apparent that the maximum bond stress in the top bars has a smaller value. The allowable bond stress as given by Sec. 1801(c) is 800 psi, and the longitudinal reinforcement is therefore satisfactory in all respects.

For the temperature reinforcement, use No. 3 bars 9 in. on centers.

SEVENTEEN

Reinforced-concrete Beams:
Working-stress Design

17-1 Introduction As demonstrated in Art. 5-4, the investigation of a composite beam by the working-stress method is most readily performed by transforming the given beam to an equivalent homogeneous beam. In the case of a reinforced-concrete member, the transformation is made by replacing the reinforcing steel with a strip of concrete having an area nA_s and located at the same distance from the neutral axis as the steel. This substitute concrete is assumed to be capable of sustaining tensile stresses.

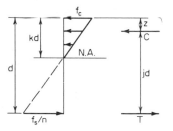

fig. 17-1 Stresses and resultant forces.

The following symbols, which are illustrated in Fig. 17-1, are to be annexed to the notational system presented in Chap. 16:

kd = distance from extreme compression fiber to neutral axis
jd = distance between action lines of C and T
z = distance from extreme compression fiber to action line of C

The allowable flexural stress in the concrete and the value of n, which are functions of the ultimate strength f_c', are presented in Table 1002(a) of the ACI Code; the allowable flexural stress in the steel is given in Sec. 1003. (Values of n are given to the nearest integer.) In all instances, we shall assume that the reinforcement is of intermediate-grade steel, having an allowable stress of 20,000 psi.

17-2   Rectangular Beams   The basic equations for the working-stress design of a rectangular beam reinforced solely in tension are as follows:

$$k = \frac{f_c}{f_c + f_s/n} \tag{17-1}$$

$$j = 1 - \frac{k}{3} \tag{17-2}$$

$$M = Cjd = \tfrac{1}{2}f_c kjbd^2 \tag{17-3}$$

$$M = \tfrac{1}{6}f_c k(3 - k)bd^2 \tag{17-4}$$

$$M = Tjd = f_s A_s jd \tag{17-5}$$

$$M = f_s pjbd^2 \tag{17-6}$$

$$M = \frac{f_s k^2(3 - k)bd^2}{6n(1 - k)} \tag{17-7}$$

$$p = \frac{f_c}{2f_s} k \tag{17-8}$$

$$p = \frac{k^2}{2n(1 - k)} \tag{17-9}$$

$$k = \sqrt{2pn + (pn)^2} - pn \tag{17-10}$$

For a given set of values of f_c, f_s, and n, M is directly proportional to the beam property bd^2. Let K denote the constant of proportionality. Then

$$M = Kbd^2 \tag{17-11}$$

where

$$K = \tfrac{1}{2}f_c kj = f_s pj \tag{17-12}$$

Example 17-1   A beam of 2500-psi concrete has a width of 12 in. and effective depth of 19.5 in.   It is reinforced with one No. 9 and two No. 7 bars.   Calculate the flexural stresses caused by a bending moment of 62 ft-kips (*a*) without applying the basic equations of reinforced-concrete beam design and (*b*) by applying these equations.

Solution

PART *a*. Refer to Fig. 17-2.

$$f_c' = 2500 \text{ psi} \qquad \therefore n = 10$$
$$A_s = 2.20 \text{ sq in.} \qquad nA_s = 22.0 \text{ sq in.}$$
$$M = 62,000 \times 12 = 744,000 \text{ in.-lb}$$

The transformed section is shown in Fig. 17-2b. By taking the statical moment of the area with respect to its centroidal axis, we obtain the following results:

$$Q_{CA} = \frac{12(kd)^2}{2} - 22.0(19.5 - kd) = 0$$

Solving, $\quad kd = 6.82$ in. $\quad$ and $\quad d - kd = 12.68$ in.

$$I = \tfrac{1}{3} \times 12 \times 6.82^3 + 22.0 \times 12.68^2 = 4806 \text{ in.}^4$$

$$f_c = \frac{Mkd}{I} = \frac{744,000 \times 6.82}{4806} = \textbf{1060 psi}$$

$$f_s = 10 \times \frac{744,000 \times 12.68}{4806} = \textbf{19,600 psi}$$

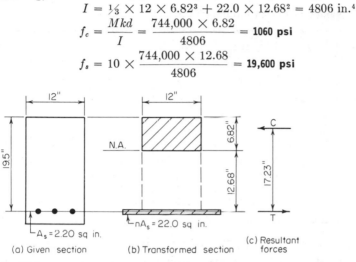

(a) Given section   (b) Transformed section   (c) Resultant forces

fig. 17-2

Alternatively, the stresses may be found by computing C and T.

$$jd = 19.5 - \frac{6.82}{3} = 17.23 \text{ in.}$$

$$C = T = \frac{M}{jd} = \frac{744,000}{17.23} = 43,200 \text{ lb}$$

But $\qquad C = \tfrac{1}{2}f_c \times 6.82 \times 12 \qquad \therefore f_c = 1060$ psi

and $\qquad T = 2.20f_s \qquad\qquad\qquad \therefore f_s = 19,600$ psi

PART *b*

$$p = \frac{A_s}{bd} = \frac{2.20}{12 \times 19.5} = 0.00940 \qquad pn = 0.0940$$

Eq. (17-10): $\quad k = \sqrt{0.1880 + (0.094)^2} - 0.094 = 0.350$

Eq. (17-2): $\quad j = 1 - \dfrac{0.350}{3} = 0.883$

Eq. (17-3): $\quad f_c = \dfrac{2M}{kjbd^2}$

$$= \frac{2 \times 744,000}{0.350 \times 0.883 \times 12 \times 19.5^2} = 1060 \text{ psi}$$

Eq. (17-5): $\quad f_s = \dfrac{M}{A_s jd} = \dfrac{744,000}{2.20 \times 0.883 \times 19.5} = 19,600 \text{ psi}$

Consider that the load on a beam is gradually increased until a limiting stress is reached.   A beam that is so proportioned that the steel and concrete simultaneously attain their respective limiting stresses is said to be in *balanced design*.   Manifestly, for each set of values of f_c' and the allowable steel stress, there is a corresponding set of values of K, k, j, and p.

Table 17-1   Values of Design Parameters at Balanced Design

f_c' and n	f_c	f_s	K	k	j	p
2500 10	1125	20,000	178	0.360	0.880	0.0101
3000 9	1350	20,000	223	0.378	0.874	0.0128
4000 8	1800	20,000	324	0.419	0.860	0.0188
5000 7	2250	20,000	423	0.441	0.853	0.0248

These values are recorded in Table 17-1.   We shall append the subscript b to a symbol when the quantity under consideration is evaluated at balanced-design conditions.

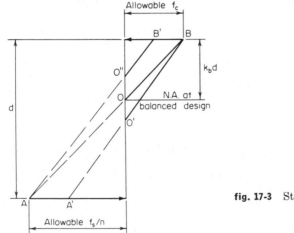

fig. 17-3   Stress diagrams.

In Fig. 17-3, AB represents the stress line of the transformed section for a beam in balanced design.   If the area of reinforcement is increased while the width and depth remain constant, the neutral axis is depressed to O', and $A'O'B$ represents the stress line under the allowable load.   On the other hand, if the width is increased while the depth and area of reinforcement remain constant, the neutral axis is elevated to O'', and $AO''B'$ represents the stress line under the allowable load.   This analysis leads to the following conclusion, which may be considered self-evident:

If the reinforcement is in excess of that needed for balanced design, the concrete is the first material to reach its limiting stress under a gradually increasing load.   If the beam size is in excess of that needed for balanced design, the steel is the first material to reach its limiting stress.

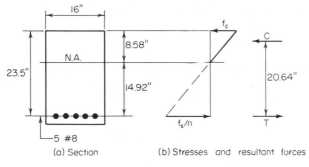

(a) Section   (b) Stresses and resultant forces

—5 #8

fig. 17-4

Example 17-2   The beam in Fig. 17-4a is made of 2500-psi concrete.   Compute the flexural capacity of the member (a) without applying the basic equations of reinforced-concrete beam design and (b) by applying these equations.

Solution

PART a

$$f_c' = 2500 \text{ psi} \qquad \therefore f_{c,\text{allow}} = 1125 \text{ psi} \qquad n = 10$$
$$A_s = 3.95 \text{ sq in.} \qquad nA_s = 39.5 \text{ sq in.}$$

For the transformed section,

$$Q_{CA} = \frac{16(kd)^2}{2} - 39.5(23.5 - kd) = 0$$

Solving,

$$kd = 8.58 \text{ in.} \qquad \text{and} \qquad d - kd = 14.92 \text{ in.}$$
$$jd = 23.5 - \frac{8.58}{3} = 20.64 \text{ in.}$$

Assume that the concrete attains its limiting stress of 1125 psi.   By proportion,

$$f_s = 10 \times 1125 \times \frac{14.92}{8.58} = 19,560 < 20,000 \text{ psi}$$

Therefore, concrete stress governs.

$$M = Cjd = \frac{1}{2} \times 1125 \times 16 \times 8.58 \times 20.64 = \textbf{1,594,000 in.-lb}$$
or $$M = Tjd = 3.95 \times 19,560 \times 20.64 = 1,594,000 \text{ in.-lb}$$

PART *b*

$$p = \frac{A_s}{bd} = \frac{3.95}{16 \times 23.5} = 0.0105 \qquad pn = 0.105$$

From Table 17-1,

$$p_b = 0.0101$$

Since the reinforcement is excessive in relation to the beam size, the concrete stress governs. Applying Eqs. (17-10) and (17-4), we obtain

$$k = \sqrt{0.210 + 0.105^2} - 0.105 = 0.365$$
$$M = \tfrac{1}{6} \times 1125 \times 0.365 \times 2.635 \times 16 \times 23.5^2$$
$$= 1{,}593{,}000 \text{ in.-lb}$$

Example 17-3 A rectangular beam of 4000-psi concrete has a width of 14 in. and effective depth of 23.5 in.   Determine the area of reinforcement if the beam is to resist a bending moment of (*a*) 220 ft-kips and (*b*) 200 ft-kips.
  Solution

$$f_{c,\text{allow}} = 1800 \text{ psi} \qquad n = 8$$

From Table 17-1,
$$j_b = 0.860 \qquad K_b = 324 \text{ psi}$$
$$M_b = K_b bd^2 = 324 \times 14 \times 23.5^2 = 2{,}505{,}000 \text{ in.-lb}$$

PART *a*

$$M = 220{,}000 \times 12 = 2{,}640{,}000 \text{ in.-lb} > M_b$$

The beam size is therefore deficient with respect to balanced design, and the concrete will be stressed to capacity.   Applying Eqs. (17-4) and (17-9), we obtain the following:

$$k(3 - k) = \frac{6M}{f_c bd^2}$$
$$= \frac{6 \times 2{,}640{,}000}{1800 \times 14 \times 23.5^2} = 1.138$$

Solving,
$$k = 0.446$$
$$p = \frac{k^2}{2n(1 - k)} = \frac{0.446^2}{16 \times 0.554} = 0.0224$$
$$A_s = pbd = 0.0224 \times 14 \times 23.5 = \textbf{7.37 sq in.}$$

This result may be verified by computing the flexural capacity of the member.
  PART *b*

$$M = 200{,}000 \times 12 = 2{,}400{,}000 \text{ in.-lb} < M_b$$

The beam size is therefore excessive with respect to balanced design, and the steel will be stressed to capacity.   We shall compute A_s by the exact method and then describe the approximate method used in practice.   Applying Eq. (17-7), we obtain the following:

$$\frac{k^2(3 - k)}{1 - k} = \frac{6nM}{f_s bd^2}$$

$$= \frac{6 \times 8 \times 2,400,000}{20,000 \times 14 \times 23.5^2} = 0.7448$$

Solving,

$$k = 0.411 \qquad j = 1 - \frac{0.411}{3} = 0.863$$

$$A_s = \frac{M}{f_s jd} = \frac{2,400,000}{20,000 \times 0.863 \times 23.5} = \textbf{5.92 sq in.}$$

The calculated value of j differs by only a negligible amount from the value $j_b = 0.860$. Consequently, in those instances where the beam size is only moderately excessive with respect to balanced design, the practice is to consider that $j = j_b$ and to solve Eq. (17-5) directly on this basis. This practice is conservative and it obviates the need for solving a cubic equation.

Example 17-4 A beam on a simple span of 13 ft is to carry a uniformly distributed load, exclusive of its own weight, of 3600 plf and a concentrated load of 17,000 lb applied at midspan. Design the section, using $f_c' = 3000$ psi.

Solution. A beam that yields balanced-design conditions would be most economical. However, balanced design generally cannot be achieved in practice, and it is preferable to make the beam size rather than the area of reinforcement slightly excessive.

There are two methods of allowing for the beam weight: First, determine the bending moment with an estimated beam weight included; second, determine the beam size required to support the external loads alone and then increase the size slightly. We shall apply the latter method. Let M_e and M_w denote the maximum bending moment induced by the external loads and beam weight, respectively. From Table 17-1,

$$K_b = 223 \text{ psi} \qquad p_b = 0.0128 \qquad j_b = 0.874$$
$$M_e = \frac{1}{4}PL + \frac{1}{8}wL^2$$
$$= \frac{1}{4} \times 17,000 \times 13 \times 12 + \frac{1}{8} \times 3600 \times 13^2 \times 12$$
$$= 1,576,000 \text{ in.-lb}$$
$$bd^2 = \frac{M}{K_b} = \frac{1,576,000}{223} = 7067 \text{ in.}^3$$

Setting $b = \frac{2}{3}d$, we obtain these results:

$$b = 14.7 \text{ in.} \qquad d = 22.0 \text{ in.}$$

Try $b = 15$ in. and $d = 22.5$ in.; if the reinforcing bars may be placed in one row, the overall depth is 25 in.

$$\text{Beam weight} = \frac{15 \times 25}{144} \times 150 = 391 \text{ plf}$$
$$M_w = \frac{1}{8} \times 391 \times 13^2 \times 12 = 99,000 \text{ in.-lb}$$
$$M = 1,576,000 + 99,000 = 1,675,000 \text{ in.-lb}$$
$$M_b = K_b bd^2 = 223 \times 15 \times 22.5^2 = 1,693,000 \text{ in.-lb}$$

The trial section is therefore adequate, and the steel is stressed to capacity.

$$A_s = \frac{M}{f_s jd} = \frac{1,675,000}{20,000 \times 0.874 \times 22.5} = 4.26 \text{ sq in.}$$

An alternative method of calculating A_s is to apply the value of p_b while setting the beam width equal to the dimension actually required to produce balanced design.

$$A_s = 0.0128 \times 15 \times \frac{1675}{1693} \times 22.5 = 4.27 \text{ sq in.}$$

Use one No. 10 and three No. 9 bars.

$$A_s = 4.27 \text{ sq in.} \qquad b_{\min} = 12.0 \text{ in.}$$

17-3 Web Reinforcement   The design of web reinforcement by the working-stress method parallels the design by the ultimate-strength method, which is covered in Art. 16-5.   Section 1201 of the ACI Code provides two alternative methods of computing the shearing stress that may be resisted by the concrete.   We shall adopt the simpler method, which expresses the allowable stress as a function solely of the ultimate strength of the concrete.   Sections 1205 and 1206 place restrictions on the beam size and stirrup spacing.

The notational system is as follows:

v = nominal shearing stress
v_c = shearing stress resisted by concrete
v' = shearing stress resisted by web reinforcement

$$v = \frac{V}{bd} \qquad\qquad (17\text{-}13)$$

$$v_c = 1.1 \sqrt{f'_c} \qquad\qquad (17\text{-}14)$$

Example 17-5   A beam of 14-in. width and 18.5-in. effective depth carries a uniform load of 3.8 klf and a concentrated midspan load of 2 kips.   The beam is simply supported and the clear distance between supports is 13 ft.   Using $f'_c = 3000$ psi and an allowable stress of 20,000 psi in the stirrups, design web reinforcement in the form of vertical U stirrups.

Solution. At face of support,

$$V = 6.5 \times 3800 + 1000 = 25,700 \text{ lb} \qquad v = \frac{25,700}{14 \times 18.5} = 99 \text{ psi}$$

At midspan,

$$V = 1000 \text{ lb} \qquad v = 4 \text{ psi}$$

The shearing-stress diagram is shown in Fig. 17-5.

$$\text{Slope of diagram} = -\frac{99 - 4}{78} = -1.22 \text{ psi per in.}$$

By Eq. (17-14), $v_c = 60$ psi.   At distance d from face of support,

$$v = 99 - 18.5 \times 1.22 = 76 \text{ psi} \qquad v' = 76 - 60 = 16 \text{ psi}$$

By Sec. 1205(b),

$$v_{\max} = 5\sqrt{f_c'} = 274 > 76 \text{ psi} \qquad \text{OK}$$

We shall establish the interval AD in which web reinforcement is required.

$$AC = \frac{99 - 60}{1.22} = 32 \text{ in.}$$

$$AD = AC + d = 32 + 18.5 = 50.5 \text{ in.}$$

The remaining calculations are similar to those in Example 16-8.

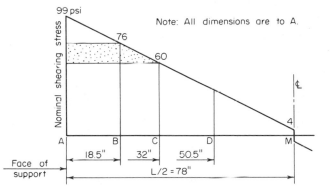

fig. 17-5   Shearing-stress diagram.

17-4 Bond Stresses   The investigation of the bond stresses in a beam under the working-stress method parallels that under the ultimate-strength method, which is covered in Art. 16-6.   The bond stress is given by the following equation:

$$u = \frac{V}{\Sigma ojd} \tag{17-15}$$

Example 17-6   A beam of 3000-psi concrete has an effective depth of 17.5 in. and is reinforced with four No. 6 bars.   Calculate the bond stress at a section where the vertical shear is 24 kips, and compare the result with the allowable stress.
Solution

$$\Sigma o = 9.4 \text{ in.} \qquad u = \frac{24,000}{9.4 \times 0.875 \times 17.5} = \textbf{167 psi}$$

The allowable stress as given by Sec. 1301 of the ACI Code is

$$u_{\text{allow}} = \frac{4.8 \sqrt{f_c'}}{D} \quad \text{but not above 500 psi}$$

$$u_{\text{allow}} = \frac{4.8 \sqrt{3000}}{0.75} = \textbf{350 psi} \quad \text{OK}$$

17-5   T Beams   When the neutral axis of a T beam falls within the web of the member, the portion of the section that lies between the neutral axis and the flange is usually disregarded in order to simplify the calculations.   The notational system is as follows:

A_f = area of flange
b = width of flange
b' = width of web
t = thickness of flange
s = center-to-center spacing of T beams
f_{c1} = stress at interior edge of flange

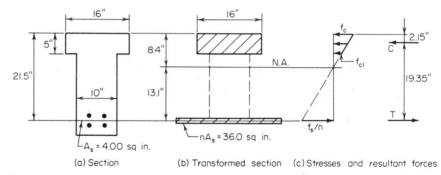

(a) Section   (b) Transformed section   (c) Stresses and resultant forces

fig. 17-6

Example 17-7   Calculate the flexural capacity of the T beam in Fig. 17-6a, using $f_c' = 3000$ psi.
Solution

$$f_{c,\text{allow}} = 1350 \text{ psi} \quad n = 9 \quad k_b = 0.378$$
$$A_f = 5 \times 16 = 80 \text{ sq in.} \quad nA_s = 9 \times 4.00 = 36.0 \text{ sq in.}$$

Assume that the centroidal axis lies within the web.

$$Q_{CA} = 80(kd - 2.5) - 36.0(21.5 - kd) = 0$$
$$kd = 8.40 \text{ in.} \quad k = \frac{8.40}{21.5} = 0.391 > k_b$$

Therefore, concrete stress governs. By proportion,

$$f_{c1} = 1350 \times \frac{3.40}{8.40} = 546 \text{ psi}$$

$$C = \tfrac{1}{2} \times 80(1350 + 546) = 75,800 \text{ lb}$$

The action line of this resultant force lies at the centroidal axis of the stress trapezoid. By Eq. (2-14),

$$z = \frac{5}{3}\left(\frac{1350 + 2 \times 546}{1350 + 546}\right) = 2.15 \text{ in.}$$

or

$$z = \frac{5}{3}\left(\frac{8.40 + 2 \times 3.40}{8.40 + 3.40}\right) = 2.15 \text{ in.}$$

$$M = Cjd = 75,800 \times 19.35 = \mathbf{1{,}467{,}000 \text{ in.-lb}}$$

Alternatively, the moment capacity may be found by assuming that the flange extends to the neutral axis and then applying the necessary correction. Let C_1 denote the resultant force in the flange if the assumed condition were true, and C_2 the resultant force in the imaginary extension of the flange.

$$C_1 = \tfrac{1}{2} \times 1350 \times 16 \times 8.40 = 90,720 \text{ lb}$$

$$C_2 = 90,720 \left(\frac{3.40}{8.40}\right)^2 = 14,860 \text{ lb}$$

$$M = 90,720\left(21.5 - \frac{8.40}{3}\right) - 14,860\left(21.5 - 5 - \frac{3.40}{3}\right)$$

$$= 1,696,000 - 228,000 = 1,468,000 \text{ in.-lb}$$

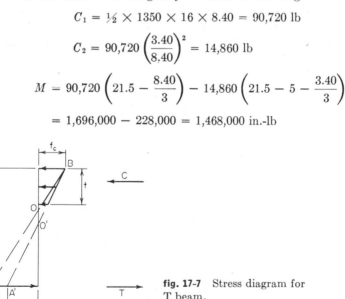

fig. 17-7 Stress diagram for T beam.

Consider that a T beam is in balanced design; the bending stresses under the allowable moment are represented by line AOB in Fig. 17-7. Now consider that the area of reinforcement is increased, causing the stress line under allowable moment to assume the position $A'O'B$. Let

T_b and M_b denote the tensile force and bending moment in the original beam, respectively, and T and M denote the corresponding quantities in the over-reinforced beam. By computing the increase in the compressive force, we obtain the following results:

$$T = T_b + \frac{bt^2x}{2d} \tag{17-16}$$

$$M = M_b + \frac{bt^2(3d - 2t)x}{6d} \tag{17-17}$$

These equations are applied in designing a T beam in which the concrete area is deficient with respect to balanced design.

Example 17-8 A girder of 2500-psi concrete has a simple span of 22 ft and is built integrally with a 5-in. slab. The girders are spaced 8 ft on centers; the overall depth is restricted to 20 in. by headroom requirements. The member carries a load of 4200 plf exclusive of the weight of its web. Design the section, using tension reinforcement only. Verify the design by computing the flexural capacity of the member.

Solution. Since the girder is built integrally with the slab that it supports, the girder and tributary slab function as a T beam. Assume a web width of 14 in. In accordance with Sec. 906(b) of the ACI Code, the effective flange width is established by means of the following calculations:

$$\frac{1}{4}L = \frac{1}{4} \times 22 \times 12 = 66 \text{ in.}$$
$$16t + b' = 16 \times 5 + 14 = 94 \text{ in.}$$
$$s = 8 \times 12 = 96 \text{ in.}$$

The effective flange width is therefore 66 in.

$$\text{Weight of web} = \frac{14 \times 15}{144} \times 150 = 219 \qquad \text{(say, 220 plf)}$$
$$w = 4200 + 220 = 4420 \text{ plf}$$

Since two rows of bars are undoubtedly required,

$$d = 20 - 3.5 = 16.5 \text{ in.}$$

The critical shear value is

$$V = w\left(\frac{L}{2} - d\right) = 4420(11 - 1.4) = 42{,}430 \text{ lb}$$
$$v = \frac{V}{b'd} = \frac{42{,}430}{14 \times 16.5} = 184 \text{ psi}$$

By Sec. 1205(b),

$$v_{\max} = 5\sqrt{f'_c} = 250 \text{ psi} \qquad \text{OK}$$

We shall compute the flexural capacity of the member at balanced design and compare this with the true moment to identify the controlling stress. Refer to Fig. 17-6 as a guide.

$$f_{c,\text{allow}} = 1125 \text{ psi} \qquad n = 10$$
$$k_b d = 0.360 \times 16.5 = 5.94 \text{ sq in.} \qquad A_f = 5 \times 66 = 330 \text{ sq in.}$$

$$f_{c1} = 1125 \times \frac{0.94}{5.94} = 178 \text{ psi}$$

$$C_b = T_b = \frac{1}{2} \times 330(1125 + 178) = 215{,}000 \text{ lb}$$

$$z_b = \frac{5}{3}\left(\frac{5.94 + 2 \times 0.94}{5.94 + 0.94}\right) = 1.89 \text{ in.} \qquad j_b d = 14.61 \text{ in.}$$

$$M_b = 215{,}000 \times 14.61 = 3{,}141{,}000 \text{ in.-lb}$$
$$M = \frac{1}{8} \times 4420 \times 22^2 \times 12 = 3{,}209{,}000 \text{ in.-lb}$$

The beam size is therefore slightly deficient with respect to balanced design, and the concrete will be stressed to capacity under the given load.

$$M - M_b = 68{,}000 \text{ in.-lb}$$

Equation (17-17) yields

$$x = \frac{68{,}000 \times 6 \times 16.5}{66 \times 25(49.5 - 10)} = 103 \text{ psi}$$

$$f_s = 20{,}000 - 10 \times 103 = 18{,}970 \text{ psi}$$

Equation (17-16) yields

$$T = 215{,}000 + \frac{66 \times 25 \times 103}{33} = 220{,}200 \text{ lb}$$

$$A_s = \frac{220{,}200}{18{,}970} = 11.61 \text{ sq in.}$$

Use five No. 11 and three No. 10 bars, placed in two rows.

$$A_s = 11.61 \text{ sq in.} \qquad b'_{\min} = 14.0 \text{ in.}$$

The allowable bond stress for a No. 11 bar is 170 psi, and the actual stress is well below this value.

In summary, the design is as follows:

Width of web: **14 in.**

Reinforcement: **Five No. 11 and three No. 10 bars**

We shall now verify the design.

$$nA_s = 116.1 \text{ sq in.}$$

For the transformed section,

$$Q_{CA} = 330(kd - 2.5) - 116.1(16.5 - kd) = 0$$

$$kd = 6.14 \text{ in.} \qquad k = \frac{6.14}{16.5} = 0.372 > k_b$$

Therefore, concrete is stressed to capacity. By proportion,

$$f_s = 10 \times 1125 \times \frac{10.36}{6.14} = 18{,}980 \text{ psi}$$

$$z = \frac{5}{3}\left(\frac{6.14 + 2 \times 1.14}{6.14 + 1.14}\right) = 1.93 \text{ in.} \qquad jd = 14.57 \text{ in.}$$

$$M_{\text{allow}} = 11.61 \times 18{,}980 \times 14.57 = 3{,}210{,}000 \text{ in.-lb} \qquad \text{OK}$$

Where the size of a T beam is excessive with respect to balanced design, the value of jd is greater than that associated with the balanced condition. The area of reinforcement may therefore be calculated by applying the value of $j_b d$ as a conservative approximation.

Example 17-9   Assume that the girder in Example 17-8 carries a total load, including the weight of web, of 4100 plf.   Calculate the area of reinforcement.
   Solution. From the preceding calculations,

$$j_b d = 14.61 \text{ in.} \qquad M_b = 3{,}141{,}000 \text{ in.-lb}$$
$$M = \tfrac{1}{8} \times 4100 \times 22^2 \times 12 = 2{,}977{,}000 \text{ in.-lb}$$

The beam size is slightly excessive with respect to balanced design, and the steel will therefore be stressed to capacity under the given load.

$$A_s = \frac{2{,}977{,}000}{20{,}000 \times 14.61} = \textbf{10.19 sq in.}$$

17-6   Doubly Reinforced Beams   Consider that compressive loads are applied to two posts, one of steel, the other of concrete.   We may assume for practical purposes that the steel member will retain the length assumed immediately following application of the load.   The concrete member, on the other hand, will continue to contract slowly for a considerable period of time if the load is sustained.   This phenomenon is termed *creep*, or *plastic flow*.   The value of E_c for a given grade of concrete is based upon the deformation of the concrete at the instant of loading; it therefore fails to afford a reliable estimate of long-term deformations.

When steel reinforcement is embedded in a region of concrete that is under compression, the initial stresses in the two materials are directly proportional to their respective moduli of elasticity.   However, since the concrete tends to continue to contract and the steel does not, the concrete exerts a compressive force on the steel and the steel exerts a tensile force on the concrete, thus engendering a flux of compressive stress from concrete to steel.

Assume that a concrete beam must be restricted to a size substantially below that corresponding to balanced design.   To compensate for this deficiency, it is necessary to reinforce the beam in compression as well as tension.   To account for the effects of plastic flow, Sec. 1102(c) of the

ACI Code provides as follows: "In doubly reinforced beams and slabs, an effective modular ratio of $2n$ shall be used to transform the compression reinforcement and compute its stress, which shall not be taken as greater than the allowable tensile stress."

The notational system is as follows:

A_s = area of tension reinforcement
A_s' = area of compression reinforcement
f_s = stress in tension reinforcement
f_s' = stress in compression reinforcement
C' = resultant force in compression reinforcement
M_1 = moment capacity of member if reinforced solely in tension to produce balanced design
M_2 = incremental moment capacity resulting from use of compression reinforcement

For simplicity, the loss in concrete area caused by the presence of the compression steel is disregarded, and it is assumed that the neutral axis occupies the same position as it would if the beam were singly reinforced at balanced design.

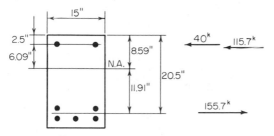

fig. 17-8   Doubly reinforced beam,

Example 17-10   A beam of 4000-psi concrete that will sustain a bending moment of 230 ft-kips is restricted to a 15-in. width and 24-in. total depth.   Design the reinforcement.
Solution. Refer to Fig. 17-8.

$$f_c = 1800 \text{ psi} \qquad n = 8 \qquad K_b = 324 \text{ psi}$$
$$k_b = 0.419 \qquad j_b = 0.860$$
$$M = 230,000 \times 12 = 2,760,000 \text{ in.-lb}$$

To ascertain whether one row of tension bars will suffice, we shall compute an approximate steel area by applying the value of j_b.

$$j_b d = 0.860 \times 21.5 = 18.49 \text{ in.}$$
$$A_s = \frac{M}{f_s j d} = \frac{2,760,000}{20,000 \times 18.49} = 7.46 \text{ sq in.}$$

The 15-in. width is inadequate for this area, and two rows of tension bars are therefore required.

$$d = 24 - 3.5 = 20.5 \text{ in.}$$
$$M_1 = K_b b d^2 = 324 \times 15 \times 20.5^2 = 2,040,000 \text{ in.-lb}$$
$$M_2 = 2,760,000 - 2,040,000 = 720,000 \text{ in.-lb}$$

For M_1: $\text{Arm} = j_b d = 0.860 \times 20.5 = 17.63 \text{ in.}$
For M_2: $\text{Arm} = 20.5 - 2.5 = 18.0 \text{ in.}$

$$T = \frac{2,040,000}{17.63} + \frac{720,000}{18.0}$$
$$= 115,700 + 40,000 = 155,700 \text{ lb}$$
$$C' = 40,000 \text{ lb}$$
$$A_s = \frac{T}{f_s} = \frac{155,700}{20,000} = 7.79 \text{ sq in.}$$
$$kd = 0.419 \times 20.5 = 8.59 \text{ in.} \qquad d - kd = 11.91 \text{ in.}$$

By proportion,

$$f_s' = 2 \times 20,000 \times \frac{6.09}{11.91} = 20,500 \text{ psi}$$

or

$$f_s' = 2 \times 8 \times 1800 \times \frac{6.09}{8.59} = 20,400 \text{ psi}$$

Therefore, set $f_s' = 20,000$ psi.

$$A_s' = \frac{C'}{f_s'} = \frac{40,000}{20,000} = 2.00 \text{ sq in.}$$

Tension steel: Five No. 11 bars $A_s = 7.80$ sq in.
Compression steel: Two No. 9 bars $A_s = 2.00$ sq in.

17-7 Deflection of Beams

When a beam is reinforced in the manner described in Sec. 1507 of the ACI Code, an investigation of its deflection is mandatory, and the limiting ratios of live-load deflection to span are presented in Sec. 909(c).

Before calculating the deflection of a beam, it is necessary to determine whether the concrete is cracked or uncracked when the member supports its working loads.   In accordance with Sec. 909(c), we may assume that the concrete is uncracked if pf_y does not exceed 500.   The deflection is evaluated by applying the moment of inertia of the transformed cracked or uncracked section, as the case may be.   If the beam is continuous, an average value of the moment of inertia is used.

Figure 17-9c is the bending-moment diagram of a continuous beam that carries a uniformly distributed load.   The deflection at midspan is as follows:

$$\Delta = \frac{L'^2}{EI} \left(\tfrac{5}{48} M_1 - \tfrac{1}{8} M_3 \right) \qquad (17\text{-}18)$$

where $L' =$ clear span.

Example 17-11 The continuous beam shown in Fig. 17-9a and b carries a total load of 3.3 klf. When considered as a T beam, the member has an effective flange width of 68 in. Compute the deflection of the beam under the stipulated load, applying the normal value of E_c. Use $f'_c = 2500$ psi and $f_y = 40,000$ psi.

Solution. The deflection will be evaluated on the basis of the maximum positive bending moment recommended in Sec. 904(c) of the ACI Code. Let A_s and A'_s denote the area of the tension and compression reinforcement, respectively.

At support:
$A_s = 4.43$ sq in.   (top)
$A'_s = 1.58$ sq in.   (bottom)

At center:
$A_s = 3.16$ sq in.   (bottom)

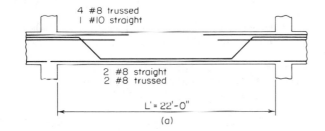

4 #8 trussed
1 #10 straight

2 #8 straight
2 #8 trussed

L' = 22'-0"

(a)

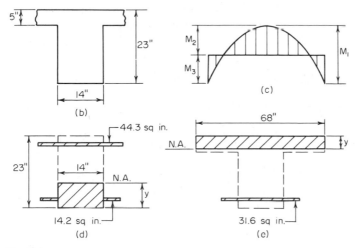

5"

23"

14"

(b)

M_2

M_3

M_1

(c)

44.3 sq in.

23"

14"

N.A.

14.2 sq in.

(d)

68"

N.A.

y

31.6 sq in.

(e)

fig. 17-9

Refer to Fig. 17-9c.

$$M_1 = \tfrac{1}{8}wL'^2 = \tfrac{1}{8} \times 3.3 \times 22^2 = 200 \text{ ft-kips}$$
$$M_2 = \tfrac{1}{16}wL'^2 = 100 \text{ ft-kips} \qquad M_3 = 100 \text{ ft-kips}$$

At the support,

$$pf_y = \frac{4.43}{14 \times 20.5} \times 40{,}000 = 617 > 500$$

Therefore, the concrete is cracked.

The transformed cracked section at the support is shown in Fig. 17-9d. We shall allow for the reduction of concrete area caused by the compression steel by using a modular ratio of $n - 1$ rather than n.

$$nA_s = 10 \times 4.43 = 44.3 \text{ sq in.} \qquad (n - 1)A_s' = 9 \times 1.58 = 14.2 \text{ sq in.}$$
$$Q_{CA} = -\tfrac{1}{2} \times 14y^2 + 44.3(20.5 - y) - 14.2(y - 2.5) = 0$$
Solving, $\qquad\qquad\qquad\qquad y = 8.16 \text{ in.}$

The moment of inertia of the section with respect to the centroidal axis is

$$I_1 = \tfrac{1}{3} \times 14 \times 8.16^3 + 14.2(8.16 - 2.5)^2 + 44.3(20.5 - 8.16)^2 = 9737 \text{ in.}^4$$

The transformed cracked section at the center is shown in Fig. 17-9e. Assume that the centroidal axis falls within the flange.

$$nA_s = 10 \times 3.16 = 31.6 \text{ sq in.}$$
$$Q_{CA} = \tfrac{1}{2} \times 68y^2 - 31.6(20.5 - y) = 0$$
Solving, $\qquad\qquad\qquad y = 3.92 < 5 \text{ in.} \qquad \text{OK}$

The moment of inertia of the section with respect to the centroidal axis is

$$I_2 = \tfrac{1}{3} \times 68 \times 3.92^3 + 31.6(20.5 - 3.92)^2 = 10{,}052 \text{ in.}^4$$
Then $\qquad\qquad\qquad I = \tfrac{1}{2}(9737 + 10{,}052) = 9895 \text{ in.}^4$

By Sec. 1102(a),

$$E_c = 145^{1.5} \times 33 \sqrt{f_c'} = 57{,}600 \sqrt{2500} = 2{,}880{,}000 \text{ psi}$$

Substituting in Eq. (17-18), we obtain

$$\Delta = \frac{22^2 \times 1728}{2880 \times 9895}\left(\frac{5}{48} \times 200 - \frac{1}{8} \times 100\right) = \mathbf{0.244 \text{ in.}}$$

Where the deflection under sustained loading is to be evaluated, it is necessary to apply the factors recorded in Sec. 909(d) of the ACI Code.

EIGHTEEN

Reinforced-concrete Columns: Ultimate-strength Design

18-1 Introduction If a concrete compression member has an unbraced length greater than three times the least lateral dimension, it must be supplied with steel reinforcement. The member is said to be *spirally reinforced* if the longitudinal reinforcement is held in position by spiral hooping, and *tied* if this reinforcement is held by means of intermittent lateral ties.

Since it is impossible in practice to secure loading that is truly concentric, the ACI Code requires that a compression member be capable of sustaining a specified minimum bending moment at ultimate-load conditions. Consequently, each compression member designed by the ultimate-strength method must be considered a beam-column even though the design load is assumed to be concentric.

A reinforced-concrete beam-column has three potential modes of failure: crushing of the concrete, which is assumed to occur when ϵ_c reaches the value of 0.003; yielding of the tension steel, which begins when its stress reaches the value f_y; and the simultaneous crushing of the concrete and yielding of the tension steel. A member that tends to fail by the third mode is said to be in *balanced design*.

211

The notational system is as follows:

P_u = ultimate axial compressive load on member
P_b = ultimate axial compressive load at balanced design
P_o = allowable ultimate axial compressive load in absence of bending moment
M_u = ultimate bending moment in member
M_b = ultimate bending moment at balanced design
t = overall depth of rectangular section or diameter of circular section

Sections 1901(a) and 1504(b) of the ACI Code establish the following values:

Spiral column:

$$\text{Minimum bending moment} = 0.05P_u t \qquad \phi = 0.75$$

Tied column:

$$\text{Minimum bending moment} = 0.10P_u t \qquad \phi = 0.70$$

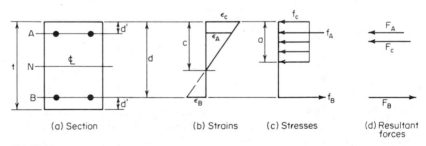

(a) Section   (b) Strains   (c) Stresses   (d) Resultant forces

fig. 18-1

Figure 18-1a is the cross section of a beam-column in which the bending moment causes rotation about axis N, inducing compression at A and tension at B. Let

ϵ_A and ϵ_B = strain of reinforcement at A and B, respectively
f_A and f_B = stress in reinforcement at A and B, respectively
F_A and F_B = resultant force in reinforcement at A and B, respectively
F_c = resultant force in concrete

For simplicity, we shall disregard the slight reduction in concrete area caused by the reinforcing steel. Compression will be considered positive and tension negative. Then

$$P_u = \phi(F_A + F_B + F_c) \tag{18-1}$$

If the steel stress is below the yield point, we obtain these relationships from the strain diagram:

$$f_A = \epsilon_c E_s \frac{c - d'}{c} \qquad f_B = \epsilon_c E_s \frac{c - d}{c} \qquad (18\text{-}2)$$

If ϵ_c has its limiting value of 0.003, these reduce to

$$f_A = 87{,}000 \frac{c - d'}{c} \qquad f_B = 87{,}000 \frac{c - d}{c} \qquad (18\text{-}2a)$$

By taking moments with respect to axis N, we obtain the following result:

$$M_u = \phi \left[F_c \frac{t - a}{2} + (F_A - F_B) \frac{t - 2d'}{2} \right] \qquad (18\text{-}3)$$

18-2   Analysis of Beam-Columns by Interaction Diagrams   To every value of the ultimate moment sustained by a given member, there corresponds a value of the allowable axial load.   An *interaction diagram* is one in which every point on the curve represents a set of simultaneous values of these two quantities.

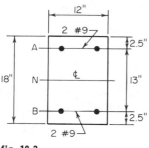

fig. 18-2

Example 18-1   A short tied compression member having the cross section shown in Fig. 18-2 will carry a bending moment with respect to axis N that induces compression at A and tension at B. The member is made of 3000-psi concrete and the steel has a yield point of 40,000 psi.   Construct the interaction diagram for this member.

Solution.   Refer to Fig. 18-3.   Consider that we start with a truly concentric load equal to the ultimate-load capacity of the member.   The entire concrete section is stressed to $0.85f'_c$ and the reinforcement at both A and B is stressed to f_y in compression.   Now consider that we displace the load toward axis A while reducing the magnitude of the load to its allowable value for the corresponding eccentricity.   The value of c decreases, and the behavior of the member passes through phases having the following boundary conditions:

Condition 1: $M_u = 0$
Condition 2: $c = t/k_1$
Condition 3: Member is at balanced design
Condition 4: Compression steel is at incipient yielding

It is necessary to investigate each of these conditions in turn, and it is recommended that the reader draw the strain diagrams representing these conditions.

$$F_c = 0.85f'_c ab = 0.85 \times 3000 \times 12a = 30{,}600a$$

At A and B, $A_s = 2.00$ sq in.

CONDITION 1

$$f_A = f_B = 40,000 \text{ psi} \qquad F_A = F_B = 80,000 \text{ lb}$$
$$F_c = 30,600 \times 18 = 550,800 \text{ lb}$$
$$P_o = 0.70(160,000 + 550,800) = 497,600 \text{ lb}$$

The minimum value of c associated with this condition is that in which the steel at B is at incipient yielding. By Eq. (18-2a),

$$40,000 = 87,000 \frac{c - 15.5}{c} \qquad c = 28.7 \text{ in.}$$

CONDITION 2

$$c = \frac{18}{0.85} = 21.18 \text{ in.} \qquad a = 18 \text{ in.}$$

By Eq. (18-2a),

$$f_A = 87,000 \frac{21.18 - 2.5}{21.18} \qquad \text{set } f_A = 40,000 \text{ psi}$$
$$f_B = 87,000 \frac{21.18 - 15.5}{21.18} = 23,300 \text{ psi}$$
$$F_c = 30,600 \times 18 = 550,800 \text{ lb}$$
$$F_A = 80,000 \text{ lb} \qquad F_B = 46,600 \text{ lb}$$
$$P_u = 0.70(80,000 + 46,600 + 550,800) = 474,200 \text{ lb}$$
$$M_u = 0.70 \times 6.5(80,000 - 46,600) = 152,000 \text{ in.-lb}$$

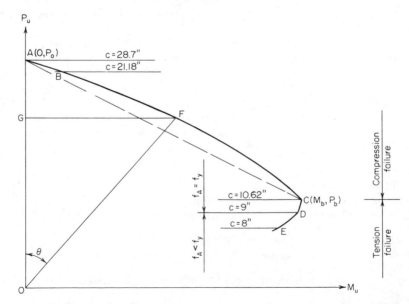

fig. 18-3   Interaction diagram.

CONDITION 3. By Eq. (18-2a),

$$f_B = 87,000 \frac{c - 15.5}{c} = -40,000 \text{ psi} \qquad c = 10.62 \text{ in.}$$

$$f_A = 87,000 \frac{10.62 - 2.5}{10.62} \qquad \text{set } f_A = 40,000 \text{ psi}$$

$$a = 0.85 \times 10.62 = 9.03 \text{ in.} \qquad F_c = 30,600 \times 9.03 = 276,300 \text{ lb}$$
$$F_A = 80,000 \text{ lb} \qquad F_B = -80,000 \text{ lb}$$
$$P_b = 0.70 \times 276,300 = 193,400 \text{ lb}$$
$$M_b = 0.70(276,300 \times 4.49 + 160,000 \times 6.5) = 1,596,000 \text{ in.-lb}$$

When $c > 10.62$, the member fails by crushing of the concrete; when $c < 10.62$, it fails by yielding of the reinforcement at B.

CONDITION 4. Since ϵ_A and ϵ_B are numerically equal, the neutral axis lies at N.

$$c = 9 \text{ in.} \qquad a = 0.85 \times 9 = 7.65 \text{ in.}$$
$$F_c = 30,600 \times 7.65 = 234,100 \text{ lb}$$
$$F_A = 80,000 \text{ lb} \qquad F_B = -80,000 \text{ lb}$$
$$P_u = 0.70 \times 234,100 = 163,900 \text{ lb}$$
$$M_u = 0.70(234,100 \times 5.18 + 160,000 \times 6.5) = 1,577,000 \text{ in.-lb}$$

When $c < 9$ in., the stress at A is below the yield point.

Having established the value of c associated with each boundary condition, we may now assign arbitrary values to c and determine the corresponding value of P_u and M_u. The following serve as illustrative calculations.

When $c = 8$ in.:

$$f_B = -40,000 \text{ psi} \qquad f_A = 40,000 \times \frac{5.5}{7.5} = 29,300 \text{ psi}$$

$$a = 6.8 \text{ in.} \qquad F_c = 30,600 \times 6.8 = 208,100 \text{ lb}$$
$$P_u = 0.70(58,600 - 80,000 + 208,100) = 130,700 \text{ lb}$$
$$M_u = 0.70(208,100 \times 5.6 + 138,600 \times 6.5) = 1,446,000 \text{ in.-lb}$$

When $c = 10$ in.:

$$f_A = 40,000 \text{ psi} \qquad f_B = -40,000 \text{ psi}$$
$$a = 8.5 \text{ in.} \qquad F_c = 30,600 \times 8.5 = 260,100 \text{ lb}$$
$$P_u = 0.70 \times 260,100 = 182,100 \text{ lb}$$
$$M_u = 0.70(260,100 \times 4.75 + 160,000 \times 6.5) = 1,593,000 \text{ in.-lb}$$

When $c = 14$ in.:

$$f_B = 87,000 \frac{14 - 15.5}{14} = -9320 \text{ psi}$$

$$a = 11.9 \text{ in.} \qquad F_c = 30,600 \times 11.9 = 364,100 \text{ lb}$$
$$P_u = 0.70(80,000 - 18,600 + 364,100) = 297,900 \text{ lb}$$
$$M_u = 0.70(364,100 \times 3.05 + 98,600 \times 6.5) = 1,226,000 \text{ in.-lb}$$

By plotting the points representing the computed values of P_u and M_u and connecting them with smooth curves, we obtain the diagram shown in Fig. 18-3.

It is important to observe that if we start with a value of P_u below P_b, any reduction in the ultimate moment is accompanied by a reduction in the allowable axial load.

18-3 Eccentrically Loaded Columns   Assume that the bending moment in a beam-column results from eccentricity of loading; let e denote the eccentricity. In Fig. 18-3, consider that we draw an arbitrary radius vector OF to the interaction diagram. Then

$$\tan \theta = \frac{M_u}{P_u} = \frac{P_u e}{P_u} = e$$

As we proceed along the interaction diagram from A to E, the value of c decreases and the value of e increases. Thus, c and e vary in the reverse manner.

To simplify the calculations associated with failure of the concrete, Sec. 1902(c) of the ACI Code permits us to replace the portion of the diagram between A and C with a straight line through those points. The equation of line AC is as follows:

$$P_u = P_o - (P_o - P_b)\frac{M_u}{M_b} \qquad (18\text{-}4a)$$

By replacing M_u with $P_u e$, we obtain

$$P_u = \frac{P_o}{1 + (P_o - P_b)e/M_b} \qquad (18\text{-}4b)$$

Example 18-2   With reference to the member analyzed in Example 18-1, compute the eccentricity of loading associated with conditions 3 and 4.

Solution. Applying the results of the preceding calculations, we obtain the following:

Condition 3: $c = 10.62$ in. $e = \dfrac{1,596,000}{193,400} = $ **8.25 in.**

Condition 4: $c = 9$ in. $e = \dfrac{1,577,000}{163,900} = $ **9.62 in.**

Example 18-3   With reference to the member analyzed in Example 18-1, compute the allowable ultimate load if the eccentricity as measured from N is (b) 9.2 in. and (b) 6 in.

Solution

PART a. As the preceding calculations disclose, an eccentricity of 9.2 in. corresponds to a point on CD. At ultimate load, the reinforcement at B is at incipient yielding and the reinforcement at A is stressed to f_y.

$$F_A = 80 \text{ kips} \qquad\qquad F_B = -80 \text{ kips}$$

$$F_c = 30.6a \quad \text{kips} \qquad \frac{P_u}{0.70} = 30.6a \quad \text{kips}$$

Applying Eq. (18-3),

$$\frac{M_u}{0.70} = 30.6a\left(9 - \frac{a}{2}\right) + 160 \times 6.5 \text{ in.-kips}$$

$$= 275.4a - 15.3a^2 + 1040$$

$$\frac{M_u}{P_u} = \frac{275.4a - 15.3a^2 + 1040}{30.6a} = 9.2$$

Solving this equation, we obtain

$$a = 8.05 \text{ in.} \qquad F_c = 246.3 \text{ kips} \qquad P_u = \textbf{172.4 kips}$$

This result may be verified by applying Eq. (18-3).

$$M_u = 0.70(246.3 \times 4.98 + 160 \times 6.5) = 1587 \text{ in.-kips}$$

$$e = \frac{1587}{172.4} = 9.2 \text{ in.} \qquad \text{OK}$$

PART *b*. An eccentricity of 6 in. corresponds to a point on line AC, and we may therefore apply Eq. (18-4*b*). From the preceding calculations,

$$P_o = 497.6 \text{ kips} \qquad P_b = 193.4 \text{ kips}$$
$$M_b = 1596 \text{ in.-kips}$$
$$P_u = \frac{497.6}{1 + 304.2 \times 6/1596} = \textbf{232.1 kips}$$

Example 18-4 The member analyzed in Example 18-1 is to carry an ultimate load of 150 kips that is eccentric with respect to axis N. Compute the maximum eccentricity with which the load may be applied.

Solution. Referring to the values of P_u obtained in Example 18-1, we find that a load of 150 kips is represented by a point between D and E in Fig. 18-3. We shall determine the corresponding value of c.

$$f_B = -40 \text{ ksi} \qquad f_A = 40\frac{c - 2.5}{15.5 - c} \quad \text{ksi}$$

$$F_c = 30.6 \times 0.85c = 26.0c \quad \text{kips}$$

$$150 = 0.70\left[26.0c + 80\left(\frac{c - 2.5}{15.5 - c} - 1\right)\right]$$

Solving,

$$c = 8.60 \text{ in.} \qquad a = 7.31 \text{ in.}$$
$$F_c = 223.7 \text{ kips} \qquad f_A = 35.36 \text{ ksi}$$
$$M_u = 0.70(223.7 \times 5.35 + 150.7 \times 6.5) = 1523 \text{ in.-lb}$$

$$e = \frac{M_u}{P_u} = \textbf{10.15 in.}$$

NINETEEN

Reinforced-concrete Columns: Working-stress Design

19-1 Introduction   The working-stress method of designing a reinforced-concrete compression member is essentially an adaptation of the ultimate-strength method. The allowable ultimate loads and bending moments are reduced by applying an appropriate factor of safety, and various simplifications in computing the ultimate values are introduced.

The notational system is as follows:

A_g = gross area of section
A_s = area of tension reinforcement
A_{st} = total area of longitudinal reinforcement
t = overall depth of rectangular section or diameter of circular section
D = diameter of circular section
P = axial load on member
f_s = allowable stress in longitudinal reinforcement
$p_g = A_{st}/A_g$
$m = f_y/0.85f_c'$

Section 913 of the ACI Code provides that p_g may range from 0.01 to 0.08. However, in the case of a circular column in which the bars are to be placed in a single circular row, the upper limit of p_g is often governed by clearance. This section also stipulates that the minimum bar size to be used is No. 5 and requires a minimum of six bars for a spirally reinforced column and four bars for a tied column.

With reference to a circular column with spiral reinforcement, the portion of the column section bounded by the outer circumference of the spiral is termed the *core* of the section. The notational system for this type of member is as follows:

A_c = area of core
D_c = diameter of core
a_s = cross-sectional area of spiral wire
g = pitch of spiral
p_s = ratio of volume of spiral reinforcement to volume of core

The minimum value of p_s established by Sec. 913 of the Code is

$$p_s = 0.45 \left(\frac{A_g}{A_c} - 1 \right) \frac{f'_c}{f_y} \tag{19-1}$$

By considering the volumes in a 1-in. length of column, we obtain the following:

$$p_s = \frac{\text{volume of spiral}}{\text{volume of core}} = \frac{a_s \pi D_c/g}{\pi D_c^2/4}$$

Then

$$a_s = \frac{g D_c p_s}{4} \tag{19-2}$$

19-2 Concentrically Loaded Columns The allowable concentric load on a short spirally reinforced column is as follows:

$$P = A_g (0.25 f'_c + f_s p_g) \tag{19-3a}$$

or

$$P = 0.25 f'_c A_g + f_s A_{st} \tag{19-3b}$$

where $f_s = 0.40 f_y$, but not to exceed 30,000 psi.

The allowable concentric load on a short tied column is as follows:

$$P = 0.85 A_g (0.25 f'_c + f_s p_g) \tag{19-4a}$$

or

$$P = 0.2125 f'_c A_g + 0.85 f_s A_{st} \tag{19-4b}$$

Example 19-1 A short circular column, spirally reinforced, is to support a concentric load of 420 kips. Design the member, using $f'_c = 4000$ psi and $f_y = 50,000$ psi.

Solution. Refer to Fig. 19-1.

$$0.25f'_c = 1.00 \text{ ksi} \qquad f_s = 20 \text{ ksi}$$

Assume the value of 0.025 for p_g. Equation (19-3a) yields

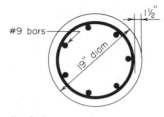

#9 bars

$$A_g = \frac{420}{1.00 + 20 \times 0.025} = 280 \text{ sq in.}$$

$$D = \sqrt{\frac{A_g}{0.785}} = 18.9 \text{ in.}$$

Set $D = 19$ in.: $\quad A_g = 0.785 \times 19^2 = 283$ sq in.

Load carried by concrete $= 283 \times 1.00 = 283$ kips

fig. 19-1

Load carried by steel $= 420 - 283 = 137$ kips

$$A_{st} = {}^{137}\!/_{20} = 6.85 \text{ sq in.}$$

Use seven No. 9 bars: $\qquad A_{st} = 7.00$ sq in.

Table 39 of the Reinforced Concrete Design Handbook reveals that the 19-in. column can accommodate eleven No. 9 bars in a single row.

The provisions of the ACI Code governing the spiral design are as follows: Section 808(c) requires 1.5 in. insulation for the spiral, and Sec. 806 restricts the pitch g to a maximum of $\frac{1}{6}D_c$.

$$D_c = 19 - 3 = 16 \text{ in.} \qquad A_c = 201 \text{ sq in.} \qquad \frac{1}{6}D_c = 2.67 \text{ in.}$$

Use a 2.5-in. spiral pitch. Equations (19-1) and (19-2) yield the following:

$$p_s = 0.45 \, ({}^{283}\!/_{201} - 1){}^{4}\!/_{20} = 0.0147$$

$$a_s = \frac{2.5 \times 16 \times 0.0147}{4} = 0.147 \text{ sq in.}$$

Use $\frac{1}{2}$-in.-diameter wire: $\qquad a_s = 0.196$ sq in.

In summary, the design is as follows:

Column size: **19-in. diameter**
Longitudinal reinforcement: **Seven No. 9 bars**
Spiral reinforcement: $\frac{1}{2}$-**in.-diameter wire, 2.5-in. pitch**

19-3   Analysis of Beam-Columns   Consider that a composite member is confected of two materials, each material having the same strength in tension and compression. Let the member be subjected simultaneously to an axial load P and bending moment M, their values being such as to induce the allowable stress in one or both materials. Let

$P_a =$ allowable axial load in absence of bending moment, as computed by dividing the allowable ultimate load by a factor of safety

M_f = allowable bending moment in absence of axial load, as computed by dividing the allowable ultimate moment by a factor of safety

The simultaneous allowable values of P and M are found by applying the interaction equation

$$\frac{P}{P_a} + \frac{M}{M_f} = 1 \tag{19-5}$$

The following are alternative forms of this equation:

$$M = M_f\left(1 - \frac{P}{P_a}\right) \qquad P = P_a\left(1 - \frac{M}{M_f}\right) \tag{19-5a}$$

$$P = \frac{P_a M_f}{M_f + P_a(M/P)} \tag{19-5b}$$

Equation (19-5), which is represented by line AB in Fig. 19-2, is also valid with respect to a reinforced-concrete member for an intermediate

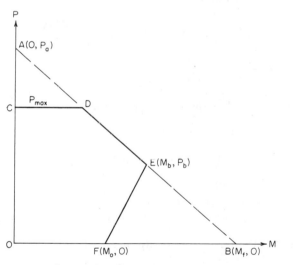

fig. 19-2 Interaction diagram.

range of values of P and M. It is inapplicable in the following instances:

1. If M is relatively small, this equation will yield a value of P in excess of that given by Eq. (19-3) or (19-4), whichever applies. Therefore, the interaction diagram must include line CD, which represents the upper bound of P.

2. If M is relatively large, the section will crack, and the equal-strength assumption underlying Eq. (19-5) becomes untenable.

Point E in the interaction diagram represents the condition that will cause cracking in the extreme concrete fiber, and point F represents the condition $P = 0$.   Let

P_b = axial load represented by point E

M_b = bending moment represented by point E

M_o = allowable bending moment in reinforced-concrete member in absence of axial load, as computed by dividing the allowable ultimate moment by a factor of safety

(The distinction between M_o and M_f is that the former applies to a cracked section and the latter to an uncracked section.   The subscript b as used by the ACI Code with reference to point E does *not* pertain to balanced design, but its use serves to illuminate the analogy with ultimate-strength analysis.)

For simplicity, the interaction diagram is assumed to be linear between E and F.   Consequently, the interaction equation for a cracked section may be expressed in one of the following forms:

$$M = M_o + \frac{P}{P_b}(M_b - M_o) \qquad P = P_b\left(\frac{M - M_o}{M_b - M_o}\right) \qquad (19\text{-}6a)$$

$$P = \frac{P_b M_o}{M_o - M_b + P_b(M/P)} \qquad (19\text{-}6b)$$

The ACI Code offers the following approximations:

For spiral column: $M_o = 0.12A_{st}f_y D_s$ $\qquad\qquad\qquad$ (19-7a)

where D_s = diameter of circle through center of longitudinal reinforcement

For symmetrical tied column: $M_o = 0.40A_s f_y(d - d')$ $\qquad$ (19-7b)

For unsymmetrical tied column: $M_o = 0.40A_s f_y jd$ $\qquad\qquad$ (19-7c)

For symmetrical spiral column: $\dfrac{M_b}{P_b} = 0.43p_g m D_s + 0.14t$ $\qquad$ (19-8a)

For symmetrical tied column: $\dfrac{M_b}{P_b} = d(0.67p_g m + 0.17)$ $\qquad$ (19-8b)

For unsymmetrical tied column: $\dfrac{M_b}{P_b} = \dfrac{p'm(d - d') + 0.1d}{(p' - p)m + 0.6}$ $\qquad$ (19-8c)

where p' = ratio of area of compression reinforcement to effective area of concrete

The value of P_a is taken as

$$P_a = 0.34f'_c A_g(1 + p_g m) \qquad (19\text{-}9)$$

The value of M_f is found by applying the section modulus of the transformed uncracked section, using a modular ratio of $2n$ to account for stress transfer between steel and concrete engendered by plastic flow. (By using a modular ratio of $2n - 1$, we also make allowance for the reduction of concrete area.)

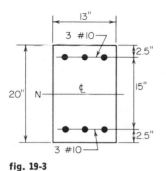

fig. 19-3

Example 19-2 A short tied member having the cross section shown in Fig. 19-3 is to resist an axial load and a bending moment that induces rotation about axis N. The member is made of 4000-psi concrete and the steel has a yield point of 50,000 psi. Calculate the values that are needed to construct the interaction diagram for this member.

Solution

$$A_g = 260 \text{ sq in.} \qquad A_s = 3.81 \text{ sq in.} \qquad A_{st} = 7.62 \text{ sq in.}$$

$$p_g = \frac{7.62}{260} = 0.0293 \qquad m = \frac{50}{0.85 \times 4} = 14.7$$

$$p_g m = 0.431 \qquad\qquad n = 8$$

Eq. (19-9): $\qquad P_a = 0.34 \times 4 \times 260 \times 1.431 = \textbf{506 kips}$

Applying a modular ratio of 15 to the uncracked section, we obtain the following:

$$I = \tfrac{1}{12} \times 13 \times 20^3 + 7.62 \times 15 \times 7.5^2 = 15{,}100 \text{ in.}^4$$

$$S = \frac{I}{c} = \frac{15{,}100}{10} = 1510 \text{ in.}^3$$

$$M_f = Sf_c = 1510 \times 1.8 = \textbf{2720 in.-kips}$$

Eq. (19-8b): $\qquad \dfrac{M_b}{P_b} = 17.5(0.67 \times 0.431 + 0.17) = 8.03 \text{ in.}$

Eq. (19-5b): $\qquad P_b = \dfrac{P_a M_f}{M_f + 8.03 P_a}$

$$= \frac{506 \times 2720}{2720 + 8.03 \times 506} = \textbf{203 kips}$$

$$M_b = 8.03 \times 203 = \textbf{1630 in.-kips}$$

Eq. (19-7b): $\qquad M_o = 0.40 \times 3.81 \times 50 \times 15 = \textbf{1140 in.-kips}$

Eq. (19-4b): $\qquad P_{\max} = 0.2125 \times 4 \times 260 + 0.85 \times 20 \times 7.62$

$$= \textbf{351 kips}$$

Example 19-3 The member analyzed in Example 19-2 is to carry an eccentric compressive load. Determine the allowable load if the eccentricity as measured from N is (a) 10 in. and (b) 6 in.

Solution. As the preceding calculations disclose, the eccentricity corresponding to point E in the interaction diagram is 8.03 in. Consequently, an eccentricity of 10 in. corresponds to a point on EF, and an eccentricity of 6 in. corresponds to a point on ED.

Applying Eq. (19-6b) with $e = 10$ in., we obtain

$$P = \frac{203 \times 1140}{1140 - 1630 + 203 \times 10} = \textbf{150 kips}$$

Applying Eq. (19-5b) with $e = 6$ in., we obtain

$$P = \frac{506 \times 2720}{2720 + 506 \times 6} = \textbf{239 kips}$$

TWENTY

Column Footings

20-1 Isolated Footings A reinforced-concrete footing supporting a single column differs from the usual type of flexural member in the following important respects: The footing is subjected to bending in all directions, its ratio of maximum vertical shear to maximum bending moment is very high, it is not reinforced in diagonal tension, and it carries a heavy load concentrated within a small area. As a result, the footing requires two-way reinforcement, its depth is usually governed by punching-shear stress below the column, and the bond stress is often the controlling criterion in selecting the reinforcing bars. Because the stress distribution in a column footing is highly complex, theory must be tempered to harmonize with empirical observations. The design of column footings is covered in Chap. 23 of the ACI Code.

Since the soil pressure is collinear with the weight of the footing and of the overlying soil, these weights do not contribute to the vertical shear or bending moment. It is convenient to visualize the footing as being subjected to an upward load transmitted by the underlying soil and a downward reaction supplied by the column, this being of course an inversion of the true form of loading. From this point of view, the footing

225

functions as an overhanging beam. The effective depth of footing is taken as the distance from the top surface to the center of the upper row of bars, the two rows being made identical to avoid confusion.

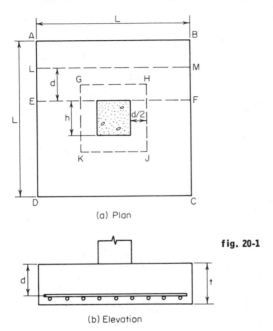

(a) Plan

fig. 20-1

(b) Elevation

Figure 20-1 shows a square footing supporting a square, centrally located concrete column. The notational system is as follows:

P = column load
p = net soil pressure (that caused by column load alone)
A = area of footing
L = side of footing
h = side of column
d = effective depth of footing
t = thickness of footing
f_b = bearing stress at face of column
v_1 = nominal shearing stress under column (also called peripheral shearing stress)
v_2 = nominal shearing stress caused by beam action
b_o = width of critical section for v_1
V_1 and V_2 = vertical shear at critical section for stresses v_1 and v_2, respectively

In accordance with Sec. 1207(b) of the ACI Code, the critical section for v_1 consists of vertical planes through $GHJK$, which lie at a distance

$d/2$ from the column faces. The critical section for v_2 is the vertical plane through LM, located at a distance d from the column face. In accordance with Secs. 2304 and 2305, the critical section for bending stress and bond stress is the vertical plane through EF at the column face. In calculating v_2, f, and u, no allowance is made for the effects of the orthogonal reinforcement.

The depth of footing as governed by v_1 may be found by solving the following equation:

$$(4v_1 + p)d^2 + h(4v_1 + 2p)d = p(A - h^2) \qquad (20\text{-}1)$$

Example 20-1 A 20-in.-square tied column reinforced with eight No. 9 bars carries a concentric load of 380 kips. Design a square footing by the working-stress method, using the following values: The allowable soil pressure is 7000 psf, $f'_c = 3000$ psi, and $f_s = 20,000$ psi. Design the dowels, using $f_y = 40,000$ psi.

Solution. The allowable stresses as recorded in Table 1002(a) of the ACI Code are as follows:

$$v_1 = 110 \text{ psi} = 15.84 \text{ ksf} \qquad v_2 = 60 \text{ psi} \qquad f_b = 1125 \text{ psi}$$

By Sec. 1301,

$$u = \frac{4.8 \sqrt{f'_c}}{\text{bar diam}} = \frac{264}{\text{bar diam}}$$

In the present instance,

$$f_b = \frac{380}{20 \times 20} = 0.95 < 1.125 \text{ ksi} \qquad \text{OK}$$

Assume that the footing weight is 6 percent of the column load.

$$A = \frac{1.06 \times 380}{7} = 57.5 \text{ sq ft}$$

Make $L = 7$ ft 8 in. $= 7.67$ ft

$$A = 58.8 \text{ sq ft} \qquad p = \frac{380}{58.8} = 6.46 \text{ ksf}$$

Substituting in Eq. (20-1), we obtain these results:

$$69.8d^2 + 127.1d = 361.8 \qquad \therefore \ d = 1.54 \text{ ft}$$

We shall test this result. In Fig. 20-1a,

$$GH = 1.67 + 1.54 = 3.21 \text{ ft}$$
$$V_1 = 6.46(58.8 - 3.21^2) = 313 \text{ kips}$$
$$v_1 = \frac{V_1}{b_o d} = \frac{313}{4 \times 3.21 \times 1.54} = 15.83 \text{ ksf} \qquad \text{OK}$$

Allowing 3 in. for insulation and assuming the use of No. 8 bars, we obtain

$$t = 1.54 \times 12 + 4.5 = 23.0 \text{ in.}$$

Setting $t = 24$ in. and $d = 19.5$ in. $= 1.63$ ft,

$$\text{Footing weight} = 58.8 \times 2 \times 0.150 = 17.64 \text{ kips}$$
$$\text{Assumed weight} = 0.06 \times 380 = 22.8 \text{ kips} \qquad \text{OK}$$

In Fig. 20-1,

$$AL = \frac{7.67 - 1.67}{2} - 1.63 = 1.37 \text{ ft}$$

$$V_2 = 380 \times \frac{1.37}{7.67} = 67.9 \text{ kips}$$

$$v_2 = \frac{V_2}{Ld} = \frac{67,900}{92 \times 19.5} = 38 < 60 \text{ psi} \qquad \text{OK}$$

The footing size is therefore satisfactory, and it now remains to design the reinforcement. In Fig. 20-1a,

$$EA = 3.00 \text{ ft} \qquad V_{EF} = 380 \times \frac{3.00}{7.67} = 148.6 \text{ kips}$$

$$M_{EF} = 148.6 \times \tfrac{1}{2} \times 3.00 \times 12 = 2675 \text{ in.-kips}$$
$$M_b = K_b L d^2 = 0.223 \times 92 \times 19.5^2 = 7801 \text{ in.-kips}$$

$$A_s = \frac{2675}{20 \times 0.874 \times 19.5} = 7.85 \text{ sq in.}$$

Try ten No. 8 bars each way.

$$A_s = 7.90 \text{ sq in.} \qquad \Sigma o = 31.4 \text{ in.}$$
$$u = \frac{V_{EF}}{\Sigma ojd} = \frac{148,600}{31.4 \times 0.874 \times 19.5} = 278 \text{ psi}$$
$$u_{\text{allow}} = {}^{264}\!\!/_1 = 264 \text{ psi}$$

The bond stress at EF is slightly excessive. However, Sec. 1301(c) of the Code, which is based upon ultimate-strength considerations, permits us to disregard the local bond stress if the average bond stress across the length of embedment is less than 80 percent of the allowable stress. Let L_e denote this length.

$$L_e = EA - 3 = 33 \text{ in.} \qquad 0.80 u_{\text{allow}} = 211 \text{ psi}$$
$$u_{\text{av}} = \frac{A_s f_s}{L_e \Sigma o} = \frac{7.90 \times 20,000}{33 \times 31.4} = 152 \text{ psi} \qquad \text{OK}$$

The function of the dowels is to transfer the compressive force in the column reinforcing bars to the footing by bond. Since this is a tied column, the maximum stress in the column reinforcement is $0.85 \times 20,000 = 17,000$ psi. Try eight No. 9 dowels; let L_e denote the required embedment length. For each bar,

$$A_s = 1.00 \text{ sq in.} \qquad \Sigma o = 3.5 \text{ in.}$$
$$u_{\text{allow}} = \frac{264}{9/8} = 235 \text{ psi} \qquad L_e = \frac{1.00 \times 17,000}{235 \times 3.5} = 20.7 \text{ in.}$$

Since the footing can provide a 21-in. embedment length, the selection of dowels is satisfactory. Section 805(c) of the Code requires that for the specified grade of steel the dowels must lap the column bars by twenty bar diameters.

$$\text{Length of lap} = 20 \times \frac{9}{8} = 22.5 \text{ in.}$$
$$\text{Length of dowels} = 20.7 + 22.5 = 43.2 \qquad (\text{say, 44 in.})$$

The footing is shown in Fig. 20-2.

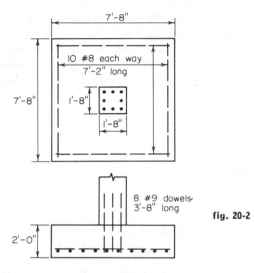

fig. 20-2

20-2 Combined Footings It is often impossible to provide an isolated, concentrically loaded footing under an exterior column because of the proximity of the property line to the column face. An eccentric footing is undesirable because it would rotate excessively. The solution lies in

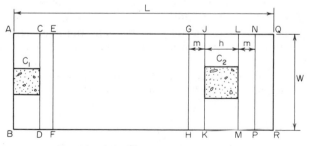

fig. 20-3 Combined footing.

using a single footing to support both the exterior column and the adjacent interior column, the footing being so proportioned that the soil pressure is approximately uniform under normal loading.

Figure 20-3 represents a combined footing supporting an exterior column C_1 and an interior column C_2. It is convenient to visualize the footing as being subjected to an upward load transmitted by the underlying soil and reactions supplied by the columns. From this point of view, the member functions as a beam that overhangs one support. However, since the footing is considerably wider than the columns, there is transverse bending as well as longitudinal bending in the vicinity of the columns. For simplicity, we shall assume that the transverse bending is confined to the regions bounded by planes AB and EF and by planes GH and NP, the distance m being $h/2$ or $d/2$, whichever is smaller. The longitudinal reinforcement will be designed by considering the combined footing as an ordinary flexural member, and the transverse reinforcement will be designed by considering members $AEFB$ and $GNPH$ as independent isolated footings.

The notational system is the same as for an isolated footing, except as follows:

P = aggregate column load
V = maximum vertical shear at a column face
p' = gross soil pressure

When a combined rectangular footing is designed for uniform soil pressure under total design load, the depth may be found by applying the following equation, in which distances are expressed in feet:

$$(Pv_2 + 0.17VL + Pp')d - 0.17Pd^2 = VLp' \qquad (20\text{-}2)$$

Example 20-2 An 18-in.-square exterior column and a 20-in.-square interior column carry loads of 250 kips and 370 kips, respectively. The column centers are 16 ft apart, and the footing cannot project beyond the face of the exterior column. Design a combined rectangular footing by the working-stress method, using $f'_c = 3000$ psi, $f_s = 20,000$ psi, and an allowable soil pressure of 5000 psf. Proportion the footing to secure uniform soil pressure under full live load.

Solution. The footing dimensions are shown in Fig. 20-4a and the reinforcement is shown in Fig. 20-5.

For uniform soil pressure, the centroid of footing must be made coincident with the resultant of column loads. In Fig. 20-4a, let Z denote the centroid.

$$P = 620 \text{ kips} \qquad x = \frac{370 \times 16}{620} = 9.55 \text{ ft}$$
$$L = 2(0.75 + 9.55) = 20.60 \text{ ft}$$

We shall make the length 20 ft 8 in. but apply the value 20.60 ft in our stress calculations.

$$\text{Net soil pressure per foot of length} = \frac{620}{20.60} = 30.1 \text{ klf}$$

The shear and bending-moment diagrams appear in Fig. 20-4.   For computing the footing depth, we have

$$V = 229.2 \text{ kips} \qquad v_2 = 60 \text{ psi} = 8.64 \text{ ksf}$$

Equation (20-2) yields

$$9260d - 105.4d^2 = 23,608 \qquad \therefore \ d = 2.63 \text{ ft}$$

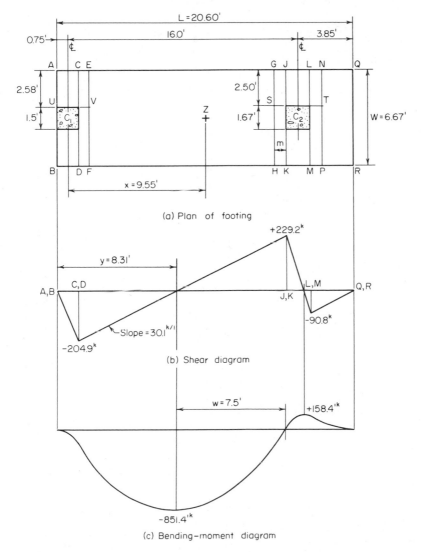

(a) Plan of footing

(b) Shear diagram

(c) Bending-moment diagram

fig. 20-4

Assume that the longitudinal steel is centered $3\frac{1}{2}$ in. from the face of footing. Make $t = 2$ ft 11 in.

$$d = 2 \text{ ft } 7\frac{1}{2} \text{ in.} = 2.63 \text{ ft} = 31.5 \text{ in.}$$

The footing width is governed by the shearing stress v_2, and the critical section lies at a distance d from the face of column C_2.

$$V = 229.2 - 2.63 \times 30.1 = 150.0 \text{ kips}$$

$$v_2 = \frac{V}{Wd} \quad \text{or} \quad W = \frac{V}{v_2 d} = \frac{150.0}{8.64 \times 2.63} = 6.60 \text{ ft}$$

Set $W = 6$ ft 8 in.

We shall check the footing size by evaluating the soil pressure.

$$\text{Footing weight} = 20.67 \times 6.67 \times 2.92 \times 0.150 = 60.4 \text{ kips}$$

$$p' = \frac{620 + 60.4}{20.67 \times 6.67} = 4.94 < 5 \text{ ksf} \qquad \text{OK}$$

$$p = 4.94 - 2.92 \times 0.150 = 4.50 \text{ ksf}$$

We shall investigate the punching shear under the columns.

At C_2:
$$b_o = 4(20 + 31.5) = 206 \text{ in.}$$

$$V = 370 - \frac{4.50 \times 51.5^2}{144} = 287 \text{ kips}$$

$$v_1 = \frac{287,000}{206 \times 31.5} = 44 < 110 \text{ psi} \qquad \text{OK}$$

At C_1:
$$b_o = 1(18 + 31.5) + 2(18 + 15.8) = 117 \text{ in.}$$

$$V = 250 - \frac{4.50 \times 49.5 \times 33.8}{144} = 198 \text{ kips}$$

$$v_1 = \frac{198,000}{117 \times 31.5} = 54 \text{ psi} \qquad \text{OK}$$

LONGITUDINAL REINFORCEMENT FOR NEGATIVE MOMENT

$$M = 851,400 \text{ ft-lb} = 10,217,000 \text{ in.-lb}$$
$$M_b = 223 \times 80 \times 31.5^2 = 17,700,000 \text{ in.-lb}$$

Therefore, the steel is stressed to capacity.

$$A_s = \frac{10,217,000}{20,000 \times 0.874 \times 31.5} = 18.6 \text{ sq in.}$$

Try fifteen No. 10 bars: $A_s = 19.1$ sq in. and $\Sigma o = 59.9$ in.   The bond stress is maximum at the point of contraflexure, where

$$M = -851.4 + \tfrac{1}{2} \times 30.1w^2 = 0 \qquad \therefore \ w = 7.5 \text{ ft}$$
$$V = 7.5 \times 30.1 = 225.8 \text{ kips}$$
$$u = \frac{225,800}{59.9 \times 0.874 \times 31.5} = 137 \text{ psi}$$
$$u_{\text{allow}} = \frac{3.4 \sqrt{3000}}{1.25} = 149 \text{ psi} \qquad \text{OK}$$

LONGITUDINAL REINFORCEMENT FOR POSITIVE MOMENT. Although the critical section lies at the face of column C_2, we shall apply the maximum moment for simplicity.

$$A_s = \frac{158,400 \times 12}{20,000 \times 0.874 \times 31.5} = 3.45 \text{ sq in.}$$

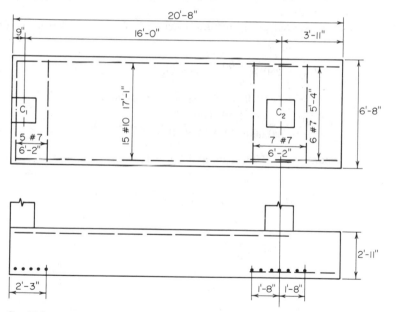

fig. 20-5

Try six No. 7 bars: $A_s = 3.60$ sq in. and $\Sigma o = 16.5$ in. We shall take LM as the critical section for bond.

$$u = \frac{90,800}{16.5 \times 0.874 \times 31.5} = 200 \text{ psi}$$
$$u_{\text{allow}} = \frac{4.8 \sqrt{3000}}{0.875} = 302 \text{ psi} \qquad \text{OK}$$

TRANSVERSE REINFORCEMENT UNDER INTERIOR COLUMN

$$V_{ST} = 370 \times \frac{2.50}{6.67} = 138.8 \text{ kips}$$

$$M_{ST} = \tfrac{1}{2} \times 138.8 \times 2.50 \times 12 = 2082 \text{ in.-kips}$$

Assume

$$d = 35 - 4.5 = 30.5 \text{ in.}$$

$$A_s = \frac{2,082,000}{20,000 \times 0.874 \times 30.5} = 3.91 \text{ sq in.}$$

Try seven No. 7 bars: $A_s = 4.20$ sq in. and $\Sigma o = 19.2$ in.

$$u = \frac{138,800}{19.2 \times 0.874 \times 30.5} = 271 \text{ psi} \qquad u_{\text{allow}} = 302 \text{ psi} \qquad \text{OK}$$

Since the critical section for v_2 falls outside the footing, shearing stress is not a criterion in this design.

TRANSVERSE REINFORCEMENT UNDER EXTERIOR COLUMN. Disregard eccentricity.

$$V_{UV} = 250 \times \frac{2.58}{6.67} = 96.8 \text{ kips}$$

$$M_{UV} = \tfrac{1}{2} \times 96.8 \times 2.58 \times 12 = 1498 \text{ in.-kips}$$

$$A_s = \frac{1,498,000}{20,000 \times 0.874 \times 31.5} = 2.72 \text{ sq in.}$$

Try five No. 7 bars: $A_s = 3.00$ sq in. and $\Sigma o = 13.7$ in.

$$u = \frac{96,800}{13.7 \times 0.874 \times 31.5} = 257 \text{ psi} \qquad \text{OK}$$

TWENTY-ONE

Cantilever Retaining Walls

Retaining walls having a height ranging from 10 to 20 ft are generally built as reinforced-concrete cantilever members. As illustrated in Fig. 21-1, a cantilever wall comprises a vertical stem to retain the soil, a horizontal base to support the stem, and in many instances a key that projects into the underlying soil to augment the resistance to sliding. Adequate drainage is an essential requirement, for the accumulation of water or ice behind the wall would greatly increase the horizontal thrust.

The active earth pressure at a given point is directly proportional to the vertical pressure at that point. Therefore, when a live load (termed a *surcharge*) is applied to the retained soil, it is convenient to replace this load with a hypothetical equivalent prism of earth.

With reference to Fig. 21-1, assume that the impounded earth has a horizontal surface. Let R denote a section at a distance y below the top, and consider the length of wall normal to the plane of the drawing as 1 ft. The notational system is as follows:

T = resultant earth thrust on QR
M = moment of this thrust with respect to R
h = height of equivalent earth prism that replaces surcharge

w = unit weight of earth
C_a = coefficient of active earth pressure
C_p = coefficient of passive earth pressure
p = soil pressure

Then
$$T = \tfrac{1}{2}C_awy(y + 2h) \qquad (21\text{-}1)$$
$$M = \tfrac{1}{6}C_awy^2(y + 3h) \qquad (21\text{-}2)$$

A cantilever retaining wall must be so proportioned that the structure is externally stable and the resultant of applied forces has the intended location. Unless the soil is highly compressible, the resultant is per-

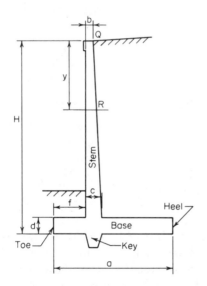

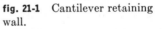

fig. 21-1   Cantilever retaining wall.

mitted to intersect the base near the forward edge of the middle third. Using the notation shown in Fig. 21-1, we may usually secure a trial section by applying the following relationships:

$$a = 0.60H \qquad\qquad b \geq 8 \text{ in.}$$
$$c = d = b + 0.045H \qquad f = \frac{a}{3} - \frac{c}{2}$$

Example 21-1   Applying the working-stress method, design a reinforced-concrete wall to retain an earth bank 14 ft high. The top surface is horizontal and supports a surcharge of 500 psf. The soil weighs 130 pcf and its angle of internal friction is 35°; the coefficient of friction of soil and concrete is 0.5. The allowable soil pressure is 4000 psf, $f_c' = 3000$ psi, and $f_y = 40,000$ psi. The base of the structure must be set 4 ft below ground level to clear the frost line, and the factor of safety (FS) against sliding and overturning should have a minimum value of 1.5.

Solution. By applying the relationships presented above, we arrive at the trial section shown in Fig. 21-2a. As we shall find, it is necessary to provide a key to develop the required resistance to sliding. The sides of the key are sloped in the manner indicated to ensure that the surrounding soil will remain undisturbed during excavation. We shall check the section.

$$h = {}^{500}\!/_{130} = 3.85 \text{ ft} \qquad \sin 35° = 0.574 \qquad \tan 35° = 0.700$$

Equation (24-13) yields

$$C_a = 0.271 \qquad C_p = 3.69$$
$$C_a w = 35.2 \text{ pcf} \qquad C_p w = 480 \text{ pcf}$$

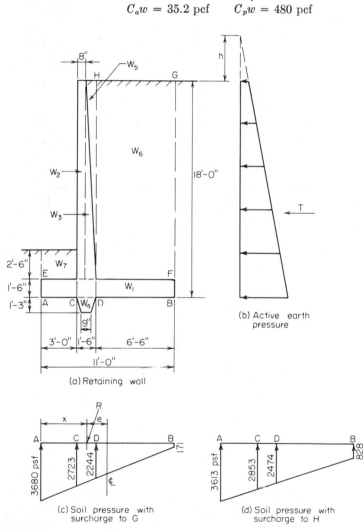

(a) Retaining wall

(b) Active earth pressure

(c) Soil pressure with surcharge to G

(d) Soil pressure with surcharge to H

fig. 21-2

Applying Eqs. (21-1) and (21-2), we obtain the following:

$$T_{AB} = \tfrac{1}{2} \times 35.2 \times 18(18 + 2 \times 3.85) = 8140 \text{ lb}$$
$$M_{AB} = \tfrac{1}{6} \times 35.2 \times 18^2(18 + 3 \times 3.85) = 56{,}200 \text{ ft-lb}$$

The critical condition with respect to stability is that in which the surcharge extends to G. The moments of the stabilizing forces with respect to the toe are

Table 21-1 Stability of Retaining Wall

Force, lb			×	Arm, ft	=	Moment, ft-lb
W_1	$1.5 \times 11 \times 150 =$	2,480		5.50		13,640
W_2	$0.67 \times 16.5 \times 150 =$	1,650		3.33		5,500
W_3	$0.5 \times 0.83 \times 16.5 \times 150 =$	1,030		3.95		4,070
W_4	$1.25 \times 1.13 \times 150 =$	210		3.75		790
W_5	$0.5 \times 0.83 \times 16.5 \times 130 =$	890		4.23		3,760
W_6	$6.5 \times 16.5 \times 130 =$	13,940		7.75		108,000
W_7	$2.5 \times 3 \times 130 =$	980		1.50		1,470
Total		21,180				137,230
Overturning moment						56,200
Net moment about A						81,030

computed in Table 21-1. Let R denote the resultant of the applied forces. In Fig. 21-2c,

$$x = \frac{81{,}030}{21{,}180} = 3.83 \text{ ft} \qquad e = 5.50 - 3.83 = 1.67 \text{ ft}$$

The fact that the resultant strikes the base within the middle third attests to the absence of uplift. Equation (5-10) yields the following:

$$p_a = \frac{21{,}180}{11}\left(1 + \frac{6 \times 1.67}{11}\right) = 3680 \text{ psf}$$

$$p_b = \frac{21{,}180}{11}\left(1 - \frac{6 \times 1.67}{11}\right) = 171 \text{ psf}$$

Check:
$$x = \frac{11}{3}\left(\frac{3680 + 2 \times 171}{3680 + 171}\right) = 3.83 \text{ ft} \qquad \text{OK}$$

$$p_c = 2723 \text{ psf} \qquad p_d = 2244 \text{ psf}$$

$$\text{FS against overturning} = \frac{137{,}230}{56{,}200} = 2.44 \qquad \text{OK}$$

Lateral displacement of the wall would produce a movement of the earth to the left of the key. Therefore, in calculating the frictional resistance to sliding, we apply the coefficient of sliding of earth on earth to the left of C and of concrete on earth to the right of C. We shall disregard the passive pressure of the layer of earth lying above the toe, since its magnitude is uncertain. The resistance to sliding is as follows:

Friction, A to C: $\qquad \frac{1}{2}(3680 + 2723) \times 3 \times 0.700 = \quad 6{,}720$ lb
Friction, C to B: $\qquad \frac{1}{2}(2723 + 171) \times 8 \times 0.5 = \quad 5{,}790$
Passive earth pressure: $\qquad\qquad \frac{1}{2} \times 480 \times 2.75^2 = \quad \underline{1{,}820}$
$$\text{Total} = 14{,}330 \text{ lb}$$

$$\text{FS against sliding} = \frac{14{,}330}{8140} = 1.76 \qquad \text{OK}$$

The trial section is adequate with respect to stability. We shall now calculate the soil pressures when the surcharge extends to H. Let W_8 denote the increased load.

$$W_8 = 500 \times 6.5 = 3250 \text{ lb} \qquad \Sigma W = 21{,}180 + 3250 = 24{,}430 \text{ lb}$$
$$M_a = 81{,}030 + 3250 \times 7.75 = 106{,}220 \text{ ft-lb}$$
$$x = \frac{106{,}220}{24{,}430} = 4.35 \text{ ft} \qquad e = 1.15 \text{ ft}$$
$$p_a = 3613 \text{ psf} \qquad\qquad p_b = 828 \text{ psf}$$
$$p_c = 2853 \text{ psf} \qquad\qquad p_d = 2474 \text{ psf}$$

DESIGN OF STEM. At base of stem,

$$y = 16.5 \text{ ft} \qquad\qquad d = 18 - 3.5 = 14.5 \text{ in.}$$
$$T_{EF} = 7030 \text{ lb} \qquad M_{EF} = 538{,}000 \text{ in.-lb}$$

The allowable shear at a distance d above the base is

$$V_{\text{allow}} = vbd = 60 \times 12 \times 14.5 = 10{,}440 \text{ lb} \qquad \text{OK}$$
$$M_b = 223 \times 12 \times 14.5^2 = 563{,}000 \text{ in.-lb}$$

Therefore, the steel is stressed to capacity.

$$A_s = \frac{538{,}000}{20{,}000 \times 0.874 \times 14.5} = 2.12 \text{ sq in.}$$

Use No. 9 bars $5\frac{1}{2}$ in. on centers.

$$A_s = 2.18 \text{ sq in.} \qquad \Sigma o = 7.7 \text{ in.}$$
$$u = \frac{7030}{7.7 \times 0.874 \times 14.5} = 72 \text{ psi} \qquad u_{\text{allow}} = 235 \text{ psi} \qquad \text{OK}$$

The reinforcement is shown in Fig. 21-3. Alternate bars will be discontinued at the point where they become superfluous. As the following calculations demonstrate, the theoretical cutoff point lies at $y = 11$ ft 7 in., where

$$M = 218{,}400 \text{ in.-lb} \qquad d = 4.5 + 10 \times \frac{11.58}{16.5} = 11.52 \text{ in.}$$
$$A_s = \frac{218{,}400}{20{,}000 \times 0.874 \times 11.52} = 1.08 \text{ sq in.} \qquad \text{OK}$$
$$T = 3930 \text{ lb} \qquad u = 101 \text{ psi} \qquad\qquad \text{OK}$$

Section 918 of the ACI Code calls for an embedment length of 13.5 in. for No. 9 bars. The alternate bars will therefore be terminated at 6 ft 1 in. above the top of base. Section 805(b) requires that special precautions be taken where more than half the bars are spliced at a point of maximum stress. To circumvent this requirement, we shall extend the short bars into the footing; only the long bars therefore require splicing. For the dowels,

$$u_{\text{allow}} = 0.75 \times 235 = 176 \text{ psi}$$

$$\text{Length of lap} = \frac{1.00 \times 20,000}{176 \times 3.5} = 33 \text{ in.}$$

DESIGN OF HEEL. Let V and M denote the shear and bending moment, respectively, at section D.

Case 1: Surcharge extending to G.

$$\text{Downward pressure } p = 16.5 \times 130 + 1.5 \times 150 = 2370 \text{ psf}$$
$$V = 6.5[2370 - \tfrac{1}{2}(2244 + 171)] = 7560 \text{ lb}$$
$$M = 12 \times 6.5^2[\tfrac{1}{2} \times 2370 - \tfrac{1}{6}(2244 + 2 \times 171)] = 383,000 \text{ in.-lb}$$

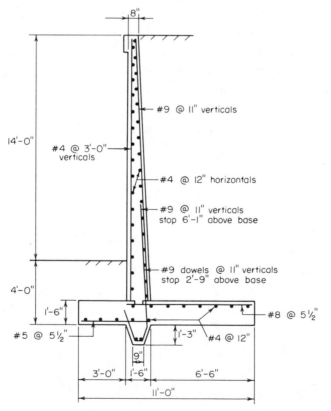

fig. 21-3

Case 2: Surcharge extending to H.

$$p = 2370 + 500 = 2870 \text{ psf}$$
$$V = 6.5[2870 - \tfrac{1}{2}(2474 + 828)] = 7920 \text{ lb} < V_{\text{allow}}$$
$$M = 12 \times 6.5^2[\tfrac{1}{2} \times 2870 - \tfrac{1}{6}(2474 + 2 \times 828)] = 379,000 \text{ in.-lb}$$
$$A_s = 2.12 \times {}^{383}\!\!\!/_{\!538} = 1.51 \text{ sq in.}$$

To maintain a uniform bar spacing throughout the member, use No. 8 bars $5\tfrac{1}{2}$ in. on centers. In the heel, tension occurs at the *top* of slab.

$$A_s = 1.72 \text{ sq in.} \qquad \Sigma o = 6.9 \text{ in.}$$
$$u = 91 \text{ psi} \qquad u_{\text{allow}} = 186 \text{ psi} \qquad \text{OK}$$

DESIGN OF TOE. We shall assume the absence of backfill on the toe but disregard the minor modification in soil pressure that results. Let V and M denote the shear and bending moment, respectively, at section C.

Downward pressure $p = 1.5 \times 150 = 225 \text{ psf}$

Case 1: Surcharge extending to G.

$$V = 3[\tfrac{1}{2}(3680 + 2723) - 225] = 8930 \text{ lb}$$
$$M = 12 \times 3^2[\tfrac{1}{6}(2723 + 2 \times 3680) - \tfrac{1}{2} \times 225] = 169,300 \text{ in.-lb}$$

Case 2: Surcharge extending to H.

$$V = 9020 \text{ lb} < V_{\text{allow}} \qquad M = 169,000 \text{ in.-lb}$$
$$A_s = 2.12 \times {}^{169}\!\!\!/_{\!538} = 0.67 \text{ sq in.}$$

Use No. 5 bars $5\tfrac{1}{2}$ in. on centers.

$$A_s = 0.68 \text{ sq in.} \qquad \Sigma o = 4.3 \text{ in.}$$
$$u = 166 \text{ psi} \qquad u_{\text{allow}} = 422 \text{ psi} \qquad \text{OK}$$

The stresses in the key are not amenable to precise calculation. Reinforcement is achieved by extending the dowels and short bars into the key and bending them.

In addition to the foregoing reinforcement, No. 4 bars are supplied to act as temperature reinforcement and spacers for the main bars.

TWENTY-TWO
Prestressed Concrete

22-1 Methods of Prestressing Prestressed-concrete construction is designed to enhance the suitability of concrete as a structural material by inducing prestresses opposite in character to the stresses resulting from gravity loads. These prestresses are created by the use of steel wires or strands, called *tendons*, that are incorporated in the member and subjected to externally applied tensile forces. This prestressing of the steel may be performed either before or after the concrete is poured. Thus two methods of prestressing a concrete beam are available: pretensioning and post-tensioning.

In *pretensioning*, the tendons are prestressed to the required degree by means of hydraulic jacks, their ends are tied to fixed abutments, and the concrete is then poured around the tendons. When hardening of the concrete has advanced to the required state, the tendons are released. The tendons now tend to contract longitudinally to their original length and to expand laterally to their original diameter, but the surrounding concrete opposes these tendencies. As a result of the longitudinal restraint, the concrete exerts a tensile force on the steel and the steel exerts a compressive force on the concrete. As a result of the lateral restraint, the tendons are deformed to a wedge shape across a relatively short distance at each end of the member. It is within this distance, termed the *transmission length*, that the steel becomes bonded to the concrete and the two materials interact, each exerting a prestressing force upon the other. However, unless greater precision is warranted, it is assumed for simplicity that the prestressing forces act at the end sections.

The tendons may be placed either in a straight line or in a series of straight-line segments, being deflected at designated points by means of holding devices. In the latter case, prestressing forces between steel and concrete occur both at the ends and at these deflection points.

In *post-tensioning*, the procedure usually consists of encasing the tendons in metal or rubber hoses, placing these in the forms, and then pouring the concrete. When the concrete has hardened, the tendons are tensioned and anchored to the ends of the concrete by means of devices called end anchorages. If the hoses are to remain in the member, the void within the hose is filled with grout. Post-tensioning has two important advantages when compared with pretensioning: it may be performed at the job site, and it permits the use of parabolic tendons.

The term *at transfer* is used to designate the instant at which the prestressing forces between steel and concrete are developed. However, in post-tensioning, where the tendons are anchored to the concrete in succession, these forces in reality are developed in steps rather than instantaneously.

22-2 Loads Sustained by Prestressed Beams Assume for simplicity that the tendons are straight and that the resultant prestressing force in these tendons lies below the centroidal axis of the concrete section. At transfer, the member cambers (deflects upward), remaining in contact with the casting bed only at the ends. Thus, the concrete beam is compelled to resist the prestressing force and to support its own weight simultaneously.

At transfer, the prestressing force in the steel diminishes because the concrete contracts under the imposed load, thereby offering only partial restraint against contraction of the steel. As time elapses, the prestressing force continues to diminish as a result of the following phenomena: relaxation of the steel, which is the tendency of the steel to undergo a reduction in stress when maintained at a constant strain, and the shrinkage and plastic flow of the concrete subsequent to transfer. Prestressed-concrete construction, to be effective, therefore requires the use of high-tensile steel in order that the reduction in prestressing force may be small in relation to the initial force. In all instances, we shall assume that the ratio of final to initial prestressing force is 0.85. Moreover, to simplify the stress calculations, we shall also assume that the full initial prestressing force exists at transfer and that the entire reduction in this force occurs during some finite interval following transfer.

There are therefore two loading states that must be considered in the design: the initial state, in which the concrete sustains the initial prestressing force and the beam weight, and the final state, in which the concrete sustains the final prestressing force, the beam weight, and all superimposed loads. Consequently, the design of a prestressed-concrete beam differs from that of a conventional type of beam in the respect that we must consider two stresses at each point, the initial stress and the final stress, and these must fall between the allowable compressive and the allowable tensile stresses. A beam is said to be in *balanced design* if the critical initial and final stresses coincide precisely with the allowable stresses.

22-3 Definitions and Notational System   The term *prestress* designates the stress induced by the *initial* prestressing force. The terms *prestress shear* and *prestress moment* refer to the vertical shear and bending moment, respectively, that the initial prestressing force induces in the concrete at a given section.

The *eccentricity* of the prestressing force is the distance from the action line of this resultant force to the centroidal axis of the section. Assume that the tendons are subjected to a uniform prestress. The locus of the centroid of the steel area along the span is termed the *trajectory* of the steel or of the prestressing force.

The sign convention is as follows: The eccentricity is positive if the action line of the prestressing force lies below the centroidal axis of the section. The trajectory has a positive slope if it inclines downward to the right. The angle between the trajectory and a horizontal line is positive if the slope of the trajectory is positive. A load is positive if it acts downward. The vertical shear at a given section is positive if the portion of the beam to the left of this section exerts an upward force on the concrete. A bending moment is positive if it induces compression above the centroidal axis and tension below it. A compressive stress is positive and a tensile stress, negative.

In the following material, it is to be understood in all instances that the given beam is prismatic.

The notational system is as follows:

Cross-sectional Properties

> A = gross area of section
> A_s = area of prestressing steel
> d = effective depth of section at ultimate strength
> h = total depth of section
> I = moment of inertia of gross area

y_b = distance from centroidal axis to bottom fiber
S_b = section modulus with respect to bottom fiber = I/y_b
k_b = distance from centroidal axis to lower kern point
k_t = distance from centroidal axis to upper kern point

Forces and Moments

F_i = initial prestressing force
F_f = final prestressing force
$\eta = F_f/F_i$
e = eccentricity of prestressing force
e_{con} = eccentricity of prestressing force having concordant trajectory
m = slope of trajectory
θ = angle between trajectory and horizontal line
w = vertical load exerted by curved tendons on concrete in unit distance along span
w_w = unit beam weight
w_s = unit superimposed load
w_{DL} = unit dead load
w_{LL} = unit live load
w_u = unit ultimate load
V_p = prestress shear
M_p = prestress moment
M_w = bending moment due to beam weight
M_s = bending moment due to superimposed load
C_u = resultant compressive force at ultimate load
T_u = resultant tensile force at ultimate load

Stresses

f'_c = ultimate compressive strength of concrete
f'_{ci} = compressive strength of concrete at transfer
f'_s = ultimate strength of prestressing steel
f_{su} = stress in prestressing steel at ultimate load
f_{bp} = stress in bottom fiber due to initial prestressing force
f_{bw} = bending stress in bottom fiber due to beam weight
f_{bs} = bending stress in bottom fiber due to superimposed loads
f_{bi} = stress in bottom fiber at initial state = $f_{bp} + f_{bw}$
f_{bf} = stress in bottom fiber at final state
   = $\eta f_{bp} + f_{bw} + f_{bs}$
f_{cai} = initial stress at centroidal axis

Camber

Δ_p = camber due to initial prestressing force
Δ_w = camber due to beam weight
Δ_i = camber at initial state
Δ_f = camber at final state

The symbols that refer to the bottom fiber are transformed to their counterparts for the top fiber by replacing the subscript b with t. For example, f_{ti} denotes the stress in the top fiber at initial state.

22-4   Calculation of Prestress Shear and Prestress Moment   Consider that a simply supported beam has the trajectory shown in Fig. 22-1a. (In these drawings, we shall exaggerate vertical distances in relation to horizontal distances for the sake of clarity.)   We wish to evaluate the prestress shear and moment induced at some interior section C.

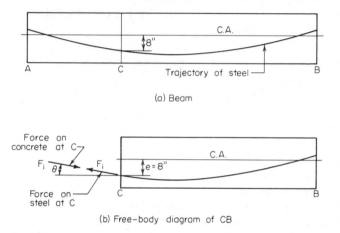

(a) Beam

(b) Free-body diagram of CB

fig. 22-1

The forces acting on the beam segment CB solely as a result of F_i are shown in Fig. 22-1b. If the composite concrete-and-steel member is regarded as a unit, the prestressing forces that the steel exerts on the concrete are purely internal; these forces therefore do not induce any reactions at the supports.   The left portion AC of the beam exerts a tensile force F_i on the tendons.   Since CB is in equilibrium, it follows that the left portion also induces compressive stresses on the concrete at C, these stresses having a resultant that is numerically equal to and collinear with F_i.

The prestress shear and moment at C are as follows:

$$V_p = -F_i \sin \theta \qquad M_p = -F_i e \cos \theta$$

Since θ is minuscule, the following approximations are admissible:

$$\sin \theta = \tan \theta \qquad \text{and} \qquad \cos \theta = 1$$

Then

$$V_p = -F_i \tan \theta = -F_i m \tag{22-1}$$

and

$$M_p = -F_i e \tag{22-2}$$

Example 22-1 The beam in Fig. 22-1a is prestressed with an initial force of 300 kips. At C, the eccentricity of this force is 8 in. and the slope of the trajectory is 0.014. Find the prestress shear and prestress moment at C.

Solution

$$V_p = -300,000 \times 0.014 = -\textbf{4200 lb}$$
$$M_p = -300,000 \times 8 = -\textbf{2,400,000 in.-lb}$$

The prestresses at a given section are as follows:

$$f_{bp} = \frac{F_i}{A} + \frac{F_i e}{S_b} \qquad f_{tp} = \frac{F_i}{A} - \frac{F_i e}{S_t} \qquad (22\text{-}3)$$

In the special case of a beam having a rectangular cross section, these equations reduce to the following:

$$f_{bp} = \frac{F_i}{A}\left(1 + \frac{6e}{h}\right) \qquad f_{tp} = \frac{F_i}{A}\left(1 - \frac{6e}{h}\right) \qquad (22\text{-}3a)$$

22-5 Stresses in Beams with Straight Tendons We wish to analyze the stresses that exist in a beam prestressed with straight tendons. As an aid to visualization, we shall construct diagrams that depict the variation in stress along the span.

Example 22-2 A 12 × 18 in. rectangular beam is subjected to an initial prestressing force of 230 kips having a constant eccentricity of 3.3 in. The beam is on a simple span of 30 ft and carries a superimposed load of 840 plf. Determine the initial and final stresses at the supports and at midspan. Construct diagrams to represent the initial and final stresses along the span.

Solution. The stresses are recorded in Table 22-1 as they are obtained.

Table 22-1   Stresses in Prestressed-concrete Beam

Type of stress	At support		At midspan	
	Bottom fiber	Top fiber	Bottom fiber	Top fiber
(a) Initial prestress, psi............	+2236	−106	+2236	−106
(b) Final prestress................	+1901	−90	+1901	−90
(c) Stress due to beam weight......	......	.....	−469	+469
(d) Stress due to superimposed load.	......	.....	−1750	+1750
Initial stress: (a) + (c)............	+2236	−106	+1767	+363
Final stress: (b) + (c) + (d)........	+1901	−90	−318	+2129

$$A = 12 \times 18 = 216 \text{ sq in.} \qquad S_b = S_t = \tfrac{1}{6} \times 12 \times 18^2 = 648 \text{ in.}^3$$
$$w_w = {}^{216}\!/_{144} \times 150 = 225 \text{ plf}$$
$$f_{bp} = \frac{230,000}{216}\left(1 + \frac{6 \times 3.3}{18}\right) = +2236 \text{ psi} \qquad f_{tp} = -106 \text{ psi}$$

At midspan,

$$M_s = \tfrac{1}{8} \times 840 \times 30^2 \times 12 = 1{,}134{,}000 \text{ in.-lb}$$

$$f_{bs} = -\frac{1{,}134{,}000}{648} = -1750 \text{ psi} \qquad f_{ts} = +1750 \text{ psi}$$

By proportion,

$$f_{bw} = -1750 \times {}^{225}\!/_{840} = -469 \text{ psi} \qquad f_{tw} = +469 \text{ psi}$$

The stresses at the supports are as follows:

$$f_{bi} = +2236 \text{ psi} \qquad f_{ti} = -106 \text{ psi}$$
$$f_{bf} = 0.85 \times 2236 = +1901 \text{ psi}$$
$$f_{tf} = 0.85(-106) = -90 \text{ psi}$$

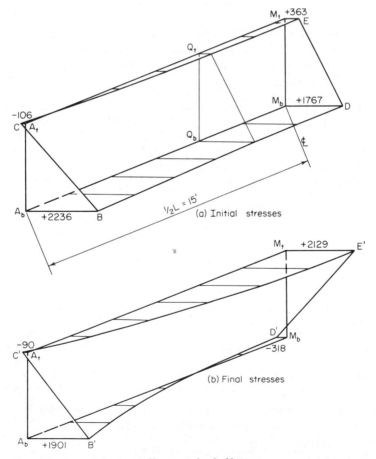

(a) Initial stresses

(b) Final stresses

fig. 22-2 Isometric stress diagrams for half-span.

The stresses at midspan are as follows:

$$f_{bi} = +2236 - 469 = +1767 \text{ psi}$$
$$f_{ti} = -106 + 469 = +363 \text{ psi}$$
$$f_{bf} = +1901 - 469 - 1750 = -318 \text{ psi}$$
$$f_{tf} = -90 + 469 + 1750 = +2129 \text{ psi}$$

In Fig. 22-2a, $A_t A_b BC$ is the initial-stress diagram at the support, and $M_t M_b DE$ is the initial-stress diagram at midspan. As we proceed along the span, the initial stress varies at the same rate as the stress due to beam weight. Consequently, lines BD and CE in this diagram are parabolic arcs having their vertices at D and E, respectively. The initial-stress diagram at an intermediate section Q is obtained by passing a plane normal to the longitudinal axis.

The final-stress diagram in Fig. 22-2b is constructed in an analogous manner. As we proceed along the span, the final stress varies at the same rate as the sum of the stresses due to beam weight and superimposed load.

An alternative method of representing the stresses is to construct two composite stress diagrams, one for the top fiber and one for the bottom fiber. The latter is

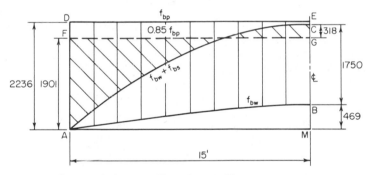

fig. 22-3 Stresses in bottom fiber along half-span.

shown in Fig. 22-3. The difference between the ordinates to lines DE and AB represents f_{bi}, and the difference between the ordinates to FG and AC represents f_{bf}.

A study of Fig. 22-2 readily discloses the following principle relevant to a beam with straight tendons carrying a uniform load: At transfer, the critical stresses occur at the supports; under full design load, the critical stresses occur at midspan if the allowable final stresses exceed η times the allowable initial stresses in absolute value.

22-6 Design for Maximum Beam Capacity and Minimum Prestressing Force The primary objective in prestressed-concrete design is to maximize the capacity of a given beam and, if the member is not in balanced design, to secure the minimum prestressing force associated with this capacity.

An increase in beam capacity is achieved through an increase (in absolute value) of the prestresses at the section having the maximum superimposed-load stresses. The allowable prestresses in turn may be increased by using a form of trajectory that enables us to take advantage of the beam-weight stresses, since these are opposite in character to the prestresses. The minimum prestressing force is obtained through the proper choice of critical stresses.

The three examples that follow, when taken as a unit, illustrate the effect of the form of trajectory on the allowable prestresses and therefore on the beam capacity. They also illustrate the method of finding the minimum prestressing force.

Example 22-3   An 8×10 in. rectangular beam, simply supported on a 20-ft span, is to be prestressed by means of straight tendons. The allowable stresses are as follows:

Initial: $+2400$ and -190 psi
Final: $+2250$ and -425 psi

Evaluate the following: the allowable unit superimposed load, the maximum and minimum prestressing force associated with this load, and the corresponding eccentricities. Check the critical stresses associated with these results.

Solution. Refer to Fig. 22-2 or 22-3 as a guide.

$$A = 80 \text{ sq in.}   \qquad S = 133 \text{ in.}^3   \qquad w_w = 83 \text{ plf}$$

At midspan,

$$M_w = \tfrac{1}{8} \times 83 \times 20^2 \times 12 = 49{,}800 \text{ in.-lb}$$

$$f_{bw} = -\frac{49{,}800}{133} = -374 \text{ psi}   \qquad f_{tw} = +374 \text{ psi}$$

The beam capacity is found by equating the critical stresses to their allowable values.

At support:

$$f_{bi} = +2400 \text{ psi}   \qquad f_{ti} = -190 \text{ psi}$$

At midspan:

$$f_{bf} = 0.85 \times 2400 - 374 + f_{bs} = -425$$
$$f_{tf} = 0.85(-190) + 374 + f_{ts} = +2250$$

Solving, $f_{bs} = -2091 \text{ psi}   \qquad f_{ts} = +2038 \text{ psi}$

Since the superimposed-load stresses at top and bottom will be numerically equal, the latter value governs the beam capacity.

$$w_s = w_w \frac{f_{ts}}{f_{tw}} = 83 \times \frac{2038}{374} = \textbf{452 plf}$$

The value of w_s was established by setting the critical values of f_{ti} and f_{tf} equal to their respective allowable values. However, since S_b is excessive for the load

w_s, there is flexibility with respect to the stresses at the bottom.   We may set the critical value of either f_{bi} or f_{bf} equal to its allowable value, or induce some intermediate condition.   As the preceding calculations reveal, f_{bf} may vary within a range of $2091 - 2038 = 53$ psi.   In the stress diagram in Fig. 22-4, OO' represents the depth of beam, and AB and EF represent the following, respectively: the stresses due to F_f and the stresses under full design load.   Points B and F

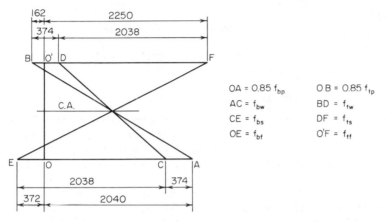

$$OA = 0.85\, f_{bp} \qquad OB = 0.85\, f_{tp}$$
$$AC = f_{bw} \qquad BD = f_{tw}$$
$$CE = f_{bs} \qquad DF = f_{ts}$$
$$OE = f_{bf} \qquad O'F = f_{tf}$$

fig. 22-4   Stresses at midspan under maximum prestressing force.

are fixed, but points A and E may be placed anywhere within the 53-psi range. Since the stress at the centroidal axis is a function solely of the prestressing force, it is evident that F_i is maximized by placing A at its limiting position to the right, i.e., by setting the critical value of f_{bi} rather than of f_{bf} equal to the allowable value.   Then

$$f_{cai} = \frac{F'_{i,\text{max}}}{A} = \tfrac{1}{2}(2400 - 190) = +1105 \text{ psi}$$

$$F_{i,\text{max}} = 1105 \times 80 = \mathbf{88{,}400 \text{ lb}}$$

$$f_{bp} = 1105 + \frac{88{,}400e}{133} = +2400 \qquad e = \mathbf{1.95 \text{ in.}}$$

The critical stresses associated with this set of values are as follows:

At support:

$$f_{bi} = +2400 \text{ psi} \qquad f_{ti} = -190 \text{ psi}$$

At midspan:

$$f_{bf} = +2040 - 374 - 2038 = -372 \text{ psi}$$
$$f_{tf} = -162 + 374 + 2038 = +2250 \text{ psi}$$

All stresses lie within the allowable range.

In like manner, the prestressing force is minimized by placing A at its limiting position to the left, i.e., by setting the critical value of f_{bf} rather than of f_{bi} equal to the allowable value.   Then

$$f_{bp} = 2400 - \frac{53}{0.85} = +2338 \text{ psi} \qquad f_{cai} = +1074 \text{ psi}$$

$$F_{i,\min} = \textbf{85,920 lb} \qquad\qquad e = \textbf{1.96 in.}$$

The critical stresses associated with this set of values are as follows:

At support:

$$f_{bi} = +2338 \text{ psi} \qquad f_{ti} = -190 \text{ psi}$$

At midspan:

$$f_{bf} = 0.85 \times 2338 - 374 - 2038 = -425 \text{ psi}$$
$$f_{tf} = +2250 \text{ psi}$$

All stresses lie within the allowable range.

Example 22-4   The beam in Example 22-3 is to be prestressed by means of tendons that are deflected at the quarter points of the span, as shown in Fig. 22-5*a*. Evaluate the following: the allowable unit superimposed load, the magnitude of the prestressing force, the eccentricity e_1 in the center interval, and the maximum and minimum allowable values of the eccentricity e_2 at the supports.   What increase in capacity has been secured by deflecting the tendons?

   Solution.   Figure 22-5*b* is a composite stress diagram for the top fiber.   The difference between an ordinate to *EFG* and the corresponding ordinate to *AHJ* represents the value of f_{ti} at the given section.   It is apparent that if *AE* does not exceed *HF*, then f_{ti} does not exceed *HF* in absolute value anywhere along the span.   Therefore, for the center interval *BC*, the critical stresses at transfer occur at the boundary sections *B* and *C*.   Analogous observations apply to the stress diagram in Fig. 22-5*c*.

   The beam-weight stresses at *B* are as follows:

$$f_{bw} = \tfrac{3}{4}(-374) = -281 \text{ psi} \qquad f_{tw} = +281 \text{ psi}$$

   The beam capacity is found by equating the critical stresses to their allowable values.

At *B*:

$$f_{bi} = f_{bp} - 281 = +2400$$
$$f_{ti} = f_{tp} + 281 = -190$$
$$f_{bp} = +2681 \text{ psi} \qquad f_{tp} = -471 \text{ psi}$$

At *M*:

$$f_{bf} = 0.85 \times 2681 - 374 + f_{bs} = -425$$
$$f_{tf} = 0.85(-471) + 374 + f_{ts} = +2250$$
$$f_{bs} = -2330 \text{ psi} \qquad f_{ts} = +2277 \text{ psi}$$

The latter value controls.

$$w_s = 83 \times \frac{2277}{374} = \textbf{505 plf}$$

$$\frac{505}{452} = 1.12$$

Capacity is increased **12 percent.**

When the foregoing calculations are compared with those in Example 22-3, it is seen that the effect of deflecting the tendons is to permit an increase of 281 psi in the absolute value of the prestress at top and bottom. The accompanying increase in f_{ts} is $0.85 \times 281 = 239$ psi.

Examination of Fig. 22-4 indicates that the value of f_{cai} is independent of the form of the trajectory. Therefore, as in the preceding example, the minimum prestressing force is

$$F_i = 85{,}920 \text{ lb}$$

$$f_{tp} = 1074 - \frac{85{,}920e_1}{133} = -471 \qquad e_1 = 2.39 \text{ in.}$$

Although not required, the value of f_{bp} is

$$f_{bp} = 1074 + [1074 - (-471)] = +2619 \text{ psi}$$

or
$$f_{bp} = 2681 - \frac{53}{0.85} = +2619 \text{ psi}$$

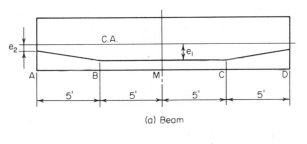

(a) Beam

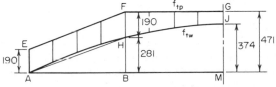

(b) Absolute values of f_{ti} along half-span

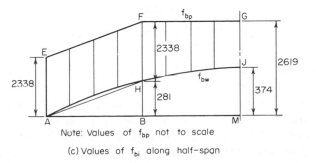

Note: Values of f_{bp} not to scale

(c) Values of f_{bi} along half-span

fig. 22-5

At the supports, the tendons may be placed an equal distance above or below the center. Then

$$e_{2,\max} = 1.96 \text{ in.} \qquad e_{2,\min} = -1.96 \text{ in.}$$

Example 22-5 The beam in Example 22-3 is to be prestressed by means of tendons lying in a parabolic arc. Evaluate the following: the allowable unit superimposed load, the magnitude of the prestressing force, the eccentricity of this force at midspan, and the increase in capacity accruing from the use of curved tendons.

Solution. Since the prestressing force has a parabolic trajectory, lines EFG in Fig. 22-5b and c will be parabolic in the present case. Therefore, it is possible to achieve the full allowable initial stresses at midspan.

The beam capacity is found by equating the critical stresses at midspan to their allowable values.

$$f_{bi} = f_{bp} - 374 = +2400$$
$$f_{ti} = f_{tp} + 374 = -190$$
$$f_{bp} = +2774 \text{ psi} \qquad f_{tp} = -564 \text{ psi}$$
$$f_{bf} = 0.85 \times 2774 - 374 + f_{bs} = -425$$
$$f_{tf} = 0.85(-564) + 374 + f_{ts} = +2250$$
$$f_{bs} = -2409 \text{ psi} \qquad f_{ts} = +2356 \text{ psi}$$

The latter value controls.

$$w_s = 83 \times \frac{2356}{374} = 523 \text{ plf}$$

$$\frac{523}{452} = 1.16$$

Capacity is increased **16 percent.**

When the foregoing calculations are compared with those in Example 22-3, it is seen that the effect of using parabolic tendons is to permit an increase of 374 psi in the absolute value of the prestress at top and bottom. The accompanying increase in f_{ts} is $0.85 \times 374 = 318$ psi.

As before, the minimum prestressing force is

$$F_i = 85,920 \text{ lb}$$

$$f_{tp} = 1074 - \frac{85,920e}{133} = -564 \qquad e = 2.54 \text{ in.}$$

An analysis of the results obtained in the preceding examples leads to the following conclusions:

1. The capacity of a given member is increased by using deflected rather than straight tendons, and the capacity is maximized by using parabolic tendons. (However, in the case of a pretensioned beam, an economy analysis must also take into account the expense incurred in deflecting the tendons.)

2. The prestressing force associated with the maximum capacity of a given member is a function of the cross-sectional area, the allowable stresses, and the ratio y_b/y_t. It is independent of the form of the trajectory.

3. If the section moduli of a given member are both in excess of the minimum required values, the minimum prestressing force is found by setting the critical values of f_{bf} and f_{ti} equal to their respective values. In this manner, points A and B in Fig. 22-4 are placed at their limiting positions to the left.

22-7 Calculation of Minimum Section Moduli

Where a beam is to be designed to carry a specified superimposed load, the required section moduli are found by estimating the cross-sectional area and then equating the critical stresses to their allowable values.

Example 22-6 A beam having a cross-sectional area of 500 sq in. sustains a beam-weight moment equal to 3500 in.-kips at midspan and a superimposed-load moment that varies parabolically from 9000 in.-kips at midspan to zero at the supports. The allowable stresses are as follows:

Initial: $+2400$ and -190 psi
Final: $+2250$ and -200 psi

The member will be prestressed by means of tendons deflected at the quarter points. Calculate the section moduli corresponding to balanced design, the magnitude of the prestressing force and its eccentricity in the center interval. Assume that the calculated eccentricity is attainable, i.e., that the centroid of the tendons will fall within the confines of the section while satisfying insulation requirements.

Solution. As Example 22-4 demonstrates, the critical initial stresses occur at the quarter point and the critical final stresses occur at midspan. Let M_w and M_s denote the beam-weight and superimposed-load moments, respectively, at midspan; the corresponding moments at the quarter points are three-fourths as large. Let e denote the eccentricity in the center interval.

STRESSES IN BOTTOM FIBER

$$f_{bi} = f_{bp} - \frac{0.75M_w}{S_b} = +2400$$

$$f_{bf} = 0.85f_{bp} - \frac{M_w}{S_b} - \frac{M_s}{S_b} = -200$$

Solving,
$$S_b = \frac{M_s + 0.3625M_w}{2240} = 4584 \text{ in.}^3$$

and
$$f_{bp} = +2973 \text{ psi}$$

STRESSES IN TOP FIBER

$$f_{ti} = f_{tp} + \frac{0.75M_w}{S_t} = -190$$

$$f_{tf} = 0.85f_{tp} + \frac{M_w}{S_t} + \frac{M_s}{S_t} = +2250$$

Solving,
$$S_t = \frac{M_s + 0.3625M_w}{2412} = \textbf{4257 in.}^3$$

and
$$f_{tp} = -807 \text{ psi}$$

With the prestresses determined, the values of F_i and e are readily secured.

$$f_{bp} = \frac{F_i}{A} + \frac{F_ie}{S_b} = +2973 \tag{a}$$

$$f_{tp} = \frac{F_i}{A} - \frac{F_ie}{S_t} = -807 \tag{b}$$

By multiplying Eq. (a) by S_b and Eq. (b) by S_t and adding the resulting equations, we obtain

$$F_i = \frac{2973S_b - 807S_t}{S_b + S_t} A = \textbf{576,500 lb}$$

Then
$$e = \frac{2973S_b}{F_i} - \frac{S_b}{A} = \textbf{14.47 in.}$$

Alternatively, since the value of F_i is independent of the depth of member, we may find this value by assuming an arbitrary depth. Set $h = 10$ in. Then

$$y_b = \frac{S_t}{S_b + S_t} h = 4.815 \text{ in.}$$

$$f_{cai} = f_{bp} - (f_{bp} - f_{tp}) \frac{y_b}{h}$$

$$= 2973 - (2973 + 807)0.4815 = +1153 \text{ psi}$$
$$F_i = 1153 \times 500 = 576,500 \text{ lb}$$

22-8   Efficiency of Cross-sectional Shapes   In selecting a beam to carry a given load, the designer is confronted with a wide choice of cross-sectional shapes, and it is therefore imperative that he fully understand the governing criteria. The following example is intended to illustrate the effect of beam span on the choice of cross section. To simplify the analysis, we shall assume that although the cross section varies with span, its shape is fixed, i.e., that all dimensions must vary by the same ratio.

Example 22-7 With reference to the beam in Example 22-6, assume that the span increases by 10 percent, thereby causing the midspan moment due to super-imposed load to increase by 21 percent. Prove that the member will be adequate with respect to flexure if all cross-sectional dimensions are increased by 7.2 percent. Compute the new eccentricity in the center interval and compare this with the original value.

Solution. The properties of the new cross section are as follows:

$$A = 500 \times 1.072^2 = 575 \text{ sq in.}$$
$$S_b = 4584 \times 1.072^3 = 5647 \text{ in.}^3$$
$$S_t = 4257 \times 1.072^3 = 5244 \text{ in.}^3$$

The midspan bending moments are as follows:

$$M_s = 9000 \times 1.21 = 10{,}890 \text{ in.-kips}$$
$$M_w = 3500 \times 1.072^2 \times 1.21 = 4867 \text{ in.-kips}$$

By repeating the calculations in Example 22-6 with these new values, we arrive at the following values for the required section moduli, prestressing force, and eccentricity:

$S_b = 5649$ in.^{3}	OK	$S_t = 5246$ in.^{3}	OK
$f_{bp} = +3046$ psi		$f_{tp} = -886$ psi	
$F_i = 662{,}800$ lb		$e = $ **16.13 in.**	

The eccentricity has increased by **11.5 percent.** In practice, it would be advantageous to increase the vertical dimensions by a greater ratio than the horizontal dimensions. Nevertheless, it is clear that as the span increases the eccentricity increases more rapidly than does the depth.

Assume that we increase the span of a beam while maintaining its cross-sectional shape and holding the unit superimposed load constant. Up to a certain critical span, the theoretical values of e and h are compatible in the respect that the tendons will fall within the confines of the section when arranged to provide the required eccentricity. Beyond the critical span, however, the theoretical values of e and h are incompatible in this respect.

For a short-span member, where difficulty in accommodating the tendons does not arise, a cross section having a shape similar to an I is the most efficient one because it yields the required section moduli with the minimum area. Since the required values of S_b and S_t differ, the area is disposed unsymmetrically about middepth. For a long-span member, on the other hand, a T section is generally the most efficient shape. The extensive flange area elevates the centroidal axis, thus enabling us to secure a reasonably large eccentricity within a limited depth.

22-9   Calculation of Prestresses by Kern Distances   In Art. 5-6 we defined the kern of a section as the central region within which a longitudinal compressive load must be applied to the member if it is to induce solely compressive stresses.   In calculating the prestresses in a concrete beam, certain advantages accrue if we establish the kern of the cross section.

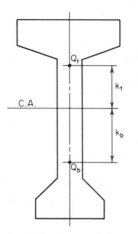

Figure 22-6 is the cross section of a beam, and Q_b and Q_t are points on the vertical centroidal axis at the extremities of the kern.   These are called the *kern points*, and the distances k_b and k_t from the centroidal axis to these points are referred to as the *kern distances*, both kern distances being taken as positive.

Consider that the prestressing force is applied at Q_t, thereby inducing zero prestress at the bottom.   Let f_{bp1} denote this stress.

$$f_{bp1} = \frac{F_i}{A} - \frac{F_i k_t}{S_b} = 0 \qquad \therefore k_t = \frac{S_b}{A}$$

fig. 22-6   Kern points.

Now consider that the prestressing force is depressed a distance $k_t + e$ to secure an eccentricity e.   Let f_{bp2} denote the prestress at the bottom.

$$f_{bp2} - f_{bp1} = f_{bp2} = \frac{\Delta M_p}{S_b} = \frac{F_i(k_t + e)}{S_b}$$

Analogous results apply with respect to k_b.   In summary,

$$k_b = \frac{S_t}{A} \qquad\qquad k_t = \frac{S_b}{A} \qquad\qquad (22\text{-}4)$$

$$f_{bp} = \frac{F_i(k_t + e)}{S_b} \qquad f_{tp} = \frac{F_i(k_b - e)}{S_t} \qquad\qquad (22\text{-}5)$$

Example 22-8   A beam has the following properties:

$$A = 850 \text{ sq in.} \qquad S_b = 11{,}400 \text{ in.}^3 \qquad S_t = 14{,}400 \text{ in.}^3$$

A prestressing force of 630 kips is applied with an eccentricity of 24 in. at a given section.   Find the prestresses at top and bottom at this section.

   Solution

$$k_b = \frac{14{,}400}{850} = 16.9 \text{ in.} \qquad k_t = \frac{11{,}400}{850} = 13.4 \text{ in.}$$

$$f_{bp} = \frac{630{,}000(13.4 + 24)}{11{,}400} = +\textbf{2067 psi}$$

$$f_{tp} = \frac{630{,}000(16.9 - 24)}{14{,}400} = -\textbf{311 psi}$$

22-10 Determination of Prestressing Force by Magnel Diagram As we have previously found, for a beam that is not in balanced design there is a range of allowable values of F_i and of e. For analytical purposes, it is convenient to construct a diagram that represents permissible sets of values of F_i and e.

Assume that the critical initial stresses and critical final stresses occur at the same section, as is true of a beam prestressed with parabolic tendons. Let f_{bi} and f_{bf} denote the *allowable* stresses in the bottom fiber. We may then write:

$$\frac{F_i(k_t + e)}{S_b} - \frac{M_w}{S_b} \leq f_{bi}$$

$$\frac{\eta F_i(k_t + e)}{S_b} - \frac{M_w + M_s}{S_b} \geq f_{bf}$$

These relationships may be transformed to the following:

$$\frac{1}{F_i} \geq \frac{k_t + e}{M_w + f_{bi}S_b} \tag{22-6a}$$

$$\frac{1}{F_i} \leq \frac{\eta(k_t + e)}{M_w + M_s + f_{bf}S_b} \tag{22-6b}$$

Similarly, let f_{ti} and f_{tf} denote the allowable stresses in the top fiber. Then

$$\frac{1}{F_i} \geq \frac{e - k_b}{M_w - f_{ti}S_t} \tag{22-6c}$$

$$\frac{1}{F_i} \leq \frac{\eta(e - k_b)}{M_w + M_s - f_{tf}S_t} \tag{22-6d}$$

If we treat the foregoing relationships as equalities and plot the straight lines by which they are represented, we obtain a diagram of the type shown in Fig. 22-7, which is called a *Magnel diagram*. Each point on these lines represents a set of values of $1/F_i$ and e at which the designated stress equals its allowable value.

When the section moduli are in excess of those corresponding to balanced design, line b has a greater inclination than a, and line d has a greater inclination than c. From the sense of each inequality, it follows that $1/F_i$ and e may be assigned any set of values represented by a point within the quadrilateral $CDEF$ or on its circumference.

The minimum prestressing force is represented by point E, and this point corresponds to the condition in which stresses f_{bf} and f_{ti} equal their allowable values. Thus, the Magnel diagram confirms the third conclusion we arrived at in Art. 22-6 by using a different approach.

Example 22-9   The following data pertain to a girder having curved tendons:

$$A = 500 \text{ sq in.} \qquad S_b = 5000 \text{ in.}^3 \qquad S_t = 5340 \text{ in.}^3$$
$$M_w = 3600 \text{ in.-kips} \qquad M_s = 9500 \text{ in.-kips}$$

The allowable stresses are as follows:

Initial: $+2400$ and -190 psi
Final: $+2250$ and -425 psi

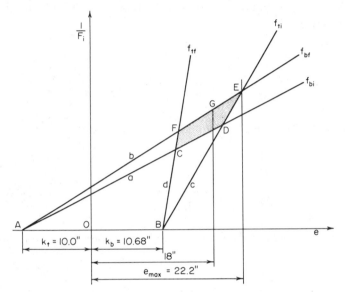

fig. 22-7   Magnel diagram.

1. Construct the Magnel diagram for this member.
2. Determine the minimum prestressing force and its eccentricity by assuming that this eccentricity is attainable.
3. Determine the prestressing force if the eccentricity is restricted to 18 in.

Solution. Substitution in Eqs. (22-6) yields the following results, in which F_i is expressed in thousands of kips:

$$\frac{1}{F_i} \geq \frac{10 + e}{15.60} \qquad (a) \qquad \frac{1}{F_i} \leq \frac{10 + e}{12.91} \qquad (b)$$

$$\frac{1}{F_i} \geq \frac{e - 10.68}{4.61} \qquad (c) \qquad \frac{1}{F_i} \leq \frac{e - 10.68}{1.28} \qquad (d)$$

The Magnel diagram for this member appears in Fig. 22-7. The values associated with point E are found in this manner:

$$\frac{1}{F_i} = \frac{10 + e}{12.91} = \frac{e - 10.68}{4.61}$$

Solving, $e = 22.2$ in. $F_i = 401$ kips

When e is restricted to 18 in., the minimum prestressing force corresponds to point G on line b. Then

$$\frac{1}{F_i} = \frac{10 + 18}{12.91} \qquad F_i = \textbf{461 kips}$$

A Magnel diagram may be constructed for a beam having any form of trajectory. For example, assume that a beam is prestressed with deflected tendons. The critical initial stresses occur at the deflection points, and the critical final stresses occur at midspan. The only modification that is needed is to replace M_w in Eqs. (22-6a) and (22-6c) with the beam-weight moment at the deflection points.

22-11 Deflection of Prestressed Beams In analyzing the elastic curve of a prestressed-concrete beam at a given stage of loading, we superpose the deflections caused by prestressing and by gravity loading, applying the moment of inertia of the gross section and the modulus of elasticity that exists at the given instant.

We shall evaluate the deflection caused by prestressing for three forms of trajectory, as follows:

Type A: The trajectory is horizontal across the entire span.

Type B: The trajectory consists of three straight lines, being horizontal across a center interval and intersecting the longitudinal axis at the ends.

Type C: The trajectory is parabolic and intersects the longitudinal axis at the ends.

The prestress-moment diagrams associated with these three cases are shown in Fig. 22-8. This problem lends itself to solution by the moment-

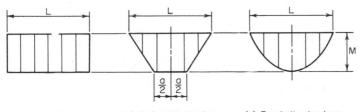

(a) Straight tendons   (b) Deflected tendons   (c) Parabolic tendons

fig. 22-8 Prestress-moment diagrams.

area method, which is presented in Art. 6-3. By symmetry, the elastic curve corresponding to F_i is horizontal at midspan, and the maximum deflection therefore equals the deviation of the elastic curve at the support from the tangent to this curve at midspan.

Consider an upward deflection (camber) as positive, and let E_c denote the modulus of elasticity of the concrete. By computing the tangential deviation, we obtain the following results in terms of the literal values shown in Fig. 22-8:

Type A: $\qquad\qquad E_c I \Delta_p = \dfrac{ML}{2}\dfrac{L}{4}$

Then $\qquad\qquad\qquad \Delta_p = \dfrac{ML^2}{8E_c I}$ $\qquad\qquad\qquad\qquad$ (22-7a)

Type B: $\qquad\qquad E_c I \Delta_p = \dfrac{Ma}{2}\left(\dfrac{L}{2}-\dfrac{a}{4}\right) + \dfrac{M}{3}\left(\dfrac{L}{2}-\dfrac{a}{2}\right)^2$

$\qquad\qquad\qquad\qquad \Delta_p = \dfrac{M(2L^2 + 2La - a^2)}{24E_c I}$ $\qquad\qquad\qquad$ (22-7b)

Type C: Refer to the AISC Manual, page 6-26.

$$E_c I \Delta_p = \frac{2}{3}\frac{ML}{2}\frac{5}{8}\frac{L}{2}$$

$$\Delta_p = \frac{5ML^2}{48E_c I}$$ $\qquad\qquad\qquad$ (22-7c)

Example 22-10   The following data pertain to a simply supported prismatic beam:

$$
\begin{array}{ll}
L = 36 \text{ ft} & I = 40{,}000 \text{ in.}^4 \\
f'_{ci} = 4000 \text{ psi} & w_w = 340 \text{ plf} \\
F_i = 430 \text{ kips} & e = 8.8 \text{ in.} \quad \text{at midspan}
\end{array}
$$

Calculate the camber of the member at transfer under each of the following conditions:

a. The tendons are straight across the entire span.

b. The tendons are deflected at the third points and the eccentricity at the supports is 1.2 in.

c. The tendons are curved parabolically and the eccentricity at the supports is 1.2 in.

Solution. In accordance with Sec. 1102 of the ACI Code,

$$E_c = 145^{1.5} \times 33 \sqrt{4000} = 3{,}644{,}000 \text{ psi}$$

PART *a.* Equation (22-7a) yields

$$\Delta_p = \frac{430{,}000 \times 8.8 \times 36^2 \times 144}{8 \times 3{,}644{,}000 \times 40{,}000} = 0.61 \text{ in.}$$

The beam-weight deflection is

$$\Delta_w = -\frac{5w_w L^4}{384E_c I} = -0.09 \text{ in.}$$

Then $\qquad\qquad\qquad \Delta_i = 0.61 - 0.09 = \textbf{0.52 in.}$

PART *b.* Consider the prestressing force to be resolved into two components, each having a magnitude of 430 kips.   The first component has a type *A* trajectory with an eccentricity of 1.2 in. The other has a type B trajectory with an eccentricity in the center interval of 7.6 in. By proportion,

$$\Delta_{pa} = 0.61 \times \frac{1.2}{8.8} = 0.08 \text{ in.}$$

$$2L^2 + 2La - a^2 = 2 \times 36^2 + 2 \times 36 \times 12 - 12^2 = 3312 \text{ sq ft}$$

Equation (22-7b) yields

$$\Delta_{pb} = \frac{430,000 \times 7.6 \times 3312 \times 144}{24 \times 3,644,000 \times 40,000} = 0.45 \text{ in.}$$

$$\Delta_i = 0.08 + 0.45 - 0.09 = \mathbf{0.44 \text{ in.}}$$

PART c. Consider the prestressing force to be resolved into two components in the same manner as in part b.

$$\Delta_{pa} = 0.08 \text{ in.}$$

Equation (22-7c) yields

$$\Delta_{pc} = \frac{5 \times 430,000 \times 7.6 \times 36^2 \times 144}{48 \times 3,644,000 \times 40,000} = 0.44 \text{ in.}$$

$$\Delta_i = 0.08 + 0.44 - 0.09 = \mathbf{0.43 \text{ in.}}$$

22-12   Limitation of Working-stress Design   In a non-prestressed beam designed on an elastic basis, the bending stresses are directly proportional to the total load carried by the member. Consequently, the working-stress method of design provides ample protection against failure if an adequate factor of safety is applied in setting the allowable stresses. In a prestressed beam, on the other hand, a direct proportionality between stress and load is lacking, and therefore the use of allowable stresses does not necessarily yield a member that has sufficient reserve strength.

As an illustration, assume that a beam having the stress diagram shown in Fig. 22-4 is subjected to a superimposed load that is 10 percent greater than its estimated capacity. The stress f_{bs} will then increase by 204 psi, and the final stress in the bottom fiber will be -576 psi instead of -372 psi. Thus a relatively small overload causes a disproportionately large increase in the tensile stress and thereby introduces the danger of cracking.

The foregoing analysis reveals that there is no set relationship between the capacity of a beam at allowable final stress and the load that will induce incipient cracking. As a result, the working-stress method of design fails to afford a reliable index of reserve strength, and it is therefore imperative that every prestressed-concrete beam be subjected to an ultimate-strength analysis to ascertain whether its reserve strength is adequate.

The method of performing this analysis is outlined in Secs. 2608 and 2609 of the ACI Code. The stress in the steel at ultimate load is a function of the reinforcement ratio p, which has the same meaning as for a non-prestressed beam. Section 2608 provides as follows:

$$f_{su} = f_s' \left(1 - \frac{0.5pf_s'}{f_c'} \right) \tag{22-8}$$

22-13 Design of Web Reinforcement   Since the diagonal tensile stresses in a prestressed beam do not vary linearly with the gravity loads, the web reinforcement must be designed at ultimate-load conditions. This subject is covered in Sec. 2610 of the ACI Code. Our notational system is as follows:

A_v = area of web reinforcement placed perpendicular to longitudinal axis

V_c' = ultimate-shear capacity of concrete

V_p' = vertical component of F_f at given section

V_u' = ultimate shear at given section

b' = width of web at centroidal axis

s = center-to-center spacing of stirrups

f_{pc}' = stress due to F_f, evaluated at centroidal axis or at junction of web and flange when centroidal axis lies in flange

The shear capacity V_c' is established by calculating the following quantities and selecting the smaller value:

$$V_{ci}' = 1.7b'd \sqrt{f_c'} \tag{22-9a}$$

where d equals the effective depth.

$$V_{cw}' = b'd(3.5 \sqrt{f_c'} + 0.3f_{pc}') + V_p' \tag{22-9b}$$

where d equals the effective depth or 80 percent of the overall depth, whichever is greater.

The web-reinforcement area is found by applying the following equations and selecting the greater value:

$$A_v = \frac{s(V_u' - \phi V_c')}{\phi d f_y} \tag{22-10a}$$

$$A_v = \frac{A_s}{80} \frac{f_s'}{f_y} \frac{s}{\sqrt{b'd}} \tag{22-10b}$$

where d equals the effective depth at section of maximum moment.

22-14 Design of Pretensioned Girder   The trend in pretensioned construction is toward the adoption of standard shapes in order to permit the constant reuse of steel forms.   Each fabricator issues a catalog listing the available shapes and their capacities, and the designer should therefore refer to a catalog to select a standard pretensioned member.

Floor and roof beams are often constructed in the form of a T or double T, several feet wide.   The flanges of these members constitute the floor or roof surface, although floor beams often have a poured-in-place concrete topping.   In many instances, the members are left exposed on the underside.

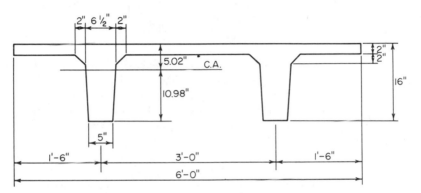

fig. 22-9 Double-T roof beam.

The following example will serve to illustrate the design of a pretensioned roof beam.

Example 22-11   The double-T beam in Fig. 22-9 has been selected for use on a simple span of 40 ft to carry the following loads:

> Roofing....... 12 psf
> Snow......... 40
> Total....... $\overline{52}$ psf

The member will be pretensioned with straight 7-wire strands, $\frac{7}{16}$ in. in diameter, having an area of 0.1089 sq in. each and an ultimate strength of 248,000 psi.   The concrete strengths are $f_c' = 5000$ psi and $f_{ci}' = 4000$ psi.   The allowable stresses are as follows:

Initial: $+2400$ and -190 psi
Final: $+2250$ and -425 psi

Investigate the adequacy of this section and design the tendons.   Compute the camber of the beam after the concrete has hardened and all dead loads are present.   For this calculation, assume that the final value of E_c is one-third of that at transfer.

Solution. The beam properties are as follows:

$$A = 316 \text{ sq in.} \qquad\qquad I = 7240 \text{ in.}^4$$
$$y_b = 10.98 \text{ in.} \qquad\qquad y_t = 5.02 \text{ in.}$$
$$S_b = 659 \text{ in.}^3 \qquad\qquad S_t = 1442 \text{ in.}^3$$
$$w_w = {}^{316}\!/_{144} \times 150 = 329 \text{ plf} \qquad w_s = 52 \times 6 = 312 \text{ plf}$$
$$\text{Total unit load} = 329 + 312 = 641 \text{ plf}$$

At midspan,

$$M_w + M_s = \tfrac{1}{8} \times 641 \times 40^2 \times 12 = 1{,}538{,}000 \text{ in.-lb}$$

$$f_{bw} + f_{bs} = - \frac{1{,}538{,}000}{659} = -2334 \text{ psi}$$

$$f_{tw} + f_{ts} = + \frac{1{,}538{,}000}{1442} = +1067 \text{ psi}$$

Let f_{bf} and f_{tf} denote the respective stresses *at midspan* and f_{bi} and f_{ti} denote the respective stresses *at the support*. The adequacy of the section may be tested by setting two critical stresses equal to their allowable values and then calculating the corresponding values of the remaining two. In accordance with our previous finding, we shall set f_{bf} and f_{ti} equal to their allowable values in order to minimize the prestressing force.

$$f_{bf} = 0.85 f_{bp} - 2334 = -425 \qquad \therefore f_{bp} = +2246 \text{ psi}$$
$$f_{ti} = f_{tp} = -190 \text{ psi}$$
$$f_{bi} = f_{bp} = +2246 < 2400 \text{ psi} \qquad \text{OK}$$
$$f_{tf} = 0.85(-190) + 1067 = +905 < 2250 \text{ psi} \qquad \text{OK}$$

The section is therefore adequate on an elastic basis. The prestressing force and its eccentricity may be most easily found by referring to the prestress diagram in Fig. 22-10.

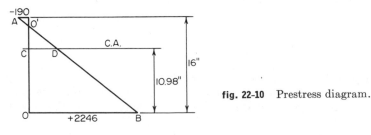

fig. 22-10   Prestress diagram.

$$f_{bp} = +2246 \text{ psi} \qquad f_{tp} = -190 \text{ psi}$$

$$\text{Slope of } AB = \frac{2246 - (-190)}{16} = 152.3 \text{ psi per in.}$$

$$\frac{F_i}{A} = CD = 2246 - 10.98 \times 152.3 = 574 \text{ psi}$$

$$F_i = 574 \times 316 = \textbf{181,400 lb}$$

$$\text{Slope of } AB = \frac{F_i e}{I} = 152.3$$

$$e = \frac{152.3 \times 7240}{181,400} = \textbf{6.07 in.}$$

With F_i and e established, the steel may now be designed. In accordance with Sec. 2606 of the ACI Code,

$$\text{Allowable initial force per strand} = 0.1089 \times 0.70 \times 248,000$$
$$= 18,900 \text{ lb}$$
$$\text{Number required} = \frac{181,400}{18,900} = 9.6$$

Use ten strands (five in each web), stressed to 18,140 lb each. In accordance with Sec. 2617(b),

$$\text{Allowable center-to-center spacing} = 4 \times \frac{7}{16} = 1\frac{3}{4} \text{ in.}$$

Use 2-in. spacing, as shown in Fig. 22-11. To locate the centroid of the steel, we have

$$y = \frac{2 \times 2 + 1 \times 4}{5} = 1.60 \text{ in.}$$

$$v = 10.98 - 6.07 - 1.60 = 3.31 \text{ in.}$$

Set $v = 3\frac{5}{16}$ in.

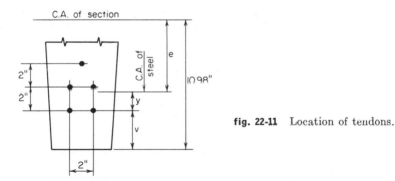

fig. 22-11 Location of tendons.

We shall now assess the ultimate strength of the member. However, it is first necessary to ascertain whether the steel index is below the limit imposed by Sec. 2609. The notational system is identical with that for a non-prestressed beam.

$$A_s = 10 \times 0.1089 = 1.089 \text{ sq in.}$$
$$d = y_t + e = 5.02 + 6.07 = 11.09 \text{ in.}$$
$$p = \frac{A_s}{bd} = \frac{1.089}{72 \times 11.09} = 0.00137$$

Applying Eq. (22-8), we obtain

$$f_{su} = 248{,}000 \left(1 - \frac{0.5 \times 0.00137 \times 248{,}000}{5000} \right) = 240{,}000 \text{ psi}$$

$$q = \frac{pf_{su}}{f_c'} = \frac{0.00137 \times 240{,}000}{5000} = 0.0658 < 0.30 \qquad \text{OK}$$

$$T_u = A_s f_{su} = 1.089 \times 240{,}000 = 261{,}400 \text{ lb}$$
$$C_u = 0.85 \times 5000 \times 72a = 261{,}400 \text{ lb}$$

$$a = 0.854 \text{ in.} \qquad d - \frac{a}{2} = 10.66 \text{ in.}$$

$$M_u = \phi T_u \left(d - \frac{a}{2} \right) = 0.90 \times 261{,}400 \times 10.66 = 2{,}500{,}000 \text{ in.-lb}$$

The ultimate moment to be resisted is computed by applying the load factors given in Sec. 1506(a).

$$w_{DL} = 329 + 12 \times 6 = 401 \text{ plf} \qquad w_{LL} = 40 \times 6 = 240 \text{ plf}$$
$$w_u = 1.5 \times 401 + 1.8 \times 240 = 1034 \text{ plf}$$
$$M_u = \tfrac{1}{8} \times 1034 \times 40^2 \times 12 = 2{,}480{,}000 \text{ in.-lb} \qquad \text{OK}$$

We shall determine the web-reinforcement area. The critical section for shear lies at a distance $d/2$ from the face of support.

$$V_u' = 1034(20 - 0.46) = 20{,}200 \text{ lb}$$

The width of web at the centroidal axis is

$$b' = 2 \left(5 + 1.5 \times \frac{10.98}{12} \right) = 12.74 \text{ in.}$$

Applying Eq. (22-9a), we have

$$V_{ci}' = 1.7 \times 12.74 \times 11.09 \sqrt{5000} = 17{,}000 \text{ lb}$$

Applying Eq. (22-9b), we have

$$d = 0.80 \times 16 = 12.8 \text{ in.} \qquad V_p' = 0$$
$$f_{pc}' = 0.85 \times 574 = +488 \text{ psi}$$
$$V_{cw}' = 12.74 \times 12.8(3.5 \sqrt{5000} + 0.3 \times 488) = 64{,}300 \text{ lb}$$
$$\therefore \ V_c' = 17{,}000 \text{ lb}$$

In applying Eqs. (22-10), we shall use $f_y = 40{,}000$ psi and set $s = 12$ in. The web-reinforcement area required at the ends is

$$A_v = \frac{12(20{,}200 - 0.85 \times 17{,}000)}{0.85 \times 11.09 \times 40{,}000} = \textbf{0.183 sq in. per ft}$$

The minimum web-reinforcement area to be supplied is

$$A_v = \frac{1.089}{80} \times \frac{248{,}000}{40{,}000} \times \frac{12}{\sqrt{12.74 \times 11.09}} = \textbf{0.085 sq in. per ft}$$

We shall calculate the camber under full dead load. From the calculation in Example 22-10,

$$E_c = \tfrac{1}{3} \times 3.644 \times 10^6 = 1.215 \times 10^6 \text{ psi}$$
$$E_c I = 1.215 \times 10^6 \times 7240 = 8.8 \times 10^9 \text{ lb-in.}^2$$
$$\Delta_{DL} = -\frac{5 \times 401 \times 40^4 \times 1728}{384 \times 8.8 \times 10^9} = -2.62 \text{ in.}$$

Equation (22-7a) yields

$$\Delta_p = \frac{0.85 \times 181,400 \times 6.07 \times 40^2 \times 144}{8 \times 8.8 \times 10^9} = 3.06 \text{ in.}$$
$$\Delta = 3.06 - 2.62 = \mathbf{0.44 \text{ in.}}$$

22-15 Design of Post-tensioned Girder In designing a post-tensioned girder having curved tendons, we may consider that the critical stresses lie at the midspan section and select a trajectory that is consonant with this assumption.

Example 22-12 The girder in Fig. 22-12 has been selected for use on a 90-ft simple span to carry the following superimposed loads: dead load, 1160 plf; live load,

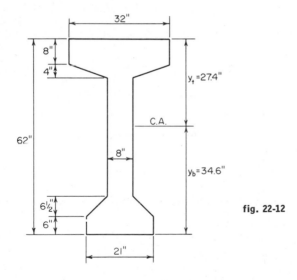

fig. 22-12

1000 plf. It will be post-tensioned with Freyssinet cables. The concrete strengths are $f'_c = 5000$ psi and $f'_{ci} = 4000$ psi. The allowable stresses are as follows:

Initial: $+2400$ and -190 psi
Final: $+2250$ and -425 psi

Complete the design of this member, and calculate the camber at transfer.

Solution. The beam properties are as follows:

$$A = 856 \text{ sq in.} \qquad I = 394,800 \text{ in.}^4$$
$$y_b = 34.6 \text{ in.} \qquad y_t = 27.4 \text{ in.}$$
$$S_b = 11,410 \text{ in.}^3 \qquad S_t = 14,410 \text{ in.}^3$$
$$w_w = 892 \text{ plf}$$

The gravity-load stresses at midspan are as follows:

$$f_{bw} = -950 \text{ psi} \qquad f_{bs} = -2300 \text{ psi}$$
$$f_{tw} = +752 \text{ psi} \qquad f_{ts} = +1820 \text{ psi}$$

We shall tentatively assume that it is possible to attain the eccentricity corresponding to the minimum prestressing force. Since the tendons will be curved, the critical stresses will be considered to occur at midspan. The adequacy of the section may be tested by equating f_{bf} and f_{ti} to their allowable values and determining the corresponding values of f_{bi} and f_{tf}.

$$f_{bf} = 0.85f_{bp} - 950 - 2300 = -425$$
$$f_{ti} = f_{tp} + 752 = -190$$
$$\therefore f_{bp} = +3324 \text{ psi} \qquad \text{and} \qquad f_{tp} = -942 \text{ psi}$$
$$f_{bi} = +3324 - 950 = +2374 < 2400 \text{ psi} \qquad \text{OK}$$
$$f_{tf} = 0.85(-942) + 752 + 1820 = +1771 < 2250 \text{ psi} \qquad \text{OK}$$

The section is therefore adequate on an elastic basis. The prestressing force

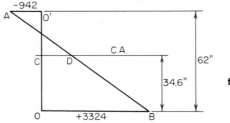

fig. 22-13 Prestress diagram.

and its eccentricity may be found by referring to the prestress diagram in Fig. 22-13.

$$\text{Slope of } AB = \frac{3324 - (-942)}{62} = 68.8 \text{ psi per in.}$$

$$\frac{F_i}{A} = CD = 3324 - 34.6 \times 68.8 = 944 \text{ psi}$$

$$F_i = 944 \times 856 = 808,100 \text{ lb}$$

$$\text{Slope of } AB = \frac{F_i e}{I} = 68.8$$

$$e = \frac{68.8 \times 394,800}{808,100} = 33.6 \text{ in.}$$

Since $y_b = 34.6$ in., this eccentricity is excessive.   It is therefore necessary to assume a feasible value of e and determine the minimum value of F_i corresponding to this eccentricity.   The Magnel diagram in Fig. 22-7 indicates that the minimum value of F_i is secured by setting f_{bf} equal to its allowable value.   The prestress f_{bp} will therefore remain $+3324$ psi.   Try

$$e = 34.6 - 3.0 = \textbf{31.6 in.}$$

$$f_{bp} = \frac{F_i}{856} + \frac{F_i \times 31.6}{11,410} = +3324$$

Solving, $F_i = \textbf{844,000 lb}$

We shall check the remaining stresses.

$$f_{tp} = \frac{844,000}{856} - \frac{844,000 \times 31.6}{14,410} = -865 \text{ psi}$$

$$f_{bi} = +3324 - 950 = +2374 \text{ psi} \qquad\qquad \text{OK}$$
$$f_{ti} = -865 + 752 = -113 \text{ psi} \qquad\qquad \text{OK}$$
$$f_{tf} = 0.85(-865) + 752 + 1820 = +1837 \text{ psi} \qquad \text{OK}$$

The properties of Freyssinet cables are recorded in the manufacturer's catalog. We shall use 12/0.276 cables.   The designation indicates that each cable consists of 12 wires of 0.276-in. diameter.   The ultimate strength is 236,000 psi.

$$A_s = 0.723 \text{ sq in. per cable}$$
$$\text{Outside diameter of cable} = 1\tfrac{5}{8} \text{ in.}$$
$$\text{Recommended final prestress} = 93,000 \text{ lb per cable}$$
$$\text{Initial prestress} = \frac{93,000}{0.85} = 109,400 \text{ lb per cable}$$

Therefore, **use eight cables** at an initial prestress of 105,500 lb each.

Section 2616 of the ACI Code requires a minimum cover of $1\tfrac{1}{2}$ in., and Sec.

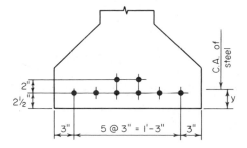

fig. 22-14 Location of tendons at midspan.

2617 permits the ducts to be bundled at the center.   We shall try the tendon pattern shown in Fig. 22-14.

$$y = \frac{6 \times 2.5 + 2 \times 4.5}{8} = 3.0 \text{ in.} \qquad \text{OK}$$

In establishing the trajectory of the prestressing force, try $e = 0$ at the supports. The prestress at the ends is therefore

$$f_{bp} = f_{tp} = \frac{844,000}{856} = +986 \text{ psi}$$

Since e varies parabolically from maximum at midspan to zero at the supports, it follows that the prestresses also vary parabolically.

The diagrams in Fig. 22-15 represent the initial and final stresses in the extreme fibers from the support to midspan. In Fig. 22-15a, the parabolic arc AB, which has its summit at B, represents f_{bp}, and the parabolic arc OC represents the absolute value of f_{bw}. The vertical distance between the arcs at a given section represents the value of f_{bi}; this value is maximum at midspan.

In Fig. 22-15b, arc $A'B'$ represents the absolute value of the final prestress, and arc OC' represents the absolute value of the gravity-load stress in the bottom fiber. The vertical distance between the arcs represents the value of f_{bf}. This stress is compressive in the interval ON and tensile in the interval NM. Analogous comments apply to Fig. 22-15c and d. The stress f_{ti} is compressive in the interval OQ and tensile in the interval QM.

Examination of the stress diagrams in Fig. 22-15 discloses that in all instances the stresses fall within the allowable range, and the trajectory is therefore satisfactory.

We shall now investigate the member for ultimate strength and ascertain whether the steel index is below the limit imposed by Sec. 2609. Ultimate-load conditions are critical at midspan.

$$d = 62 - 3 = 59.0 \text{ in.} \qquad A_s = 8 \times 0.723 = 5.784 \text{ sq in.}$$

$$p = \frac{A_s}{bd} = \frac{5.784}{32 \times 59.0} = 0.00306$$

Applying Eq. (22-8), we obtain

$$f_{su} = 236,000 \left(1 - \frac{0.5 \times 0.00306 \times 236,000}{5000} \right) = 219,000 \text{ psi}$$

$$T_u = A_s f_{su} = 5.784 \times 219,000 = 1,267,000 \text{ lb}$$

$$\text{Concrete area under stress} = \frac{1,267,000}{0.85 \times 5000} = 298 \text{ sq in.}$$

This is the shaded area in Fig. 22-16, as the following calculation proves:

$$32 \times 9.53 - 4.59 \times 1.53 = 305 - 7 = 298 \text{ sq in.}$$
$$\text{Area of } ABCD = 8 \times 9.53 = 76.24 \text{ sq in.}$$

By proportion, the steel area A_{sr} that is required to balance the force in this web strip is

$$A_{sr} = 5.784 \times \frac{76.24}{298} = 1.48 \text{ sq in.}$$

$$q = \frac{A_{sr} f_{su}}{b' d f_c'} = \frac{1.48 \times 219,000}{8 \times 59.0 \times 5000} = 0.137 < 0.30 \qquad \text{OK}$$

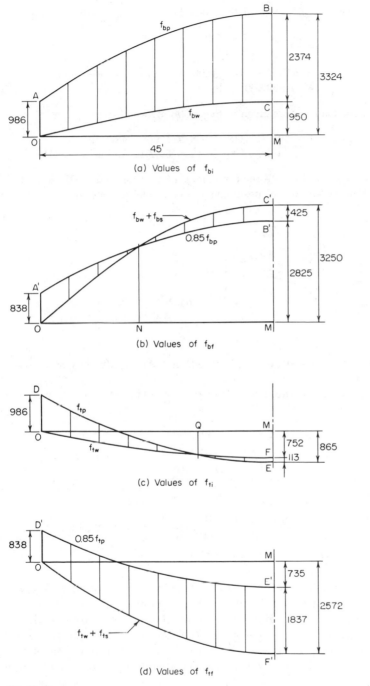

(a) Values of f_{bi}

(b) Values of f_{bf}

(c) Values of f_{ti}

(d) Values of f_{tf}

fig. 22-15

To locate the centroidal axis of the shaded area in Fig. 22-16, we have

$$m = \frac{305 \times 4.77 - 7(9.53 - 0.51)}{298} = 4.67 \text{ in.}$$

$$M_u = \phi T_u(d - m) = 0.90 \times 1,267,000(59.0 - 4.67)$$
$$= 61,950,000 \text{ in.-lb}$$

Applying the load factors given in Sec. 1506(a), we obtain

$$w_u = 1.5(892 + 1160) + 1.8 \times 1000 = 4878 \text{ plf}$$
$$M_u = \tfrac{1}{8} \times 4878 \times 90^2 \times 12 = 59,270,000 \text{ in.-lb} \qquad \text{OK}$$

The calculations for web-reinforcement area are similar to those in Example 22-11. For the method of designing the end blocks, refer to G. Winter et al.:

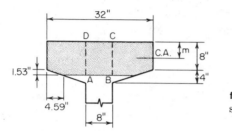

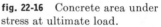

fig. 22-16   Concrete area under stress at ultimate load.

"Design of Concrete Structures," 7th ed., Art. 11.13, McGraw-Hill Book Company, New York, 1964.

We shall compute the camber at transfer. The value of E_c was found in Example 22-10.

$$E_c I = 3.644 \times 10^6 \times 394,800 = 1.44 \times 10^{12} \text{ lb-in.}^2$$

$$\Delta_w = -\frac{5 \times 892 \times 90^4 \times 1728}{384 \times 1.44 \times 10^{12}} = -0.91 \text{ in.}$$

Equation (22-7c) yields

$$\Delta_p = \frac{5 \times 844,000 \times 31.6 \times 90^2 \times 144}{48 \times 1.44 \times 10^{12}} = 2.25 \text{ in.}$$

$$\Delta_i = 2.25 - 0.91 = \textbf{1.34 in.}$$

22-16   Alternative Methods of Analysis for Parabolic Trajectories

Where the prestressing force has a parabolic trajectory, the prestress shear and moment at a given section may be evaluated by two alternative methods. One method considers the action of the prestressing force at the given section; the other method considers the action of the prestressing force within the interval between the support and the given section.

Figure 22-17 shows the prestressing forces acting on the concrete in an interval AC of a beam. Let w denote the vertical component of the radial force exerted by the steel on the concrete in a unit longitudinal distance, this force being positive if directed downward. Let V_{pq} and

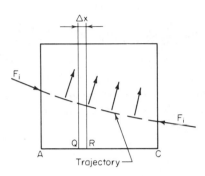

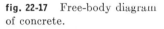

fig. 22-17 Free-body diagram of concrete.

V_{pr} denote the prestress shear at Q and R, respectively. Applying Eq. (22-1), we have

$$V_{pr} - V_{pq} = -F_i(m_r - m_q) \qquad \therefore \frac{dV_p}{dx} - -F_i \frac{dm}{dx}$$

Let the subscripts a, m, and b refer to the section at the left support, midspan, and right support, respectively; let L denote the beam span. Applying Eqs. (2-20) and (5-1), we have

$$\frac{dV_p}{dx} = -\frac{4F_i}{L^2}(e_a - 2e_m + e_b) = -w$$

$$\therefore w = \frac{4F_i}{L^2}(e_a - 2e_m + e_b) \tag{22-11}$$

This result discloses that when the trajectory is parabolic w is uniform across the span. The radial forces are always directed toward the center of curvature, since the tendons seek to become straight when subjected to tensile forces at their ends.

Example 22-13 The beam in Fig. 22-18 is subjected to an initial prestressing force of 860 kips on a parabolic trajectory. The eccentricities are as follows:

$$e_a = 1 \text{ in.} \qquad e_m = 30 \text{ in.} \qquad e_b = -3 \text{ in.}$$

Evaluate the prestress shear and prestress moment at section C by each of the following methods: (a) by applying the properties of the trajectory at C and (b) by considering the prestressing action of the steel on the concrete in interval AC.

Solution

PART *a*. The eccentricity and slope of the trajectory at C are found by applying Eqs. (2-18) and (2-19).

$$e_a - 2e_m + e_b = 1 - 60 - 3 = -62 \text{ in.}$$

$$3e_a - 4e_m + e_b = 3 - 120 - 3 = -120 \text{ in.}$$

$$e_c = 2(-62)\left(\frac{20}{100}\right)^2 + 120\,\frac{20}{100} + 1 = 20.04 \text{ in.}$$

$$m_c = 4\,\frac{-62}{12}\,\frac{20}{100^2} - \frac{-120}{12 \times 100} = 0.0587$$

$$V_{pc} = -F_i m_c = -860{,}000 \times 0.0587 = \mathbf{-50{,}480\ lb}$$

$$M_{pc} = -F_i e_c = -860{,}000 \times 20.04 = \mathbf{-17{,}230{,}000\ in.\text{-}lb}$$

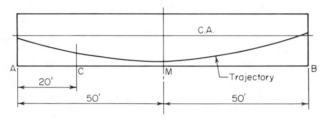

fig. 22-18

PART *b*. Equation (22-11) yields

$$w = \frac{4F_i}{L^2}\,\frac{-62}{12} = -0.002067 F_i \qquad \text{plf}$$

By Eq. (2-21*a*),

$$m_a = -\,\frac{-120}{100 \times 12} = 0.1 \qquad V_{pa} = -0.1F_i$$

$$V_{pc} = V_{pa} - 20w = F_i(-0.1 + 20 \times 0.002067)$$
$$= -0.0587F_i = -50{,}480 \text{ lb}$$

$$M_{pc} = M_{pa} + V_{pa} \times 240 - 20w \times 120$$
$$= F_i(-1 - 0.1 \times 240 + 20 \times 0.002067 \times 120)$$
$$= -20.04F_i = -17{,}230{,}000 \text{ in.-lb}$$

22-17   Prestress Moments in Continuous Beams   We shall now analyze the prestress moments that exist in a continuous beam.   Figure 22-19 illustrates a two-span beam subjected to a prestressing force that has a parabolic trajectory in each span, and Fig. 22-20 shows the forces on the concrete in span AB caused solely by prestressing.   Since the portions AB and BC are constrained to undergo an identical rotation at B, there exists at this section a bending moment M_{kb} in addition to that resulting from the eccentricity of F_i. This moment M_{kb} induces reactions at the supports. Thus, at every section of the beam there is a moment caused by continuity of the member as well as the moment $-F_ie$. We shall refer to the former as the *continuity moment* and the latter as the *eccen-*

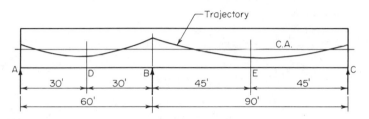

fig. 22-19

tricity moment. The numerical value of the continuity moment is directly proportional to the distance from the given section to the end support.

The continuity moment at the interior support may be readily evaluated by adopting the second method of analysis presented in Art. 22-16, since this renders the continuous member amenable to analysis by the theorem of three moments or moment distribution. Alternatively, this continuity moment may be found directly by means of an equation.

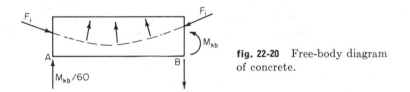

fig. 22-20 Free-body diagram of concrete.

With reference to Fig. 22-19, let the subscripts 1 and 2 refer to span AB and BC, respectively, and let the subscripts d and e refer to the midspan sections. Then

$$M_{kb} = F_i\left(\frac{e_b}{2} + \frac{L_1 e_d + L_2 e_e}{L_1 + L_2}\right) \tag{22-12}$$

Example 22-14 The continuous beam in Fig. 22-19 has a prestressing force of 96 kips. The eccentricities are as follows:

$$e_a = -0.40 \text{ in.} \qquad e_d = +0.60 \text{ in.} \qquad e_b = -1.20 \text{ in.}$$
$$e_e = +0.64 \text{ in.} \qquad e_c = -0.60 \text{ in.}$$

Construct the prestress-moment diagram for this member, indicating all significant values.

278   *Comprehensive Structural Design Guide*

Solution. Equation (22-12) yields the following:

$$M_{kb} = F_i\left(\frac{-1.20}{2} + \frac{60 \times 0.60 + 90 \times 0.64}{60 + 90}\right) = 0.024F_i$$

Combining this with the eccentricity moment of $1.20F_i$, we obtain $1.224F_i$ as the prestress moment at B.

$$M_{pa} = \frac{0.40}{12} \times 96,000 = 3200 \text{ ft-lb}$$

$$M_{pb} = \frac{1.224}{12} \times 96,000 = 9792 \text{ ft-lb}$$

$$M_{pc} = \frac{0.60}{12} \times 96,000 = 4800 \text{ ft-lb}$$

$$M_{pd} = -F_i e_d + M_{kd} = \frac{F_i(-0.60 + \frac{1}{2} \times 0.024)}{12}$$
$$= -4704 \text{ ft-lb}$$

$$M_{pe} = \frac{F_i(-0.64 + \frac{1}{2} \times 0.024)}{12} = -5024 \text{ ft-lb}$$

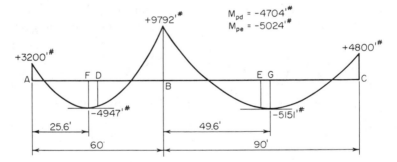

fig. 22-21   Prestress-moment diagram.

The prestress-moment diagram is shown in Fig. 22-21.   The maximum negative moments are found by applying Eqs. (2-22).

$$AF = 25.6 \text{ ft} \qquad M_{pf} = -4947 \text{ ft-lb}$$
$$BG = 49.6 \text{ ft} \qquad M_{pg} = -5151 \text{ ft-lb}$$

22-18   Principle of Linear Transformation   With reference to the continuous beam in Fig. 22-19, consider that the trajectory of the prestressing force is displaced in the following manner: The eccentricities at A and C remain constant, and the change in eccentricity at a given section is directly proportional to the distance from the given section to A or C depending on whether the section is in AB or BC, respectively.   Thi modification is referred to as a *linear transformation.* We wish to assess the effect of a linear transformation on the prestress moments.

Let PS_1 and PS_2 denote, respectively, the original prestressing system and the system resulting from the linear transformation; let e' denote the change in eccentricity at B during the transformation. Let PS_3 denote

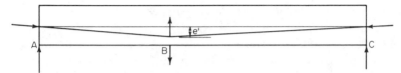

fig. 22-22   Hypothetical prestressing system and forces exerted on concrete.

a prestressing system in which the force has the same value as in PS_1 and PS_2 and the trajectory has the rectilinear form shown in Fig. 22-22. From Eq. (22-2), we deduce that the prestress moments will be the same whether the beam is subjected to PS_2 alone or to a combination of PS_1 and PS_3.

Under the system PS_3 shown in Fig. 22-22, the steel exerts three forces on the concrete: one at each end, and one at the deflection point above the interior support, the latter resulting from the change in direction of the prestressing force. Because we consider the horizontal component of the prestressing force to be equal to the force itself, it follows that the force acting at the deflection point has no horizontal component. Since the three forces that the steel exerts on the concrete are applied directly at the supports, their vertical components do not induce bending. Similarly, since the forces at A and C are applied at the centroidal axis, their horizontal components do not induce bending. Consequently, system PS_3 does not induce any prestress moments whatsoever. Since PS_2 is equivalent to the combination of PS_1 and PS_3 with respect to flexure, it follows that the prestress moments associated with PS_2 and those associated with PS_1 are identical. Thus, the linear transformation of the trajectory was not accompanied by any change in prestress moments. Manifestly, this conclusion applies regardless of whether the original trajectory is curved or rectilinear.

We thus arrive at the highly important *principle of linear transformation* for a two-span continuous beam: *The prestress moments remain constant when the trajectory of the prestressing force is transformed linearly.* This principle is widely applied in plotting a trial trajectory for a continuous beam.

Equation (22-12) affords an alternative method of proving the principle of linear transformation. By setting the change in eccentricity at the midspan sections equal to one-half that at B, we find that the change in continuity moment at B is $F_i e'$, which precisely balances the change in eccentricity moment. Thus, the prestress moment at B remains constant, and this condition obtains throughout the member.

Two points warrant emphasis. First, in a linear transformation, the eccentricities at the end supports remain constant. Second, the system PS_2 is equivalent to the combination of PS_1 and PS_3 with respect to flexure but not with respect to axial stresses.

22-19   Concordant Trajectories   From our analysis of a two-span continuous beam, the following conclusions have emerged:

1. The prestress moment M_p consists of two elements: an eccentricity moment $-F_i e$ and a continuity moment M_k. The latter varies linearly from zero at the ends to its maximum numerical value at the interior support.

2. In a linear transformation, the change in $-F_i e$ is offset by a compensatory change in M_k, the result being that M_p remains constant.

Equation (22-12) reveals that we may assign a set of values to the eccentricity at the interior support and at the two midspan sections that will cause a zero continuity moment at the interior support, and therefore throughout the member. Consequently, at any section in the continuous beam, we have $M_p = -F_i e$. A trajectory that is characterized by this condition is referred to as a *concordant trajectory*.

Assume that we are given a nonconcordant trajectory. Manifestly, we may transform this linearly to secure one that is concordant. Since M_p remains constant during the linear transformation, the concordant trajectory may be plotted simply by equating the final eccentricity at each section to $-M_p/F_i$. An alternative method is to apply Eq. (22-12) to find the required change in eccentricity at the interior support.

Example 22-15   With reference to the beam in Example 22-14, transform the trajectory linearly to secure a concordant trajectory.

Solution.   Refer to Fig. 22-21. As before,

$$e_a = -0.40 \text{ in.} \quad \text{and} \quad e_c = -0.60 \text{ in.}$$

Then
$$e_d = \frac{4704 \times 12}{96,000} = +0.588 \text{ in.}$$

$$e_b = -\frac{9792 \times 12}{96,000} = -1.224 \text{ in.}$$

$$e_e = \frac{5024 \times 12}{96,000} = +0.628 \text{ in.}$$

As an alternative method of solution, let e' denote the increase in eccentricity at B during the linear transformation. Setting M_{kb} in Eq. (22-12) equal to zero we obtain

$$\frac{-1.20 + e'}{2} + \frac{60(0.60 + 0.5e') + 90(0.64 + 0.5e')}{150} = 0$$

Solving, $e' = -0.024$ in.

Then $e_b = -1.20 - 0.024 = -1.224$ in.

$$e_d = +0.60 - 0.012 = +0.588 \text{ in.}$$

$$e_e = +0.64 - 0.012 = +0.628 \text{ in.}$$

Example 22-16 The beam in Fig. 22-19 is to sustain an initial prestressing force of 72 kips having an eccentricity of -2 in. at B. Design a trajectory that will yield the prestress moments recorded in Fig. 22-21.

Solution. We shall first plot a concordant trajectory by setting $e = -M_p/F_i$.

$$e_a = -\frac{3200 \times 12}{72,000} = -0.533 \text{ in.}$$

$$e_d = +0.784 \text{ in.} \qquad e_b = -1.632 \text{ in.}$$

$$e_e = +0.837 \text{ in.} \qquad e_c = -0.800 \text{ in.}$$

The revisions in eccentricity during the linear transformation are as follows:

$$\Delta e_b = -2 - (-1.632) = -0.368 \text{ in.}$$

$$\Delta e_a = \Delta e_c = 0 \qquad \Delta e_d = \Delta e_e = -0.184 \text{ in.}$$

The final eccentricities are as follows:

$$e_a = -0.533 \text{ in.} \qquad e_b = -2 \text{ in.} \qquad e_c = -0.800 \text{ in.}$$

$$e_d = +0.784 - 0.184 = +0.600 \text{ in.} \qquad e_e = +0.837 - 0.184 = +0.653 \text{ in.}$$

22-20 Design of Continuous Beams Consider that a beam is to be continuous over two equal spans and support a uniformly distributed load. Assume that we have arrived at a satisfactory section and now wish to design the prestressing system, using a parabolic trajectory. An exact method of design consists of the following steps: First, write equations for the prestress moment, beam-weight moment, and the maximum and minimum potential superimposed-load moments, expressing each moment in terms of the distance x from a given section to the exterior support for that span. Second, apply these equations to identify the sections at which the initial and final stresses are critical. Third, design the prestressing system to restrict the critical stresses to their allowable range.

The exact method of design that we have outlined is not particularly laborious when applied to a prismatic beam carrying a uniform load. Nevertheless, in practice the prestressing system is designed by an approximate method that is intended to obviate the need for applying calculus. This method consists of dividing each span into a suitable number of intervals and analyzing the stresses at each boundary section.

It assumes that the maximum and minimum potential superimposed-load moments at a section occur under one of the following conditions of loading rather than under a condition of partial loading:

1. Load on entire left span, none on right span
2. Load on entire right span, none on left span
3. Load across entire beam

We shall adopt the approximate method of design for illustrative purposes.

If the trajectory is made symmetrical about the center support, the vertical component w of the force exerted by the steel on the concrete in a unit longitudinal distance is uniform across the entire length of member. If in addition the eccentricity at the ends is set equal to zero, the prestress-moment diagram has the same form as the bending-moment diagram of a non-prestressed beam continuous over two equal spans and subjected to a uniform load across its entire length.   It therefore follows that the prestress moments at the boundary sections previously referred to have specific *relative* values, although their absolute values are functions of the magnitude and trajectory of the prestressing force.

The design of the prestressing system by the approximate method may be performed in the following manner: Evaluate the relative prestress moments at the boundary sections and select a trajectory having ordinates directly proportional to these moments.   The trajectory thus fashioned is concordant.   Compute the prestressing force that is required to restrict the stresses to their allowable range.   Then transform the concordant trajectory linearly to secure one that lies entirely within the confines of the section.   Although the number of satisfactory concordant trajectories is infinite, the one to be selected is of course that which requires the minimum prestressing force.   Therefore, the selection of the trajectory and the calculation of the prestressing force are blended into one operation.

Example 22-17   A T beam that is continuous over two spans of 120 ft each is to carry a uniformly distributed live load of 880 plf.   The cross section has the following properties:

$$A = 1440 \text{ sq in.} \qquad I = 752,000 \text{ in.}^4$$
$$y_b = 50.6 \text{ in.} \qquad y_t = 23.4 \text{ in.}$$

The allowable stresses are as follows:

Initial: $+2400$ and -60 psi
Final: $+2250$ and -60 psi

Assume that the minimum possible distance from the extremity of the section to the centroidal axis of the prestressing steel is 9 in.   Design the prestressing system, using a parabolic trajectory.

Solution

$$S_b = 14,860 \text{ in.}^3 \qquad S_t = 32,140 \text{ in.}^3$$
$$k_b = 22.32 \text{ in.} \qquad k_t = 10.32 \text{ in.} \qquad w_w = 1500 \text{ plf}$$

We shall divide the left span into five intervals, as shown in Fig. 22-23. (The greater the number of intervals chosen, the more reliable are the results.) Let

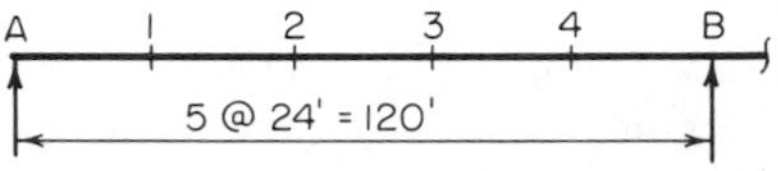

fig. 22-23 Division of span into intervals.

C_1, C_2, and C_3 denote the bending-moment coefficients associated with the loading conditions previously enumerated. The values of these coefficients at the boundary sections are recorded in Table 22-2. By way of illustration, we shall present

Table 22-2   Calculations for Two-span Continuous Beam

Line	Section	1	2	3	4	B
1	C_1	+0.0675	+0.0950	+0.0825	+0.0300	−0.0625
2	C_2	−0.0125	−0.0250	−0.0375	−0.0500	−0.0625
3	C_3	+0.0550	+0.0700	+0.0450	−0.0200	−0.1250
4	f_{bw}	−959	−1221	−785	+349	+2180
5	f_{bs1}	−691	−972	−844	−307	+640
6	f_{bs2}	+128	+256	+384	+512	+640
7	f_{tw}	+444	+565	+363	−161	−1008
8	f_{ts1}	+319	+450	+390	+142	−296
9	f_{ts2}	−59	−118	−177	−237	−296
10	e_{con}	+17.19	+21.87	+14.06	−6.25	−39.05
11	f_{bp}	+2148	+2513	+1903	+318	−2243
12	f_{tp}	+185	+16	+298	+1031	+2215
13	$0.85f_{bp}$	+1826	+2136	+1618	+270	−1906
14	$0.85f_{tp}$	+157	+14	+253	+876	+1883

At midspan: $C_3 = +0.0625$ and $e_{con} = +19.53$

the calculations pertaining to section 3. Refer to Case 29 on page 2-130 of the AISC Manual, which represents condition 1.

$$R_1 = \tfrac{7}{16}wL \qquad R_3 = -\tfrac{1}{16}wL$$

The bending moment at section 3 is

$$M = \tfrac{7}{16}wL \times 0.6L - \tfrac{1}{2}w(0.6L)^2 = 0.0825wL^2$$
$$C_1 = \frac{M}{wL^2} = +0.0825$$

By interchanging the spans, we obtain condition 2.   At section 3,

$$M = -\tfrac{1}{16}wL \times 0.6L = -0.0375wL^2 \qquad C_2 = -0.0375$$
$$C_3 = C_1 + C_2 = +0.0825 - 0.0375 = +0.0450$$

At midspan, $C_3 = +0.0625$

Since the gravity loads induce the maximum positive moment at section 2 and the maximum negative moment at section B, the prestressing system will be designed to satisfy the requirements at these sections.   (However, the stresses at all boundary sections will be evaluated for completeness.)   The Magnel diagram for section 2 is similar to that in Fig. 22-7, but that for section B is radically different.

$$M_w = C_3 \times 1500 \times 120^2 \times 12 = 259,200,000C_3 \qquad \text{in.-lb}$$

$$f_{bw} = -\frac{259,200,000C_3}{14,860} = -17,440C_3$$

For the live-load stresses, let the subscripts 1 and 2 refer to the respective loading conditions.   By proportion,

$$f_{bs1} = \frac{880}{1500}(-17,440)C_1 = -10,230C_1 \qquad f_{bs2} = -10,230C_2$$

$$f_{tw} = 8065C_3 \qquad f_{ts1} = 4731C_1 \qquad f_{ts2} = 4731C_2$$

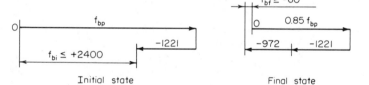

Initial state   Final state

(a) Limiting values of f_{bp} at section 2

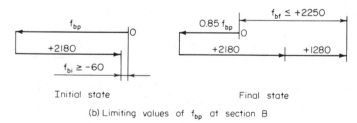

Initial state   Final state

(b) Limiting values of f_{bp} at section B

fig. 22-24

By substituting the values of the moment coefficients, we obtain the gravity-load stresses recorded in Table 22-2.

Since S_t far exceeds S_b, it is evident that the bottom-fiber stresses will be critical. We shall demarcate the allowable range of values of f_{bp} at sections 2 and B. Refer to Fig. 22-24.

At section 2: $$f_{bp} \leq +3621 \text{ psi} \tag{a}$$
$$0.85f_{bp} \geq 1221 + 972 - 60$$
$$\therefore f_{bp} \geq +2509 \text{ psi} \tag{b}$$
At section B: $$f_{bp} \geq -2240 \text{ psi} \tag{c}$$
$$0.85f_{bp} \leq -(2180 + 1280) + 2250$$
$$f_{bp} \leq -1424 \text{ psi} \tag{d}$$

Assume that we have a concordant trajectory that is symmetrical about the center support and has zero eccentricity at the ends. As previously stated, the prestress-moment diagram has the same form as the bending-moment diagram for loading condition 3; the values of C_3 therefore represent the relative values of the eccentricity. Then

$$\frac{e_b}{e_2} = \frac{-0.1250}{+0.0700} = -1.786 \qquad \therefore e_b = -1.786e_2$$

By substituting the limiting values of f_{bp} in Eq. (22-5), with e_b expressed in terms of e_2, we arrive at the following results:

$$\frac{1}{F_i} \geq \frac{k_t + e_2}{3621S_b} \qquad (a') \qquad\qquad \frac{1}{F_i} \leq \frac{k_t + e_2}{2509S_b} \qquad (b')$$

$$\frac{1}{F_i} \geq \frac{1.786e_2 - k_t}{2240S_b} \qquad (c') \qquad\qquad \frac{1}{F_i} \leq \frac{1.786e_2 - k_t}{1424S_b} \qquad (d')$$

By treating these relationships as equalities and plotting the straight lines by which they are represented, we obtain the composite Magnel diagram in Fig. 22-25. The shaded area represents the region of permissible sets of values of e_2 and $1/F_i$. The minimum allowable value of F_i is given by point A, at the intersection of lines b' and c'. Then

$$\frac{10.32 + e_2}{2509} = \frac{1.786e_2 - 10.32}{2240}$$

Solving, $\qquad e_2 = 21.87 \text{ in.} \qquad F_i = \textbf{1,160,000 lb}$

With e_2 determined, the concordant trajectory may be plotted by applying the values of C_3. For example, at section 1 and at midspan,

$$e_1 = +21.87 \times \frac{0.0550}{0.0700} = +17.19 \text{ in.}$$

$$e_m = +21.87 \times \frac{0.0625}{0.0700} = +19.53 \text{ in.}$$

The results are recorded on line 10 in Table 22-2. It is apparent that this concordant trajectory is satisfactory in the respect that it may be linearly transformed to one falling within the confines of the section; the formal proof will appear later.

The values of f_{bp} and f_{tp}, which are recorded on lines 11 and 12 in the table, are found by applying Eq. (22-5). For example, at section 1,

$$f_{bp} = \frac{1,160,000(10.32 + 17.19)}{14,860} = +2148 \text{ psi}$$

$$f_{tp} = \frac{1,160,000(22.32 - 17.19)}{32,140} = +185 \text{ psi}$$

The reduced values of the prestresses are recorded on lines 13 and 14.

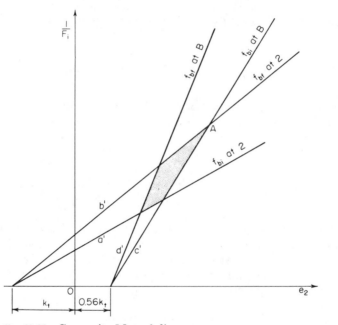

fig. 22-25   Composite Magnel diagram.

The prestressing system may be checked by investigating the stresses at every boundary section.

Section 1: $f_{bi} = -959 + 2148 = +1189$ psi
 $f_{bf} = -959 - 691 + 1826 = +176$ psi
 $f_{ti} = +444 + 185 = +629$ psi
 $f_{tf} = +444 + 319 + 157 = +920$ psi

Section 2: $f_{bi} = -1221 + 2513 = +1292$ psi
 $f_{bf} = -1221 - 972 + 2136 = -57$ psi
 $f_{ti} = +565 + 16 = +581$ psi
 $f_{tf} = +565 + 450 + 14 = +1029$ psi

Section 3: $f_{bi} = -785 + 1903 = +1118$ psi
 $f_{bf} = -785 - 844 + 1618 = -11$ psi
 $f_{ti} = +363 + 298 = +661$ psi
 $f_{tf} = +363 + 390 + 253 = +1006$ psi

Section 4: $f_{bi} = +349 + 318 = +667$ psi

$f_{bf} = +349 - 307 + 270 = +312$ psi

or $f_{bf} = +349 + 512 + 270 = +1131$ psi

$f_{ti} = -161 + 1031 = +870$ psi

$f_{tf} = -161 - 237 + 876 = +478$ psi

or $f_{tf} = -161 + 142 + 876 = +857$ psi

Section B: $f_{bi} = +2180 - 2243 = -63$ psi

$f_{bf} = +2180 + 1280 - 1906 = +1554$ psi

$f_{ti} = -1008 + 2215 = +1207$ psi

$f_{tf} = -1008 - 592 + 1883 = +283$ psi

In all instances, the stresses lie within the allowable range.

The true trajectory may now be established by linearly transforming the concordant trajectory. The imposed limits are as follows:

$$e_{\max} = y_b - 9 = 41.6 \text{ in.}$$
$$e_{\min} = -(y_t - 9) = -14.4 \text{ in.}$$

Try $e_b = -14$ in. Since the displacement of the trajectory at midspan is one-half that at B, the eccentricity at midspan is

$$e_m = +19.53 + \tfrac{1}{2}(39.05 - 14) = +32.06 \text{ in.}$$

The maximum eccentricity is found by applying Eq. (2-22b).

$$e_s = -\frac{1}{8}\frac{(-4 \times 32.06 - 14)^2}{-2 \times 32.06 - 14} = +32.4 < 41.6 \text{ in.} \qquad \text{OK}$$

The final trajectory is therefore defined by the following values:

$$e_a = 0 \qquad e_m = +32.06 \text{ in.} \qquad e_b = -14 \text{ in.}$$

The member must be checked for ultimate-strength capacity. The procedure is the same as in the preceding examples.

The calculations pertaining to any quantity that varies parabolically across the span may be readily checked by verifying that the values at uniformly spaced sections have equal "second differences." For example, with respect to the values of $0.85f_{bp}$ on line 13, the verification is as follows:

```
+1826        +2136        +1618        +270        -1906
       -310         +518        +1348       +2176
            -828         -830         -828
```

The values on the second and third lines represent the differences between successive values on the preceding line.

In Example 22-17, we found that the maximum eccentricity of the prestressing force as governed by the allowable stresses is considerably below the upper limit set by the beam dimensions. Referring to Fig. 22-25, assume that we arbitrarily remove the restrictions imposed by line c'. It then becomes possible to increase e_2 to the value corresponding to a maximum eccentricity of 41.6 in. and thereby reduce the value of F_i. This revision in the prestressing system causes the initial tensile stress at B to become excessive, but the condition may be remedied by supplying non-prestressed reinforcement over the interior support. Since the excess tension at transfer extends across a comparatively short distance, the saving accruing from the reduction in prestressing force would more than offset the cost of the added reinforcement.

Example 22-18   With reference to Example 22-17, design the prestressing system if this is to be supplemented with non-prestressed reinforcement.
   Solution. We shall try the following values:

$$e_a = 0 \qquad e_m = +41 \text{ in.} \qquad e_b = -14 \text{ in.}$$

The maximum eccentricity as given by Eq. (2-22b) is

$$e_s = -\frac{1}{8}\frac{(-4 \times 41 - 14)^2}{-2 \times 41 - 14} = +41.3 \text{ in.}$$

The upper limit is $+41.6$ in., and the trial trajectory is therefore satisfactory.
   To analyze the stresses, we shall secure a hypothetical concordant trajectory by linearly transforming the true trajectory.   Let y denote the upward displacement at B; refer to the values of C_3 in Table 22-2.

$$\frac{e_m}{e_b} = \frac{41 - \frac{1}{2}y}{-14 - y} = \frac{+0.0625}{-0.1250} \qquad y = 34 \text{ in.}$$

$$e_a = 0 \qquad e_m = +24 \text{ in.} \qquad e_b = -48 \text{ in.}$$

$$e_1 = -48 \times \frac{+0.0550}{-0.1250} = +21.12 \text{ in.}$$

$$e_2 = +26.88 \text{ in.} \qquad e_3 = +17.28 \text{ in.} \qquad e_4 = -7.68 \text{ in.}$$

Applying the relationship (b') in Example 22-17, we have

$$F_i = \frac{2509 \times 14,860}{10.32 + 26.88} = \textbf{1,000,000 lb}$$

The introduction of non-prestressed reinforcement has served to reduce the prestressing force by 14 percent.
   The stresses at the boundary sections are recorded in Table 22-3.   At sections 1 through 4, the final stresses are based upon loading condition 1.   The slight discrepancy between the final stress at section 2 and the allowable value of -60 psi arises from the degree of precision inherent in these calculations.   With the exception of f_{bi} at B, all stresses at the boundary sections lie within the allowable range.
   To establish the interval within which non-prestressed reinforcement is required, we shall write an equation for f_{bi}.   Since f_{bp} and f_{bw} vary parabolically across the span, their sum f_{bi} also varies in this manner.   Let x denote the dis-

Table 22-3 Calculations for Two-span Continuous Beam

Section	1	2	3	4	B
e_{con}	+21.12	+26.88	+17.28	−7.68	−48.00
f_{bp}	+2116	+2503	+1857	+178	−2535
f_{tp}	+37	−142	+157	+933	+2188
$0.85f_{bp}$	+1799	+2128	+1578	+151	−2155
$0.85f_{tp}$	+31	−121	+133	+793	+1860
f_{bi}	+1157	+1282	+1072	+527	−355
f_{bf}	+149	−65	−51	+193	+1305
f_{ti}	+481	+423	+520	+772	+1180
f_{tf}	+794	+894	+886	+774	+260

tance from the interior support to a given section. The equation for f_{bi} is found by applying Eq. (2-18); we shall use the initial-stress values at sections B, 3, and 1.

$$-355 - 2 \times 1072 + 1157 = -1342$$
$$3(-355) - 4 \times 1072 + 1157 = -4196$$
$$f_{bi} = -2684\left(\frac{x}{96}\right)^2 + 4196\frac{x}{96} - 355$$

When $f_{bi} = -60$ psi, $x = 7.08$ ft. The tensile stress at transfer is therefore excessive in an interval of only 14.16 ft. The non-prestressed reinforcement is designed for the excess tension.

As shown in Fig. 22-20, the prestressing force in a continuous beam induces reactions at the supports, and these reactions may be readily evaluated by computing the continuity moment at any section.

Example 22-19 With reference to the beam in Example 22-17, compute the reactions at the supports caused by the initial prestressing force.

Solution. The prestress moment at a given section may be written in the following forms:

$$M_p = -F_i e + M_k \quad \text{and} \quad M_p = -F_i e_{con}$$
$$\therefore M_k = F_i(e - e_{con})$$

Substituting the values of eccentricity at section B, we have

$$M_{kb} = 1160(-14 + 39.05) = 29{,}060 \text{ in.-kips}$$
$$R_a = \frac{29{,}060}{120 \times 12} = \textbf{20.2 kips} \qquad R_b = \textbf{−40.4 kips}$$

Alternatively, M_{kb} may be found by applying Eq. (22-12). Since the member is symmetrical, this reduces to

$$M_{kb} = F_i\left(\frac{e_b}{2} + e_m\right) = F_i(-7 + 32.06)$$

TWENTY-THREE
Composite Steel-and-concrete Beams

23-1 Introduction When a steel member supports a concrete slab, the steel and a portion of the tributary slab may be considered to function as a composite steel-and-concrete beam. There are two types of composite beams: those in which the steel is completely encased in concrete for fireproofing, and those in which the portion of the steel member below the concrete slab remains exposed. In the former, composite action is assumed to result from the natural bond of the two materials; in the latter, composite action is secured through the use of shear connectors welded to the top flange of the steel member.

The design of a composite steel-and-concrete beam is governed by Sec. 1.11 of the Specification of the American Institute of Steel Construction, adopted 1963. By convention, the composite section is analyzed by transforming it to an equivalent homogeneous section of steel, using the gross concrete area. The effects of plastic flow of the concrete are usually ignored in building design.

In the following material, it is to be understood that the grade of steel is ASTM A36. The symbol t denotes the slab thickness, and the superscripts c and n refer to the composite and noncomposite section, respectively.

23-2 Beams with Encased Steel   For this type of member, loads that
are applied prior to hardening of the concrete are carried by the steel
alone unless the member is provided with temporary shoring; loads that
are applied after hardening of the concrete are carried by the composite
member.   Since the concrete is poured monolithically and the steel is
fully encased within the concrete, the composite member is considered
to be continuous.   For a uniformly distributed load, the bending moments
in the composite member are usually assumed to be the following:

At midspan: $M = \frac{1}{20}wL^2$
At support: $M = -\frac{1}{12}wL^2$

Example 23-1   A concrete floor slab is to be supported by steel beams spaced
10 ft on centers and having a span of 28 ft 6 in.   The steel will be encased in
concrete with a minimum cover of 2 in. all around, and it will remain unshored
during construction.   The slab has been designed as $4\frac{1}{2}$ in. thick, with $f'_c = 3000$
psi.   The loading includes the following: live load, 120 psf; finished floor and
ceiling, 25 psf.   The steel beams have been tentatively designed as 16WF40.
Review the design.

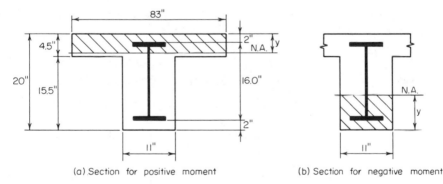

(a) Section for positive moment   (b) Section for negative moment

fig. 23-1   Steel beam encased in concrete.

Solution. Refer to Fig. 23-1.   Let the subscripts c, ts, and bs refer to the extreme
fiber of concrete, top of steel, and bottom of steel, respectively.   The properties
of the 16WF40 are as follows:

$$A = 11.77 \text{ sq in.} \qquad d = 16.00 \text{ in.}$$
$$I = 515.5 \text{ in.}^4 \qquad S = 64.4 \text{ in.}^3$$
$$\text{Flange width} = 7 \text{ in.}$$

In accordance with Sec. 1.11.2 of the AISC Specification and Table 1002(a) of the
ACI Code, we have

$$f_s = 24,000 \text{ psi} \qquad f_c = 1350 \text{ psi} \qquad n = 9$$

Section 1.11.1 of the AISC Specification restricts the effective width of the concrete in the composite beam to the lowest of the following values:

$$\tfrac{1}{4}L = \tfrac{1}{4} \times 28.5 \times 12 = 85.5 \text{ in.}$$
$$\text{Spacing of beams} = 120 \text{ in.}$$
$$16t + \text{haunch} = 16 \times 4.5 + 11 = 83 \text{ in.} \quad \text{(governs)}$$

We shall analyze the transformed section with respect to positive moment. The width of steel that replaces the concrete is

$$\tfrac{83}{9} = 9.22 \text{ in.}$$

Assume that the neutral axis lies within the flange. Taking statical moments with respect to this axis, we obtain

$$\tfrac{1}{2} \times 9.22y^2 - 11.77(10 - y) = 0 \quad \therefore y = 3.93 \text{ in.}$$
$$y_c = 3.93 \text{ in.} \qquad |y_{bs}| = 18 - 3.93 = 14.07 \text{ in.}$$
$$I = \tfrac{1}{3} \times 9.22 \times 3.93^3 + 515.5 + 11.77(10 - 3.93)^2$$
$$= 1136 \text{ in.}^4$$
$$S_c = \frac{1136}{3.93} = 289.1 \text{ in.}^3 \qquad S_{bs} = \frac{1136}{14.07} = 80.7 \text{ in.}^3$$

We shall analyze the transformed section with respect to negative moment. The width of steel that replaces the concrete is

$$\tfrac{11}{9} = 1.22 \text{ in.}$$

Taking statical moments with respect to the neutral axis, we obtain

$$11.77(10 - y) - \tfrac{1}{2} \times 1.22y^2 = 0 \quad \therefore y = 7.26 \text{ in.}$$
$$|y_c| = 7.26 \text{ in.} \qquad y_{ts} = 18 - 7.26 = 10.74 \text{ in.}$$
$$I = \tfrac{1}{3} \times 1.22 \times 7.26^3 + 515.5 + 11.77(10 - 7.26)^2$$
$$= 759.5 \text{ in.}^4$$
$$S_c = \frac{759.5}{7.26} = 104.6 \text{ in.}^3 \qquad S_{ts} = \frac{759.5}{10.74} = 70.7 \text{ in.}^3$$

The loads carried by the noncomposite member are as follows:

Slab: $\qquad \dfrac{4.5}{12} \times 150 \times 10 = 563 \text{ plf}$

Haunch: $\qquad \dfrac{11 \times 15.5}{144} \times 150 = 178$

Steel: $\qquad\qquad\qquad\qquad\qquad \underline{40}$

$$w^n = 781 \text{ plf}$$

The load carried by the composite member is

$$w^c = 145 \times 10 = 1450 \text{ plf}$$

The conditions at midspan are as follows:

$$M^n = \tfrac{1}{8} \times 781 \times 28.5^2 \times 12 = 951,500 \text{ in.-lb}$$
$$M^c = \tfrac{1}{20} \times 1450 \times 28.5^2 \times 12 = 706,600 \text{ in.-lb}$$

$$f_c = \frac{706,600}{289.1 \times 9} = 272 \text{ psi} \qquad \text{OK}$$

$$f_{bs} = \frac{951,500}{64.4} + \frac{706,600}{80.7} = 23,530 \text{ psi} \qquad \text{OK}$$

The conditions at the support are as follows:
By proportion, $M^c = 706,600 \times \tfrac{20}{12} = 1,177,700$ in.-lb

$$f_c = \frac{1,177,700}{104.6 \times 9} = 1251 \text{ psi} \qquad \text{OK}$$

$$f_{ts} = \frac{1,177,700}{70.7} = 16,660 \text{ psi} \qquad \text{OK}$$

The design is therefore satisfactory with respect to flexure, and we must now investigate the adequacy of the composite beam with respect to horizontal shear. This subject is treated in Art. 5-5. Where the bending moment is positive, a horizontal-shear failure would occur along the surface *abcd* in Fig. 23-2*a*. Resistance to shear flow is provided by bond between the steel and concrete along *bc* and by the pure-shear strength of the concrete along *ab* and *cd*. (The term *pure shear*

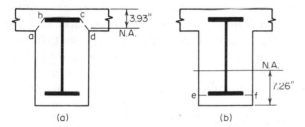

fig. 23-2   Critical planes for horizontal shear.

is used to distinguish this from shear that serves as a measure of diagonal tension.) The allowable stresses in bond and pure shear are usually taken as $0.03f'_c$ and $0.12f'_c$, respectively.

$$bc = 7 \text{ in.} \qquad ab = \sqrt{2.5^2 + 2^2} = 3.2 \text{ in.}$$
$$q_{\text{allow}} = 7 \times 90 + 2 \times 3.2 \times 360 = 2934 \text{ pli}$$

For the positive-moment interval, the maximum shear flow manifestly occurs at the section of contraflexure. Assume that this section lies at a distance of $0.2L$ from the support. The shear at this section is

$$V^c = 1450 \times 0.3 \times 28.5 = 12,400 \text{ lb}$$

For simplicity, we shall compute the shear flow at the neutral axis, where it is maximum, rather than at *abcd*.

$$Q = \tfrac{1}{2} \times 9.22 \times 3.93^2 = 71.20 \text{ in.}^3$$

$$q = \frac{VQ}{I} = \frac{12,400 \times 71.20}{1136} = 777 \text{ pli} \qquad \text{OK}$$

Where the bending moment is negative, a horizontal-shear failure would occur along the surface *ef* in Fig. 23-2*b*, and the section of maximum shear flow lies at the support.

$$q_{\text{allow}} = 7 \times 90 + 2 \times 2 \times 360 = 2070 \text{ pli}$$
$$Q = 1.22 \times 2(7.26 - 1) = 15.27 \text{ in.}^3$$
$$V^c = \tfrac{1}{2} \times 1450 \times 28.5 = 20,660 \text{ lb}$$

$$q = \frac{20,660 \times 15.27}{759.5} = 415 \text{ pli} \qquad \text{OK}$$

As these calculations disclose, mechanical shear connectors are not required to secure composite action; however, the steel is wrapped with wire mesh.

23-3   Beams with Exposed Steel   A commentary concerning the design of this type of member appears in the AISC Manual, pages 2-86 to 2-91. Although the relevant portion of the AISC Specification ostensibly pertains to elastic design, in reality it is based upon the ultimate-strength behavior of a composite beam. Loads that are present before the concrete has hardened are supported by the steel alone; loads that are present after the concrete has hardened are considered to be supported by the composite member, regardless of whether these loads originated before or after hardening. If the steel member is simply supported, the composite member is also considered to be simply supported.

Example 23-2   A concrete floor slab is to be supported by steel beams spaced 11 ft on centers and having a span of 36 ft. The beams will be supplied with shear connectors to secure composite action of the steel and concrete. The slab will be 5 in. thick and made of 3000-psi concrete; it will bear directly on the top flange of the steel. The loading includes the following: live load, 200 psf; finished floor, ceiling, and partition, 30 psf. In addition, each girder will carry a dead load of 10 kips applied as a concentrated load at midspan prior to hardening of the concrete. Conditions at the job site preclude the use of temporary shoring. Design the interior girders, limiting the total depth of steel to 20 in. if possible.

   Solution. Let the subscripts 1, 2, and 3 refer to the following loads, respectively: dead loads applied before hardening of the concrete, dead loads applied after hardening of the concrete, and live loads. Let the subscripts *b*, *ts*, and *tc* refer to the bottom of member, top of steel, and top of concrete, respectively.

The slab weighs 63 plf; assume that the steel weighs 80 plf.

$$w_1 = 63 \times 11 + 80 = 773 \text{ plf}$$
$$w_2 = 30 \times 11 = 330 \text{ plf} \qquad w_3 = 200 \times 11 = 2200 \text{ plf}$$
$$M_1 = 12(\tfrac{1}{8} \times 0.773 \times 36^2 + \tfrac{1}{4} \times 10 \times 36) = 2583 \text{ in.-kips}$$
$$M_2 = \tfrac{1}{8} \times 0.330 \times 36^2 \times 12 = 642 \text{ in.-kips}$$
$$M_3 = \tfrac{1}{8} \times 2.200 \times 36^2 \times 12 = 4277 \text{ in.-kips}$$
$$M^c = 2583 + 642 + 4277 = 7502 \text{ in.-kips}$$
$$M^n = 2583 \text{ in.-kips}$$
$$M_{DL} = 2583 + 642 = 3225 \text{ in.-kips} \qquad M_{LL} = 4277 \text{ in.-kips}$$

In the composite member, the maximum steel stress occurs at the bottom; in the noncomposite member, it occurs at the top of steel if a bottom-flange cover plate is used. For an allowable bending stress of 24 ksi, the required section moduli are as follows:

Composite section: $\qquad S_b = \dfrac{7502}{24} = 312.6 \text{ in.}^3$

Noncomposite section: $\qquad S_{ts} = \dfrac{2583}{24} = 107.6 \text{ in.}^3$

We shall select a trial section by assuming tentatively that the composite-design tables in the AISC Manual are applicable in the present instance. Referring to page 2-99 of the Manual, we find that a composite section consisting of a 5-in. concrete slab, an 18WF55 steel beam, and a cover plate having an area of 9 sq in. provides $S_b = 317.5$ in.^{3} Referring to page 2-113, we find that the noncomposite section provides $S_{ts} = 113.7$ in.^{3} Since unshored construction is to be used, the section must comply with Formula (17) of Sec. 1.11.2.2 of the Specification.

$$1.35 + 0.35 \frac{M_{LL}}{M_{DL}} = 1.35 + 0.35 \times \frac{4277}{3225} = 1.81$$

$$\frac{S_b^c}{S_b^n} = \frac{317.5}{213.6} = 1.49 \qquad \text{OK}$$

The flange width of the 18WF55 is 7.53 in. The minimum allowable distance between the edge of cover plate and edge of beam flange equals the size of the fillet weld that will be used plus $\frac{5}{16}$ in. We shall use a 9 × 1 in. plate, and our section therefore coincides with that presented in the AISC Manual, which has a cover-plate thickness t_p of 1 in.

In summary, the trial section is as follows:

18WF55 and bottom-flange cover plate, 9 × 1 in.

We shall check the trial section. The AISC composite-design tables are constructed by assuming that the effective width of the concrete equals sixteen times the slab thickness plus the flange width of the steel. In the present instance, the effective width as governed by Sec. 1.11.1 is as follows:

$$\tfrac{1}{4}L = \tfrac{1}{4} \times 36 \times 12 = 108 \text{ in.}$$
$$\text{Spacing of beams} = 132 \text{ in.}$$
$$16t + 7.53 = 16 \times 5 + 7.53 = 87.53 \text{ in.} \qquad \text{(governs)}$$

We may therefore apply the cross-sectional properties recorded in the AISC table. The moment of inertia presented in this table is that of an equivalent homogeneous section of steel.

$$y_{tc} = 5 + 18.12 + 1 - 16.50 = 7.62 \text{ in.}$$
$$S_{tc} = \frac{I}{y_{tc}} = \frac{5242}{7.62} = 687.9 \text{ in.}^3$$

In accordance with Table 1002(a) of the ACI Code,

$$f_c = 1350 \text{ psi} \qquad \text{and} \qquad n = 9$$
$$f_c = \frac{M^c}{nS_{tc}} = \frac{7{,}502{,}000}{9 \times 687.9} = 1210 \text{ psi} \qquad \text{OK}$$

The relevant properties of the 18WF55 are as follows:

$$A = 16.19 \text{ sq in.} \qquad d = 18.12 \text{ in.}$$
$$I = 890 \text{ in.}^4 \qquad S = 98.2 \text{ in.}^3$$
$$\text{Flange thickness} = 0.630 \text{ in.}$$

For the transformed section,

$$\text{Flange width} = \frac{87.53}{9} = 9.726 \text{ in.}$$

We shall determine the section moduli of the transformed section without the cover plate. Take statical moments with respect to the centroidal axis of the steel, and let y_m denote the distance from this axis to the centroidal axis of the transformed section.

Element	A, sq in.	y, in.	Ay, in.^{3}	Ay^2, in.^{4}	I_o, in.^{4}
18WF55......	16.19	0	0	0	890
Slab.........	48.63	11.56	562.2	6499	101
Total......	64.82	.....	562.2	6499	991

$$y_m = \frac{562.2}{64.82} = 8.67 \text{ in.}$$

By Eq. (2-11), the moment of inertia of the transformed section with respect to its centroidal axis is

$$I = 6499 + 991 - 64.82 \times 8.67^2 = 2618 \text{ in.}^4$$
$$|y_b| = 9.06 + 8.67 = 17.73 \text{ in.}$$
$$y_{tc} = 9.06 + 5 - 8.67 = 5.39 \text{ in.}$$
$$S_b = \frac{2618}{17.73} = 147.7 \text{ in.}^3 \qquad S_{tc} = \frac{2618}{5.39} = 485.7 \text{ in.}^3$$

The value of S_b may be verified by applying the value of the K factor in the AISC table. This factor is defined in the following manner:

$$K^2 = 1 - \frac{S_b \text{ (without plate)}}{S_b \text{ (with plate)}}$$
$$S_b \text{ (without plate)} = 317.5(1 - 0.73^2) = 148 \text{ in.}^3 \qquad \text{OK}$$

In Fig. 23-3, let C denote the section at which the cover plate in the composite

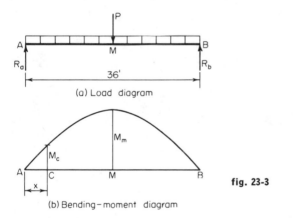

(a) Load diagram

(b) Bending-moment diagram

fig. 23-3

section becomes superfluous with respect to flexure. For the composite section, we have the following:

$$w = 0.773 + 0.330 + 2.200 = 3.303 \text{ klf} \qquad P = 10 \text{ kips}$$
$$M_m = 7502 \text{ in.-kips} \qquad R_a = 64.45 \text{ kips}$$

The allowable values of M_c are as follows:

For concrete: $M_c = \dfrac{485.7 \times 9 \times 1.35}{12} = 491.8 \text{ ft-kips}$

For steel: $M_c = \dfrac{147.7 \times 24}{12} = 295.4 \text{ ft-kips} \qquad \text{(governs)}$

$$R_a x - \tfrac{1}{2} w x^2 = 295.4 \qquad x = 5.30 \text{ ft}$$

We shall investigate the stresses at C in the noncomposite section.

$$w = 0.773 \text{ klf} \qquad P = 10 \text{ kips} \qquad R_a = 18.91 \text{ kips}$$
$$M_c = 18.91 \times 5.30 - \tfrac{1}{2} \times 0.773 \times 5.30^2 = 89.4 \text{ ft-kips}$$
$$f_b = f_{ts} = \frac{89.4 \times 12}{98.2} = 10.9 \text{ ksi} \qquad \text{OK}$$

The welding of the cover plate to the beam flange is designed in the manner illustrated in Example 12-4.

The design of the shear connectors is governed by Sec. 1.11.4 of the AISC Specification. We shall use $\frac{3}{4}$-in. studs, 3 in. high; these have a capacity of 11.5 kips each, as recorded in Table 1.11.4 of the Manual. From the AISC table on page 2-112, $V_h = 453.4$ kips. Then

$$\text{Total number of connectors} = 2 \times \frac{453.4}{11.5} = 80$$

These are to be uniformly spaced across the span.

TWENTY-FOUR

Soil Mechanics

The basic notational system is as follows:

c = unit cohesion
s = specific gravity
V = volume
W = total weight
w = specific weight
ϕ = angle of internal friction
τ = shearing stress
σ = normal stress

24-1 Composition of Soils In a three-phase soil mass, the voids, or pores, between the solid particles are occupied by moisture and entrapped air. A mass that contains moisture but not air is said to be fully saturated and constitutes a two-phase system.

Let the subscripts s, w, and a refer to the solids, moisture, and air, respectively. Where a subscript is omitted, the reference is to the entire mass.   The following nomenclature is used:

e = void ratio = $(V_w + V_a)/V_s$
n = porosity = $(V_w + V_a)/V$
MC = moisture content = W_w/W_s
S = degree of saturation = $V_w/(V_w + V_a)$

If the metric system is used,

$$W = s_s V_s + V_w \qquad (24\text{-}1)$$

When a soil mass is submerged in water, the (apparent) weight of the mass equals the true weight less the buoyant force of the water.

Example 24-1   A specimen of moist soil weighing 122 g has an apparent specific gravity of 1.82.   The specific gravity of the solids is 2.53.   After the specimen is oven dried, the weight is 104 g.   Compute the void ratio, porosity, moisture content, and degree of saturation of the original mass.

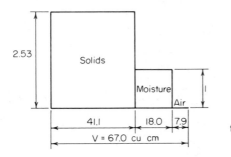

fig. 24-1   Soil ingredients.

Solution.   Refer to Fig. 24-1.   A horizontal line represents volume, a vertical line represents specific gravity, and the area of a rectangle represents the weight of the respective ingredient in grams.

$$W = 122 \text{ g} \qquad W_s = 104 \text{ g} \qquad W_w = 122 - 104 = 18 \text{ g}$$

$$V = \frac{122}{1.82} = 67.0 \text{ cu cm}$$

$$V_s = \frac{104}{2.53} = 41.1 \text{ cu cm} \qquad V_w = 18.0 \text{ cu cm}$$

$$V_a = 67.0 - (41.1 + 18.0) = 7.9 \text{ cu cm}$$

$$e = \frac{18.0 + 7.9}{41.1} = \textbf{63.0 percent}$$

$$n = \frac{18.0 + 7.9}{67.0} = \textbf{38.7 percent}$$

$$MC = \frac{18}{104} = \textbf{17.3 percent}$$

$$S = \frac{18.0}{18.0 + 7.9} = \textbf{69.5 percent}$$

Example 24-2 A specimen of sand has a porosity of 35 percent, and the specific gravity of the solids is 2.70. Compute the specific weight of this soil in pounds per cubic foot in the saturated and in the submerged state.

Solution. Set $V = 1$ cu cm. Then

$$V_w + V_a = nV = 0.35 \text{ cu cm} \qquad V_s = 0.65 \text{ cu cm}$$

Saturated state: $W = 2.70 \times 0.65 + 0.35 = 2.105$ g
                       $w = 2.105 \times 62.4 = \textbf{131.4 pcf}$

Submerged state: $W = 2.105 - 1 = 1.105$ g
or $W = (2.70 - 1)0.65 = 1.105$ g
                       $w = 1.105 \times 62.4 = \textbf{69.0 pcf}$

24-2 Flow of Water through Soil The seepage of moisture through pervious soil demands careful investigation, for this motion may adversely influence the structural properties of the soil. As water percolates through soil, the hydraulic head that induces flow diminishes in the direction of flow as a result of friction and viscous drag. The drop in head in a unit distance is termed the *hydraulic gradient;* it is denoted by i.

When water that is flowing upward has a sufficient momentum to float the soil particles, a *quicksand* condition exists. Let i_c denote the minimum gradient that causes quicksand. By equating the buoyant force on a soil mass to the submerged weight, we obtain the following result:

$$i_c = \frac{s_s - 1}{1 + e} \tag{24-2}$$

Example 24-3 Soil having a void ratio of 1.05 contains particles having a specific gravity of 2.72. Compute the hydraulic gradient that will produce a quicksand condition.

Solution. Equation (24-2) yields

$$i_c = \frac{2.72 - 1}{1 + 1.05} = \textbf{0.84}$$

The velocity of water flow through a soil is a function of the hydraulic gradient and the hydraulic conductivity, or *coefficient of permeability,* of the soil. Darcy's law of laminar flow is as follows:

$$v = ki \tag{24-3}$$

where k = coefficient of permeability
       v = velocity of flow

24-3 Flow Nets It is often necessary to analyze the flow of water under a structure in order to ascertain its effects. The path traversed by a water particle in flowing through a soil mass is termed a *flow line, stream* *line,* or *path of percolation.* A line that is the locus of points in the soil mass at which the head on the water has some assigned value is termed an *equipotential line.* A diagram consisting of flow lines and equipotential lines is called a *flow net.* A flow net is illustrated in Fig. 24-2a, where water flows under a dam under a head H. Lines AB and CD are flow lines and EF and GH are equipotential lines.

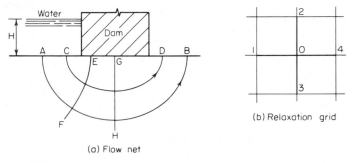

(a) Flow net

(b) Relaxation grid

fig. 24-2

Since a water particle in flowing from one equipotential line to another of smaller head will traverse the shortest path, it follows that flow lines and equipotential lines intersect at right angles, thus forming a system of orthogonal curves. In a flow net, the equipotential lines should be so spaced that the difference in head between successive lines is a constant, and the flow lines should be so spaced that the discharge through the space between successive lines is a constant. A flow net constructed in accordance with these rules illuminates the basic characteristics of the flow. For example, a close spacing of equipotential lines signifies a rapid loss of head in that region.

We shall develop the mathematical basis of constructing flow nets. Let h denote the head on the water at a given point and dL denote an elemental distance along the flow line. Equation (24-3) may be written in this form:

$$v = -k \frac{dh}{dL}$$

Let x and z denote a horizontal and vertical coordinate axis, respectively. By investigating the two-dimensional flow through an elemental rectangular prism of homogeneous, isentropic soil and combining the foregoing equation with the equation of continuity, we obtain the following result:

$$\frac{\partial^2 h}{\partial x^2} + \frac{\partial^2 h}{\partial z^2} = 0 \qquad (24\text{-}4)$$

This is a particular form of the general Laplace equation. It is analogous to the following: the equation for the flow of an electric current through a conducting sheet of uniform thickness, and the equation of the trajectory of principal stress. (This is a curve that is tangent to the direction of a principal stress at each point along the curve.) The seepage of moisture through soil may therefore be investigated by analogy with either the flow of an electric current or the stresses in a body. In the latter method, it is merely necessary to load a body in a manner that produces identical boundary conditions and then to ascertain the directions of the principal stresses.

As an illustration of the principal-stress analogy, refer to Fig. 24-2a and consider the surface directly below the dam to be subjected to a uniform pressure. Principal-stress trajectories may be readily constructed by applying the principles of elasticity. In the flow net, flow lines correspond to the minor-stress trajectories and equipotential lines correspond to the major-stress trajectories. It may be demonstrated that in this case the flow lines are ellipses having their foci at the edges of the base of the dam and the equipotential lines are hyperbolas.

A flow net may also be constructed by an approximate, trial and error procedure based on the method of relaxation. Consider that the area through which discharge occurs is covered with a grid of squares, a part of which is shown in Fig. 24-2b. If it is assumed that the hydraulic gradient is constant within each square, Eq. (24-4) leads to the following result:

$$h_1 + h_2 + h_3 + h_4 - 4h_0 = 0 \qquad (24\text{-}5)$$

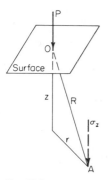

fig. 24-3

Trial values are assigned to each node in the grid, and the values are adjusted until a consistent set of values is obtained. With the approximate head at each node thus established, it becomes a simple matter to draw equipotential lines. The flow lines are then drawn normal thereto.

24-4   Calculation of Soil Pressure   With reference to Fig. 24-3, consider that we wish to evaluate the vertical stress σ_z at A caused by a concentrated vertical load P applied at O. Let R denote the length of OA and r and z denote the length of OA as projected on a horizontal and vertical plane, respectively. The Boussinesq equation is as follows:

$$\sigma_z = \frac{3Pz^3}{2\pi R^5} \qquad (24\text{-}6)$$

Although this equation is derived by assuming an idealized homogeneous mass, its results have been found to agree reasonably well with those obtained experimentally for true soil masses.

Example 24-4   A concentrated vertical load of 6 kips is applied at the ground surface. Compute the vertical pressure caused by this load at a point 3.5 ft below the surface and 4 ft from the action line of the force.

   Solution

$$P = 6000 \text{ lb} \qquad r = 4 \text{ ft} \qquad z = 3.5 \text{ ft}$$
$$R = \sqrt{4^2 + 3.5^2} = 5.32 \text{ ft}$$
$$\sigma_z = \frac{3 \times 6000 \times 3.5^3}{2\pi \times 5.32^5} = \textbf{28.8 psf}$$

With reference to Fig. 24-4a, consider that we wish to evaluate the resultant vertical force F on the rectangular area *abcd* caused by a con-

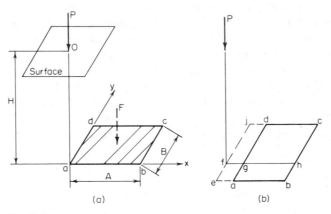

            (a)   (b)

fig. 24-4

centrated vertical load P, where a lies on the action line of P. Let

$$C = A^2 + H^2 \qquad D = B^2 + H^2 \qquad E = A^2 + B^2 + H^2$$
$$\theta = \sin^{-1} H \sqrt{\frac{E}{CD}} \qquad \text{degrees}$$

By applying Eq. (24-6) and integrating, we obtain the following result:

$$\frac{F}{P} = 0.25 - \frac{\theta}{360°} + \frac{ABH}{2\pi \sqrt{E}} \left(\frac{1}{C} + \frac{1}{D} \right) \qquad (24\text{-}7)$$

Example 24-5   A concentrated vertical load of 20 kips is applied at the ground surface. Determine the resultant vertical force caused by this load on a rectangular area 3 ft by 5 ft that lies 2 ft below the surface and has one vertex on the action line of the applied load.

Solution

$$A = 3 \text{ ft} \qquad B = 5 \text{ ft} \qquad H = 2 \text{ ft}$$
$$C = 13 \text{ ft}^2 \qquad D = 29 \text{ ft}^2 \qquad E = 38 \text{ ft}^2$$
$$\theta = \sin^{-1} 0.6350 = 39.4°$$
$$\frac{F}{P} = 0.25 - 0.109 + 0.086 = 0.227$$
$$F = 20 \times 0.227 = \textbf{4.54 kips}$$

The resultant force on an area such as $abcd$ in Fig. 24-4b may be found by expressing the area in this manner:

$$abcd = ebhf - eagf + fhcj - fgdj$$

The forces on the areas on the right side of this equation are superposed to find the force on $abcd$.

The determination of vertical soil pressures may be expedited by referring to the various charts and diagrams that have been devised for this purpose.

24-5 Shearing Capacity of Soil   Since failure of a soil mass is characterized by the sliding of one part past the other, a soil failure is one of shear. Resistance to sliding springs from two sources: cohesion of the soil and internal friction. However, it is generally not possible to determine how the resistance to shear failure is divided between the cohesion and the friction. If the shearing stress at a given point exceeds the cohesive strength, it is usually assumed for simplicity that the soil has mobilized its maximum potential cohesive resistance plus whatever frictional resistance is needed to prevent failure. The mass therefore remains in equilibrium if the ratio of the computed frictional stress to the normal stress is below the coefficient of internal friction of the soil. A mass that is on the verge of failure is said to be in *limit equilibrium*.

Consider a soil prism in a state of triaxial stress. Let Q denote a point in this prism and P a plane through Q. Let

c = unit cohesive strength of soil
σ = normal stress at Q on plane P
σ_1 = maximum normal stress at Q
σ_3 = minimum normal stress at Q
τ = shearing stress at Q on plane P
θ = angle between P and plane on which σ_1 occurs
ϕ = angle of internal friction of soil

Refer to Fig. 24-5a. (An explanation of Mohr's circle of stress is presented in Art. 3-4.) The shearing stress ED on plane P may be

resolved into the cohesive stress *EG* and the frictional stress *GD*.   W∢
may therefore write

$$\tau = c + \sigma \tan \alpha$$

The maximum value of α associated with point Q is found by drawing th∢
tangent *FH*.

Assume that failure impends at Q.   Two conclusions may be drawn
The angle between *FH* and the base line *OAB* equals ϕ, and the angl∢
between the plane of impending rupture and the plane on which σ_1 occur∢
equals one-half angle *BCH*.

The shearing capacity of a soil may be appraised by means of a∢
unconfined compression test, in which a soil specimen is subjected to ∢
vertical load without being restrained horizontally.   The load is increase∢
until failure occurs.   The stress σ_1 thus occurs on a horizontal plane

Example 24-6   In an unconfined compression test on a soil sample, it was foun∢
that when the axial stress reached 2040 psf the soil ruptured along a plane makin∢
an angle of 56° with the horizontal.   Applying graphical construction, find th
cohesion and angle of internal friction of this soil.

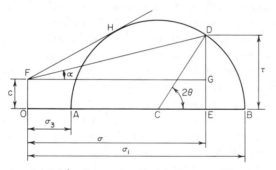

(a) Mohr's diagram for triaxial-stress condition

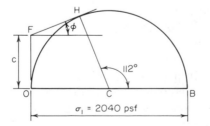

(b) Mohr's diagram for unconfined compression test

fig. 24-5

Solution. Refer to Fig. 24-5b.

$$\sigma_1 = 2040 \text{ psf} \qquad \sigma_3 = 0$$
$$\text{Angle } BCH = 2 \times 56° = 112°$$

At H, draw a line tangent to the circle, intersecting the vertical line through O at F. By measurement, we obtain

$$c = OF = \mathbf{688 \text{ psf}} \qquad \phi = \mathbf{22°}$$

In general, in an unconfined compression test, we have

$$c = \tfrac{1}{2}\sigma_1 \cot \theta' \qquad \phi = 2\theta' - 90° \qquad (24\text{-}8)$$

where θ' denotes the angle between the plane of failure and the plane on which σ_1 occurs. In the special case where frictional resistance is negligible, we have

$$\phi = 0 \qquad \text{and} \qquad c = \tfrac{1}{2}\sigma_1$$

An alternative means of appraising the shearing capacity is the *triaxial compression test*, in which a soil specimen is placed in a closed container surrounded by a liquid. While the horizontal stress σ_3 remains equal to the liquid pressure, the vertical stress is increased until failure occurs. Let σ_1 denote the vertical stress at impending failure, and let

$$S = \sigma_1 + \sigma_3 \qquad D = \sigma_1 - \sigma_3$$

By referring to Fig. 24-5a, we obtain the following result:

$$D - S \sin \phi = 2c \cos \phi \qquad (24\text{-}9a)$$
or
$$c = \tfrac{1}{2}(D \sec \phi - S \tan \phi) \qquad (24\text{-}9b)$$

Consider that two samples of a soil are loaded to failure in a triaxial compression test. Since the right side of Eq. (24-9a) represents a constant that is characteristic of the soil, we have

$$D_1 - S_1 \sin \phi = D_2 - S_2 \sin \phi$$
or
$$\sin \phi = \frac{D_2 - D_1}{S_2 - S_1} \qquad (24\text{-}10)$$

where the subscripts correspond with the sample numbers.

Example 24-7 Two samples of a soil were subjected to triaxial compression tests, and it was found that failure occurred under the following principal stresses:

Sample 1: $\qquad \sigma_1 = 6960 \text{ psf} \qquad \sigma_3 = 2000 \text{ psf}$
Sample 2: $\qquad \sigma_1 = 9320 \text{ psf} \qquad \sigma_3 = 3000 \text{ psf}$

Find the cohesion and angle of internal friction of this soil, both trigonometrically and graphically.

Solution

TRIGONOMETRIC METHOD

$$S_1 = 8960 \text{ psf} \qquad D_1 = 4960 \text{ psf}$$
$$S_2 = 12{,}320 \text{ psf} \qquad D_2 = 6320 \text{ psf}$$
$$\sin \phi = \frac{6320 - 4960}{12{,}320 - 8960} \qquad \phi = 23° \, 53'$$

Substituting either set of values in Eq. (24-9*b*), we obtain

$$c = 729 \text{ psf}$$

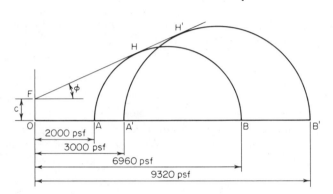

fig. 24-6 Composite Mohr's diagram for triaxial compression tests.

GRAPHICAL METHOD. In Fig. 24-6, draw the Mohr's circle associated with each set of principal stresses. Draw the envelope (common tangent) FHH', and measure OF and the angle of inclination of the envelope.

In practice, three or four samples should be tested and the average value of ϕ and c determined.

24-6 Earth Thrust on Retaining Walls   The thrust exerted on a canti-lever retaining wall by the backfill may be evaluated by applying the theory of earth pressure formulated by Rankine or that formulated by Coulomb.

Rankine's theory applies to a uniform mass of dry cohesionless soil. It considers the state of stress at the instant of impending failure caused by a slight yielding of the wall.   Let

h = vertical distance from soil surface to given point
p = resultant pressure on vertical plane at given point
o = ratio of shearing stress to normal stress on given plane
θ = angle of inclination of earth surface

The quantity *o* may also be defined as the tangent of the angle between the resultant stress on a plane and a line normal to this plane; it is accordingly termed the *obliquity* of the resultant stress.

Consider the elemental soil prism *abcd* in Fig. 24-7*a*, where faces *ab* and *dc* are parallel to the surface of the backfill and faces *bc* and *ad* are vertical.

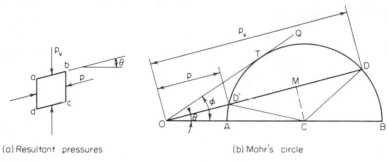

(a) Resultant pressures   (b) Mohr's circle

fig. 24-7

The resultant pressure p_v on *ab* is vertical and *p* is parallel to the surface. Thus, the resultant stresses on *ab* and *bc* have the same obliquity, namely, tan θ. (Stresses having equal obliquities are called *conjugate* stresses.) Since failure impends, there is a particular plane for which the obliquity of stress is tan ϕ.

Figure 24-7*b* is the Mohr's circle associated with a soil prism. It is constructed in the following manner: Using a suitable scale, draw line *OD* making an angle θ with the base line, where *OD* represents p_v. Draw line *OQ* making an angle ϕ with the base line. Draw a circle that has its center *C* on the base line, passes through *D*, and is tangent to *OQ*. Line *OD'* represents *p*. Draw *CM* perpendicular to *OD*. Then

$$p = OD' = OC \cos \theta - \sqrt{(CD')^2 - (CM)^2}$$

But $\qquad CD' = CT = OC \sin \phi \qquad$ and $\qquad CM = OC \sin \theta$

$$\therefore \ p = OC(\cos \theta - \sqrt{\sin^2 \phi - \sin^2 \theta})$$
$$= OC(\cos \theta - \sqrt{\cos^2 \theta - \cos^2 \phi})$$

Similarly, $\qquad p_v = OC(\cos \theta + \sqrt{\cos^2 \theta - \cos^2 \phi})$

But $\qquad p_v = wh$

$$\therefore \ p = \frac{\cos \theta - \sqrt{\cos^2 \theta - \cos^2 \phi}}{\cos \theta + \sqrt{\cos^2 \theta - \cos^2 \phi}} \, wh \qquad (24\text{-}11)$$

The lateral pressure that accompanies a slight displacement of the wall *away from* the retained soil is termed *active pressure;* that which accompanies a slight displacement of the wall *toward* the retained soil is termed *passive pressure.* By an analogous procedure, the passive pressure is found to be

$$p = \frac{\cos \theta + \sqrt{\cos^2 \theta - \cos^2 \phi}}{\cos \theta - \sqrt{\cos^2 \theta - \cos^2 \phi}} \, wh \qquad (24\text{-}12)$$

The equations for active and passive pressure are often written in the following manner:

$$p_a = C_a wh \qquad p_p = C_p wh \qquad (24\text{-}13)$$

where the subscripts identify the type of pressure and C_a and C_p are the coefficients appearing in Eqs. (24-11) and (24-12), respectively.

In the special case where $\theta = 0$, these coefficients reduce to the following:

$$C_a = \frac{1 - \sin \phi}{1 + \sin \phi} = \tan^2 (45° - \tfrac{1}{2}\phi) \qquad (24\text{-}14)$$

$$C_p = \frac{1 + \sin \phi}{1 - \sin \phi} = \tan^2 (45° + \tfrac{1}{2}\phi) \qquad (24\text{-}15)$$

Moreover, the planes of failure make an angle of $45° + \tfrac{1}{2}\phi$ with the principal planes.

Example 24-8 A retaining wall supports sand weighing 100 pcf and having an angle of internal friction of 34°. The back of the wall is vertical, and the surface of the backfill is inclined at an angle of 15° with the horizontal. Applying Rankine's theory, calculate the active earth pressure on the wall at a point 12 ft below the top.

Solution

$$w = 100 \text{ pcf} \qquad h = 12 \text{ ft}$$
$$\theta = 15° \qquad \phi = 34°$$

By substituting the trigonometric values in Eq. (24-11), we obtain

$$p = 0.321 \times 100 \times 12 = \textbf{385 psf}$$

Coulomb's theory of earth pressure postulates that as the retaining wall yields, the soil tends to rupture along a plane passing through the heel of the wall. With reference to Fig. 24-8a, assume that BC is the plane of rupture. As shown in Fig. 24-8b, the wedge ABC is held in equilibrium by three forces: its weight W, the resultant pressure R of the soil beyond the plane of rupture, and the resultant pressure P of the wall, which of course is equal and opposite to the thrust of the earth on the wall. Let denote the angle of friction between the soil and wall. The forces R and P have the indicated directions.

By selecting a trial wedge and computing its weight, we may readily find the corresponding value of P by drawing the force polygon. The problem is to identify the wedge that yields the maximum value of P. Rebhann's theorem, which we shall now formulate, is of considerable assistance in this regard.

In Fig. 24-8a, line BD makes an angle ϕ with the horizontal, and lines AE and CF make an angle $\delta + \phi$ with the back of wall. Lines AE and

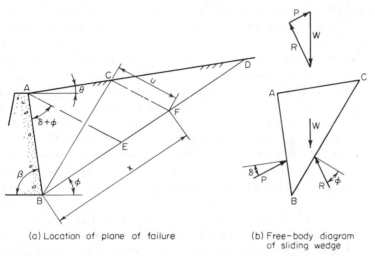

(a) Location of plane of failure
(b) Free-body diagram of sliding wedge

fig. 24-8

CF therefore make an angle $\beta - \delta$ with BD. Triangle BCF is similar to the triangle of forces in Fig. 24-8b. Then

$$P = W \frac{u}{x} \qquad \text{where } W = w \times \text{area } ABC$$

By setting $dP/dx = 0$, we arrive at Rebhann's theorem, which states the following: The wedge that exerts the maximum thrust on the wall is that for which triangles ABC and BCF have equal areas.

If BC is the true plane of rupture, the following equations result:

$$x^2 = BE \times BD \qquad (24\text{-}16)$$

$$u = \frac{AE \times BD}{x + BD} \qquad (24\text{-}17)$$

$$P = \tfrac{1}{2}wu^2 \sin (\beta - \delta) \qquad (24\text{-}18)$$

However, there are many situations that do not lend themselves to analysis by Rebhann's theorem. For example, the backfill may be non-homogeneous, the earth surface may be curved, a surcharge may be applied over part of the surface, etc. In these situations, graphical analysis affords the simplest means of solution.   The procedure consists of selecting a trial wedge, computing its weight and the surcharge it carries, and finding P by constructing the force polygon in the manner shown in Fig. 24-8*b*.   After several trial wedges have been investigated, the maximum value of P will become apparent.

If the backfill is cohesive, the active pressure on the retaining wall is reduced.   However, in view of the difficulty of appraising the cohesive capacity of a disturbed soil, most designers prefer to disregard cohesion.

24-7   Stability of Embankments   To determine whether an embankment is stable, it is necessary to evaluate both the forces or moments that tend to cause sliding and the forces or moments that may be relied upon to oppose sliding.   Failure of an embankment is assumed to occur along a circular arc through its toe, the mass of soil above the arc of failure rotating about an axis through the center of this arc.   The basic problem therefore is to identify the arc along which failure is most likely to occur.   Unfortunately, there is no direct way of doing this, and it becomes necessary to follow a cut and try procedure, investigating a series of assumed arcs of failure.

The stability of an embankment is usually investigated by means of the *method of slices*, also known as the *Swedish method*.   This method consists of dividing the soil mass above an assumed arc of failure into a series of vertical strips, evaluating the disturbing and stabilizing forces associated with each strip, and aggregating the results.

The method of slices may be explained by referring to the embankment in Fig. 24-9, where O is the center of an assumed arc of failure AC. The soil mass above the arc is divided into the indicated strips, and the strips are numbered.   Taking a 1-ft length of embankment, the weight W of each strip is determined, and a vector representing the weight is drawn.   At the point where the action line of W intersects arc AC, this force is resolved vectorially into a component N normal to the arc and a component T tangential to the arc.   It is assumed that the lateral forces on each strip approximately balance one another and may therefore be ignored.

With reference to strip 8, the force T has a clockwise moment with respect to an axis through O.   The tendency of the strip to rotate in a clockwise direction about this axis is resisted by the frictional and cohesive forces developed along the arc.   The stability of the embankment is measured by comparing the total moment of the tangential forces with the total moment of the maximum potential frictional and cohesive forces.

Since the soil mass in Fig. 24-9 tends to rotate in a clockwise direction, we shall consider a tangential force as positive if its moment with respect to an axis through O is clockwise, and negative if this moment is counter-clockwise. Let

r = radius of arc AC
L = length of arc AC
c = unit cohesive strength of soil
C = maximum potential cohesive force along arc AC
F = maximum potential frictional force along arc AC
ΣN = sum of normal forces
ΣT = algebraic sum of tangential forces
DM = disturbing moment
SM = stabilizing moment

Then
$$F = \Sigma N \tan \phi \qquad C = cL \qquad \text{(24-19)}$$

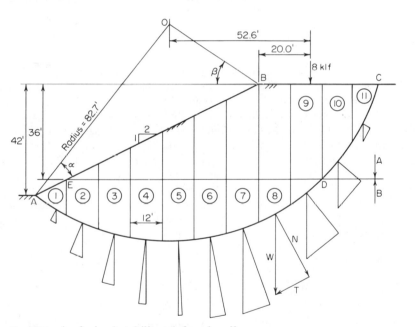

fig. 24-9 Analysis of stability of slope by slices.

In the absence of external loads, the moment that induces failure is

$$DM - r\Sigma T \qquad \text{(24-20)}$$

The moment that opposes failure is

$$SM = r(F + C) \qquad \text{(24-21)}$$

To secure the first assumed arc of failure, Fellenius recommend applying the values recorded in the accompanying table.

Slope (vertical to horizontal)	α	β
1:0.58	29°	40°
1:1	28	37
1:1.5	26	35
1:2	25	35
1:3	25	35
1:5	25	37

Example 24-9 Investigate the stability of the slope in Fig. 24-9. The properti of the upper and lower soil strata, designated as A and B, respectively, are a follows:

A: $w = 110$ pcf $c = 0$ $\phi = 28°$
B: $w = 122$ pcf $c = 650$ psf $\phi = 10°$

Stratum A is 36 ft deep.   A surcharge of 8000 plf is applied 20 ft from the edg

Solution. Setting $\alpha = 25°$ and $\beta = 35°$, locate the center O of the first trial ar draw the arc AC. By scaling, the radius is found to be 82.7 ft.   Draw th boundary line ED of the two strata, and scale the central angle AOD. B calculation, the length of arc AD is found to be 120 ft.   By scaling, the horizont distance from O to the applied load is found to be 52.6 ft.

Starting at the toe, divide the soil mass above AC into vertical strips of 12- width, and number the strips. For simplicity, consider that D lies on th boundary line between strips 9 and 10, although this is not strictly true. B scaling the dimensions or using a planimeter, determine the volume of soil i each strip and then compute the weight of soil.   For example, with respect t strip 5, we have

Volume of soil A = 252 cu ft
Volume of soil B = 278 cu ft
Weight of soil = $252 \times 110 + 278 \times 122 = 61,600$ lb

The results are recorded in Table 24-1.

Using a suitable scale, draw a vector directly below each strip to represent th weight of soil.   (Theoretically, the vector should lie on the vertical line throug the center of gravity of the soil, but such refinement is not warranted in th analysis.   For the interior strips, place each vector on the vertical centerline Resolve the soil weights vectorially into their N and T components, and sca these vectors.   Total the normal forces acting on soil A and those acting o soil B; total the tangential forces.

Applying Eq. (24-20) and making allowance for the effect of the surcharge, w obtain

$$DM = 82.7 \times 115 + 52.6 \times 8 = 9930 \text{ ft-kips}$$

Table 24-1   Stability Analysis of Slope

Strip	Weight, kips	Normal component, kips	Tangential component, kips
1	10.3	8.9	−5.2
2	28.1	26.0	−10.7
3	41.9	40.6	−10.4
4	53.0	52.7	−5.5
5	61.6	61.5	2.6
6	67.7	66.5	12.8
7	71.0	67.0	23.4
8	67.1	58.8	32.4
9	54.8	43.0	34.0
10	38.3	24.9	29.1
11	14.3	7.0	12.5
Total, 1 to 9.........		425.0	
Total, 10 and 11......		31.9	
Grand total..........		456.9	115.0

Equations (24-19) yield

$$F = 425 \tan 10° + 31.9 \tan 28° = 91.9 \text{ kips}$$
$$C = 0.65 \times 120 = 78.0 \text{ kips} \qquad F + C = 169.9 \text{ kips}$$

Equation (24-21) yields

$$SM = 82.7 \times 169.9 = 14{,}050 \text{ ft-kips}$$

The factor of safety for this arc is

$$FS = \frac{SM}{DM} = \frac{14{,}050}{9930} = 1.41$$

Other assumed arcs of failure should be investigated in the same manner.

24-8   Capacity of Piles   When the soil directly underlying a structure is of relatively poor quality, recourse is had to the use of bearing piles to transmit the load of the structure to the earth.   An *end-bearing* pile is one that is driven to bear on a firm stratum of soil and transmits the load primarily by compression at its tip.   A *friction*, or *floating*, pile is one that is embedded in plastic soil and transmits the load primarily by tangential forces, termed *skin friction*, at its surface.

Assigning an allowable load to a bearing pile driven into a given soil stratum is a complex problem that has been approached by two distinct methods.   The first method requires a laboratory analysis of a soil specimen to determine its structural properties and the application of a so-called static formula to compute the allowable load. The second method seeks to correlate the bearing capacity of a pile with the energy expended in driving a specimen pile and has led to the development of so-called dynamic formulas. Of the latter, we shall apply the Redtenbacker formula as being the most rational. Let

A = cross-sectional area of pile
E = modulus of elasticity
h = height of fall of ram
L = length of pile
P = allowable load on pile
R = reaction of soil on pile
s = penetration per blow
W = weight of falling ram
w = weight of pile

By considering the work performed by the soil in bringing the pile to rest, the work performed in compressing the pile, and the energy delivered to the pile, we arrive at the following result:

$$Rs + \frac{R^2 L}{2AE} = \frac{W^2 h}{W + w} \tag{24-22}$$

Example 24-10   A 16 × 16 in. pile of 3000-psi concrete, 45 ft long, is reinforced with eight No. 7 bars. The pile is driven by a double-acting steam hammer. The weight of the ram is 4600 lb and the energy delivered is 17,000 ft-lb per blow. It is found that the average penetration caused by the final blows is 0.42 in. Compute the bearing capacity of the pile by applying Redtenbacker's formula and using a factor of safety of 3.

Solution. We shall transform the composite area of the pile to an equivalent area of concrete.

$$\text{Area of No. 7 bar} = 0.60 \text{ sq in.} \qquad n = 9$$
$$A = 16 \times 16 + 8(9 - 1)0.60 = 294 \text{ sq in.}$$

$$w = \frac{16 \times 16}{144} \times 0.150 \times 45 = 12 \text{ kips}$$

$$s = 0.42 \text{ in.} \qquad L = 540 \text{ in.} \qquad E_c = 3160 \text{ ksi}$$
$$W = 4.6 \text{ kips} \qquad Wh = 17 \text{ ft-kips} = 204 \text{ in.-kips}$$

Substituting in Eq. (24-22), we have

$$0.42R + \frac{540}{2 \times 294 \times 3160} R^2 = \frac{4.6 \times 204}{4.6 + 12}$$

$$R = 84.8 \text{ kips} \qquad P = \frac{R}{3} = \textbf{28.3 kips}$$

When friction piles are compactly spaced, the area of soil that is needed to support an individual pile overlaps that needed to support the adjacent ones. Consequently, the capacity of a group of friction piles is less than the value obtained by aggregating the capacities of the piles composing the group. Let

P = capacity of group
P_i = capacity of individual pile
m = number of rows
n = number of piles per row
d = diameter of pile
s = center-to-center spacing of piles
θ = $\tan^{-1} d/s$, degrees

The value of P may be found by applying the Converse-Labarre equation:

$$\frac{P}{P_i} = mn - \frac{\theta}{90°} [m(n-1) + n(m-1)] \qquad (24\text{-}23)$$

Example 24-11 A structure is to be supported by twelve friction piles of 10-in. diameter. These will be arranged in four rows of three piles each at a spacing of 3 ft in both directions. A test pile was found to have an allowable load of 32 kips. Determine the load that may be carried by this pile group.

Solution

$$P_i = 32 \text{ kips} \qquad m = 4 \qquad n = 3 \qquad d = 10 \text{ in.} \qquad s = 36 \text{ in.}$$
$$\theta = \tan^{-1} 1\%6 = 15.5°$$
$$\frac{P}{32} = 12 - \frac{15.5}{90} (4 \times 2 + 3 \times 3) \qquad P = \textbf{290 kips}$$

Bibliography

Abbett, R. W.: "American Civil Engineering Practice," Wiley, vols. I and II, 1956, vol. III, 1957.

Beedle, L. S., et al.: "Structural Steel Design," Ronald, 1964.

————: "Plastic Design of Steel Frames," Wiley, 1958.

Benjamin, J. R.: "Statically Indeterminate Structures," McGraw-Hill, 1959.

Borg, S. F.: "Fundamentals of Engineering Elasticity," Van Nostrand, 1962.

———— and J. J. Gennaro: "Advanced Structural Analysis," Van Nostrand, 1959.

Canadian Institute of Timber Construction: "Timber Construction," Ottawa, 1959.

Chellis, R. D.: "Pile Foundations," 2d ed., McGraw-Hill, 1961.

Chi, M., and F. A. Biberstein: "Theory of Prestressed Concrete," Prentice-Hall, 1963.

Connolly, W. H.: "Design of Prestressed Concrete Beams," McGraw-Hill, 1960.

Den Hartog, J. P.: "Advanced Strength of Materials," McGraw-Hill, 1952.

Dunham, C. W.: "Theory and Practice of Reinforced Concrete," 4th ed., McGraw-Hill, 1966.

————: "Advanced Reinforced Concrete," McGraw-Hill, 1964.

————: "Foundations of Structures," 2d ed., McGraw-Hill, 1962.

Ferguson, P. M.: "Reinforced Concrete Fundamentals," 2d ed., Wiley, 1965.

Fitzgerald, R. W.: "Strength of Materials," Addison-Wesley, 1967.

Frankel, J. P.: "Principles of the Properties of Materials," McGraw-Hill, 1957.

Gaylord, E. H., and C. N. Gaylord: "Design of Steel Structures," McGraw-Hill, 1957.

Gere, J. M., and W. Weaver, Jr.: "Analysis of Framed Structures," Van Nostrand, 1965.

318

Grinter, L. E.: "Design of Modern Steel Structures," 2d ed., Macmillan, 1960.
Hoadley, A.: "Essentials of Structural Design," Wiley, 1964.
Hodge, P. G.: "Plastic Analysis of Structures," McGraw-Hill, 1959.
Huntington, W. C.: "Earth Pressures and Retaining Walls," Wiley, 1957.
Jensen, A.: "Applied Strength of Materials," 2d ed., McGraw-Hill, 1967.
————: "Statics and Strength of Materials," 2d ed., McGraw-Hill, 1967.
Karol, R. H.: "Soils and Soil Engineering," Prentice-Hall, 1960.
La Londe, W. S., Jr., and M. F. Janes: "Concrete Engineering Handbook," McGraw-Hill, 1961.
Leontovich, V.: "Frames and Arches," McGraw-Hill, 1959.
Libby, J. R.: "Prestressed Concrete," Ronald, 1961.
Lincoln Electric Co.: "Procedure Handbook of Arc Welding Design and Practice," 11th ed., Cleveland, 1957.
Lothers, J. E.: "Advanced Design in Structural Steel," Prentice-Hall, 1960.
Moore, H. F., and M. B. Moore: "Textbook of the Materials of Engineering," 8th ed., McGraw-Hill, 1953.
Norris, C. H., and J. B. Wilbur: "Elementary Structural Analysis," 2d ed., McGraw-Hill, 1960.
———— et al.: "Structural Design for Dynamic Loads," McGraw-Hill, 1959.
Parcel, J. I., and R. B. B. Moorman: "Analysis of Statically Indeterminate Structures," Wiley, 1955.
Preston, H. K.: "Practical Prestressed Concrete," McGraw-Hill, 1960.
Ritter, L. J., Jr., and R. J. Paquette: "Highway Engineering," 3d ed., Ronald, 1967.
Roark, R. J.: "Formulas for Stress and Strain," 4th ed., McGraw-Hill, 1965.
Rogers, G. L., and M. L. Causey: "Mechanics of Engineering Structures," Wiley, 1962.
Sanks, R. L.: "Statically Indeterminate Structural Analysis," Ronald, 1961.
Scofield, W. F., and W. H. O'Brien: "Modern Timber Engineering," 4th ed., Southern Pine Association, New Orleans, 1954.
Seely, F. B.: "Resistance of Materials," 4th ed., Wiley, 1956.
———— and J. O. Smith: "Advanced Mechanics of Materials," 2d ed., Wiley, 1952
Shanley, F. R.: "Mechanics of Materials," McGraw-Hill, 1967.
Spangler, M. G.: "Soil Engineering," 2d ed., International Textbook, 1960.
Sutherland, H., and H. L. Bowman: "Structural Theory," 4th ed., Wiley, 1950.
Terzaghi, K.: "From Theory to Practice in Soil Mechanics," Wiley, 1960.
———— and R. B. Peck: "Soil Mechanics in Engineering Practice," Wiley, 1948.
————: "Theoretical Soil Mechanics," Wiley, 1943.
Timber Engineering Company: "Timber Design and Construction Handbook," McGraw-Hill, 1956.
Timoshenko, S. P., and D. H. Young: "Theory of Structures," 2d ed., McGraw-Hill, 1965.
———— and ————: "Elements of Strength of Materials," 4th ed., Van Nostrand, 1962.
———— and S. Woinowsky-Krieger: "Theory of Plates and Shells," 2d ed., McGraw-Hill, 1959.
————: "Strength of Materials," 3d ed., Van Nostrand, part I, 1955, part II, 1956.
Tschebotarioff, G. P.: "Soil Mechanics, Foundations, and Earth Structures," McGraw-Hill, 1951.
U.S. Department of Agriculture, Forest Products Laboratory: "Wood Handbook" (Agriculture Handbook 72), Government Printing Office, 1955.
Urquhart, L. C.: "Civil Engineering Handbook," 4th ed., McGraw-Hill, 1959.

Viest, I. M., R. S. Fountain, and R. C. Singleton: "Composite Construction in Steel and Concrete," McGraw-Hill, 1958.

Wang, C. K., and C. L. Eckel: "Elementary Theory of Structures," McGraw-Hill, 1957.

Wang, C. T.: "Applied Elasticity," McGraw-Hill, 1953.

White, L., and E. A. Prentis: "Cofferdams," 2d ed., Columbia University Press, 1956.

Williams, C. D., and E. C. Harris: "Structural Design in Metals," 2d ed., Ronald, 1957.

Winter, G., L. C. Urquhart, C. E. O'Rourke, and A. H. Nilson: "Design of Concrete Structures," 7th ed., McGraw-Hill, 1964.

INDEX

Index

PRAYER

THAT
GETS
RESULTS

PRA

Clarion Call Marketing

Y E R

THAT
GETS
RESULTS

The Key to Your Survival

BENNY HINN

PRAYER THAT GETS RESULTS

© 2005 Clarion Call Marketing

Published by Clarion Call Marketing
P.O. Box 610010
Dallas, TX 75261

All Scripture quotations, unless otherwise indicated, are taken from the
King James Version.

ISBN: 1-59574-044-9

Printed in the United States of America
2005—First Edition
10 9 8 7 6 5 4 3 2 1

contents

TODAY'S GREATEST NEED

*Call unto me, and I will answer thee, and
shew thee great and mighty things, which
thou knowest not.*

—Jeremiah 33:3

W hat is the greatest need facing the church today?

Prayer!

A survey of 1,300 ministry leaders from around the world were asked that question. Participants were given a list of 3,700 different issues. They were also provided an opportunity for additional input. Most of the answers were fairly predictable: abortion (#10), marriage (#7), and apathy (#6). Numbers 5 to 2, respectively, were doctrine, evangelism, leadership, and discipleship.

Number 1?

It is prayer.[1]

The greatest need facing today's Christians, according to top leaders, is the need for more ongoing, passionate prayer in both personal and church life! It is the most pressing challenge facing believers today. It is the greatest need in the church today!

God Almighty wants to birth prayer in your heart. It is the answer to your relationship with Him. It is the key to your survival in today's world in the coming days. Without prayer that gets results, we will be powerless and impotent in the midst of these troubled and confusing times.

How about you? What would your life be like if you could move into the powerful, overwhelming, all-encompassing, eternal presence of God without fail, anytime you desired? How different would your life be? Your conversations? Your relationships? Your thoughts? Your goals? Your actions?

What would it be like to receive answers to prayer, time after time? How would your life truly change if you could be in contact daily with your heavenly Father?

It is possible to enjoy the presence of God every day and to have your prayers answered. How do I know? The Bible is filled with promises that God answers prayer:

*And the LORD said unto him, I have heard
thy prayer and thy supplication, that thou
hast made before me: I have hallowed this
house, which thou hast built, to put my name
there for ever; and mine eyes and mine heart
shall be there perpetually.* (1 Kings 9:3)

*The LORD hath heard my supplication; the
LORD will receive my prayer.* (Psalm 6:9)

*Ask, and it shall be given you; seek, and ye
shall find; knock, and it shall be opened unto
you. For every one that asketh receiveth; and
he that seeketh findeth; and to him that
knocketh it shall be opened.* (Luke 11:9-10)

*Let us therefore come boldly unto the throne
of grace, that we may obtain mercy, and find
grace to help in time of need.* (Hebrews 4:16)

*For the eyes of the Lord are over the righteous,
and his ears are open unto their prayers.*
(1 Peter 3:12)

*The effectual fervent prayer of a righteous
man availeth much.* (James 5:16)

God Almighty sent His Son to earth to die for our salvation and to provide eternal redemption, but also to restore the broken bonds of fellowship that man enjoyed with God before the Fall.

God sent His Holy Spirit to be our Helper in order that we might live a life of power and communion with Him, yet many today do not know this glorious privilege. They ask:

- Does God hear when I call?
- Is the Lord involved in every area of my life?
- Can I know Him intimately?
- Does He answer prayer?
- How can I learn to hear His voice?
- Does God intervene in the affairs of man?

The answer is a resounding *yes*!

Are you ready for an intimate walk with the Lord—a walk you have hungered for and longed for with all your being? As you read this book, I pray that the Lord will begin to show you how and empower you to live a life of prayer that gets results.

THE MODEL PRAYER

This is how the

Master teaches us to pray:

He brings us into the

Father's living presence.

What we pray there

must avail.

Andrew Murray

---

one

Scripture records: *"And it came to pass, that, as he was praying in a certain place, when he ceased, one of his disciples said unto him, Lord, teach us to pray"* (Luke 11:1).

One of the greatest requests in the Word of God is the one made to the Lord Jesus by His disciples— *"Lord, teach us to pray"*—a cry that still echoes in the hearts of those who long to follow Him.

Why did the disciple make such an urgent request? It is because of the great and mighty hunger that dwelled in their hearts for the knowledge of God.

Effective prayer is God's invitation into His limitlessness. Prayer crosses the border of time into eternity. And in response to the disciple's request, *"Teach us to pray,"* the answer given by the Lord Jesus so long ago is as fresh and applicable right now as it was when He first offered the model prayer. He knew that a good example is worth a thousand sermons. He lived it daily. As a result, we not only have His teaching that came as a result of the disciple's request, but we have an example, a model prayer, and a powerful pattern which we can follow.

And as we begin our study of prayer, I can think of no better place to start than with the Master's model prayer.

A PATTERN FOR PRAYER

What the Lord Jesus taught is often called the "Lord's Prayer." Actually, the "Lord's Prayer" is found in John 17. This one should actually be called the disciple's prayer. The Lord said, *"After this manner pray ye."* He gave a model prayer—a pattern for those who would follow His example. It is the foundation upon which we can build a life of prayer. It is a foundation, not a formula; a standard to follow, not a rigid ritual.

The Lord Jesus gave us clear instructions that are vital as we build a life of prayer, calling daily upon Him. He said:

> *And when thou prayest, thou shalt not be as the hypocrites are: for they love to pray standing in the synagogues and in the corners of the streets, that they may be seen of men. Verily I say unto you, They have their reward. But thou, when thou prayest, enter into thy closet, and when thou hast shut thy door, pray to thy Father which is in secret; and thy Father which seeth in secret shall reward thee openly.* (Matthew 6:5-6)

But when ye pray, use not vain repetitions, as the heathen do: for they think that they shall be heard for their much speaking. Be not ye therefore like unto them: for your Father knoweth what things ye have need of, before ye ask him. (Matthew 6:7-8)

Years ago, *Moody Monthly* ran this eye-opening paragraph:

It is not the arithmetic of our prayers, how many they are; nor the rhetoric of our prayers, how eloquent they be; nor the geometry of our prayers, how long they may be; nor the music of our prayers, how sweet our voice may be; nor the logic of our prayers, how argumentative they may be; nor the method of our prayers, how orderly they may be; or even the theology of our prayers, how good the doctrine—which God cares for. Fervency of spirit is that which availeth much.[1]

Fervency of spirit is the key. Relationship is born of fervency. Fellowship springs from fervency. And I pray as we begin studying what the Lord Jesus taught us, that God's power and presence will be released upon your life, filling your heart with His knowledge.

"Our Father" (Matthew 6:9)

True prayer is impossible without the knowledge of God as heavenly Father. Only the Holy Spirit can reveal Him as Father to our hearts. This takes place at salvation, when we are born again and surrender our lives to Jesus Christ as our Lord and Savior.

And at that moment of salvation, the Holy Spirit reveals God's omnipotence, God's omniscience, and God's omnipresence, the One who is all-powerful, all-knowing, and rules all—the One from whom nothing is hidden—God Almighty.

And when the Lord Jesus taught us to begin with, "Our Father," He was also telling us to surrender to our heavenly Father completely, obeying and loving Him at all times.

Strong, effective, and fervent prayer begins when the Holy Spirit reveals God Almighty as *Abba* Father.

"Which art in heaven" (Matthew 6:9)

"Which art in heaven," speaks of recognition. When we come to God as Father, we recognize His authority both in heaven and on earth.

We say with the psalmist, *"Let all the earth fear the LORD: let all the inhabitants of the world stand in awe of him"* (Psalm 33:8). We declare that He rules in heaven and on the earth: *"For by him were all things created, that are in heaven, and that are in earth, visible and invisible, whether they be thrones, or dominions, or principalities, or powers: all things were created by him, and for him"* (Colossians 1:16).

"Hallowed be thy name" (Matthew 6:9)

When we come to God, we sanctify His holy name. We honor and glorify His blessed name. Prayer is impossible unless we stand in awe at the mention of His name. The name of the Lord is revealed throughout His Word as:

Elohim—"Creator"—is used 2,570 times in the Old Testament, first in Genesis 1:1: *"In the beginning God created the heaven and the earth."* God was the Creator—the Creator of everything—long before He was our Father. The name Elohim is always connected to creation and power.

Jehovah or Yahweh—occurs 6,823 times in the Old Testament. An example is in Genesis 2:7: *"And the*

LORD God formed man of the dust of the ground, and breathed into his nostrils the breath of life; and man became a living soul." The name Jehovah is revealed in connection with the creation of Adam and deals with God's covenant with His people, and it is also used throughout the Old Testament in connection with God's covenants with the children of Israel.

El Shaddai—"God Almighty, my Supply, my Nourishment"—the third name of God, used seven times in the Old Testament, was revealed to Abraham:

> *And when Abram was ninety years old and nine, the LORD appeared to Abram, and said unto him, I am the Almighty God; walk before me, and be thou perfect. And I will make my covenant between me and thee, and will multiply thee exceedingly.* (Genesis 17:1-2)

Adonai—"Master and LORD"—is used in Genesis 18:2. When Abraham saw God coming in the noon of the day with two angels to destroy Sodom and Gomorrah, he ran to meet them before the tent door, bowed himself before them, and said, *"[Adonai!] My LORD, if now I have found favour in thy sight, pass not away, I pray thee, from thy servant"* (verse 3), and he became the great intercessor, for Scripture tells us, *"And Abraham drew near, and said, Wilt thou also destroy the righteous with the wicked?"* (verse 23).

Written 434 times in the Old Testament, this name indicates "mastership" and "ownership." Calling the Lord Adonai acknowledges His outright ownership over our lives totally, and when we call Him <u>Adonai,</u> we say to Him, "<u>We are Your servants forever.</u>"

Jehovah Jireh—"The Lord my Provider" and "my Vision," or "the One I see"—occurs only once in the Old Testament (Genesis 22:14). In the ultimate act of obedience, Abraham took Isaac to Mount Moriah as God commanded to sacrifice his son.

And when Abraham approached the place where he was to build an altar, Isaac asked: *"Behold the fire and the wood: but where is the lamb for a burnt offering?"* (Genesis 22:7). Abraham told his son, *"God will provide himself a lamb for a burnt offering: so they went both of them together"* (verse 8). He bound his son to the altar, and as he stretched his hand to slay Isaac, the angel of the Lord stopped him: *"And he said, Lay not thine hand upon the lad, neither do thou any thing unto him: for now I know that thou fearest God, seeing thou hast not withheld thy son, thine only son from me"* (verse 12).

Abraham was shown a ram caught in a nearby thicket. When he looked and saw the sacrifice God had provided as a substitute for Isaac, he called the name of that place Jehovahjireh: *"And Abraham called the name of that place Jehovahjireh: as it is said to this day, In the mount of the LORD it shall be seen"* (verse 14).

And at that moment God revealed His Son's death on the cross to Abraham. The Lord Jesus said, *"Your father Abraham rejoiced to see my day: and he saw it, and was glad"* (John 8:56).

Jehovah Rophe—"the LORD who heals"—is used only once in the Old Testament. In Exodus 15:26, the Lord made a healing covenant with the children of Israel after their deliverance from Egypt:

> *And said, If thou wilt diligently hearken to the voice of the LORD thy God, and wilt do that which is right in his sight, and wilt give ear to his commandments, and keep all his statutes, I will put none of these diseases upon thee, which I have brought upon the Egyptians: for I am the LORD that healeth thee.*

Jehovah Nissi—"the Lord my Victory" or "the Lord is my Banner"—is used only once in the Word of God (Exodus 17:15) In this memorable passage of Scripture, Amalek's army came to fight with the children of Israel. During the battle, as long as Moses held up the rod, Israel prevailed. When his hands became heavy and he lowered the rod, Amalek prevailed. Finally Aaron and Hur held up his hands as he held up the rod until the battle was won. Afterward, *"Moses built an altar, and called the name of it Jehovahnissi"* (Exodus 17:15).

Jehovah Mikkadesh, Jehovah M'Kaddesh—"The Lord my Sanctifier"—makes us whole and sets us apart to be holy. *Mikkadesh* comes from the Hebrew word *qâdash, which* means "sanctify," "holy," or "dedicate."

It is recorded in the Scriptures, *"And the LORD spake unto Moses, saying, Speak thou also unto the children of Israel, saying, Verily my sabbaths ye shall keep: for it is a sign between me and you throughout your generations; that ye may know that I am the LORD that doth sanctify you"* (Exodus 31:12-13; see also Leviticus 20:7-9).

Jehovah Tsidkenu—first used in Jeremiah 23:5-6 then again in Jeremiah 33:16—is filled with meaning.

Tsedek, from which *Tsidkenu* is derived, means "to be stiff," "to be straight," or "righteous." When the two words are combined, Jehovah Tsidkenu, we have "the Lord who is our Righteousness." He becomes our righteousness as we accept His Son Jesus as our Lord and Savior:

> *Behold, the days come, saith the LORD, that*
> *I will raise unto David a righteous Branch, and*
> *a King shall reign and prosper, and shall execute*
> *judgment and justice in the earth. In his days*
> *Judah shall be saved, and Israel shall dwell*
> *safely: and this is his name whereby he shall*
> *be called, THE LORD OUR RIGHTEOUSNESS.*
> (Jeremiah 23:5-6)

Jehovah Shalom—"the LORD my Peace" or "the LORD is Peace"—is used 170 times in the Old Testament. It was revealed to Gideon after the Lord called and commanded him to smite the Midianites: *"Then Gideon built an altar there unto the LORD, and called it Jehovah-shalom"* (Judges 6:24).

Jehovah Rohi, Jehovah Ro'eh—"my Shepherd"—occurs in Genesis 48:15; 49:24, and Psalm 23:1; 80:1. The root word for *Rohi* means "shepherd," and it also means "intimate friendship" or "close companionship." So when David wrote, *"The LORD is my shepherd, I shall not want"* (Psalm 23:1), he was speaking of the bond of intimacy the Lord desires to have with His people, as a Shepherd who guides His sheep, protecting and nurturing them.

Jehovah Shammah—"His Presence" or "the LORD is there"—is used only once in the Bible, in Ezekiel 48:35, the last verse of Ezekiel's prophetic book. *Shammah* is derived from the Hebrew word *sham*, which can be translated as "there," spoken of by Ezekiel the prophet after he was shown the millennium temple and the glory of God.

There are other names for the Lord used throughout God's Word, but these twelve reveal His heart and His nature. When you say "Our Father" in prayer, you declare who God is. You approach His presence with love and reverence, and you walk into the Holy of Holies as you call Him, "my Elohim, my Jehovah, my El Shaddai, my Adonai, my Jehovah Jireh, my Jehovah Rophe, my Jehoval Nissi, my Jehovah Mikkadesh, my Jehovah Tsidkenu, my Jehovah Shalom, my Jehovah Rohi, and my Jehovah Shammah."

"Thy kingdom come" (Matthew 6:10)

What is God's kingdom? It is a vibrant relationship, for *"Behold, the kingdom of God is within you"* (Luke 17:21). The Bible also makes it clear that the kingdom of God is not a natural kingdom, but it is a heavenly one in the Holy Ghost: *"For the kingdom of God is not meat and drink; but righteousness, and peace, and joy in the Holy Ghost"* (Romans 14:17).

It is a kingdom of eternal power: *"For the kingdom of God is not in word, but in power"* (1 Corinthians 4:20).

When you pray, "Thy kingdom come," you are asking God to release His righteousness, His peace, His joy, and His power—through the Holy Spirit—upon your heart and your life.

"Thy will be done in earth, as it is in heaven" (Matthew 6:10)

There is a secret will—known only to God—and a revealed will for each of us. Deuteronomy 29:29 declares: *"The secret things belong unto the LORD our God: but those things which are revealed belong unto us and to our children for ever, that we may do all the words of this law."*

The secret, unseen will of God is already set in motion. Our prayer cannot change His secret will: *"And he doeth according to his will in the army of heaven, and among the inhabitants of the earth: and none can stay his hand, or say unto him, What doest thou?"* (Daniel 4:35).

Yet there is a revealed or expressed will that satan can oppose. We do not need much discernment to look around and see that God's expressed will is not always being obeyed throughout the earth. We can find what the Lord's revealed will is through diligent Bible study. For example, God is not willing that any should perish (2 Peter 3:9), nor is it His will that sin should dominate your life (Romans 6:14). It is His will to redeem you from destruction, to surround you with lovingkindness and tender mercies (Psalm 103:4), and to satisfy your mouth with good things so your youth is renewed like the eagles (Psalm 103:5). And all these blessings will be ours when we pray, "Thy will be done."

"Give us this day our daily bread" (Matthew 6:11)

The Lord taught us to pray first by coming to our heavenly Father in adoration and humility. Then He commanded us to ask for the things that we need for daily living. "Daily bread" speaks of total dependence upon the Lord for daily nourishment and suste- nance—first, as we receive His Word to nourish our spirits, and then for all our physical needs.

The Word of God teaches us that the Lord knows our needs intimately and knows us better than we know ourselves. Yet we receive nothing until we ask. James 4:2 declares, *"Ye have not, because ye ask not."*

It is imperative that you ask for the things you need, and you must ask in faith in order to receive: *"And this is the confidence that we have in him, that, if we ask any thing according to his will, he heareth us: And if we know that he hear us, whatsoever we ask, we know that we have the petitions that we desired of him"* (1 John 5:14-15).

By asking specifically and in faith, you acknowl- edge your dependence upon the Lord continually.

It is His will to answer every prayer that you pray in faith, but like blind Bartimaeus, you must ask in order to receive:

> *And Jesus answered and said unto him, What wilt thou that I should do unto thee? The blind man said unto him, Lord, that I might*

receive my sight. And Jesus said unto him, Go thy way; thy faith hath made thee whole. And immediately he received his sight, and followed Jesus in the way. (Mark 10:51-52)

"And forgive us our debts" (Matthew 6:12)

As we continue in this glorious life of prayer, we move from dependence to repentance. Prevailing prayer always includes both truths—dependence and repentance.

Proverbs 28:13 declares, *"He that covereth his sins shall not prosper: but whoso confesseth and forsaketh them shall have mercy."*

The Lord promises: *"If we confess our sins, he is faithful and just to forgive us our sins, and to cleanse us from all unrighteousness"* (1 John 1:9). Without confession, there is no forgiveness.

"As we forgive our debtors" (Matthew 6:12)

Forgiveness is a two-way street. We are forgiven as we forgive others. The Lord Jesus wanted us to understand this truth when He underlined the importance of forgiveness, saying: *"For if ye forgive men their trespasses, your heavenly Father will also forgive you; but if ye forgive not their trespasses, neither will your Father forgive your trespasses"* (Matthew 6:14-15).

Effective prayer is only possible when our relationship is right with God and with His people. There are two sins from which there is no forgiveness: blasphemy against the Holy Spirit (Mark 3:22-30) and unforgiveness.

To be forgiven, we must forgive. Without forgiving others, prayer is empty and powerless. So today—from your heart—forgive, forgive, forgive!

"And lead us not into temptation, but deliver us from evil" (Matthew 6:13)

It is God's will that we ask for His guidance and protection. And as we do, He will lead us into a life of righteousness and into that place of refuge as promised in Psalm 91:2: *"I will say of the LORD, He is my refuge and my fortress: my God; in him will I trust."*

Asking for guidance and protection will bring us into God's strength against the enemy of our souls and will cause him to flee: *"When I cry unto thee, then shall mine enemies turn back: this I know; for God is for me"* (Psalm 56:9).

Only then will God hide you in the secret of His presence: *"Thou shalt hide them in the secret of thy presence from the pride of man: thou shalt keep them secretly in a pavilion from the strife of tongues"* (Psalm 31:20).

"For thine is the kingdom, and the power, and the glory, for ever. Amen." (Matthew 6:13)

True, effective, and victorious prayer begins with God the Father, and it ends with God the Father, for He is *"Alpha and Omega, the beginning and the end, the first and the last"* (Revelation 22:13).

t w o

PRAYER IN THE LIFE OF OUR WONDERFUL LORD JESUS

Prayer does not fit us for the greater works;

prayer is the greater work. We think of prayer

as a common sense exercise of our higher powers

in order to prepare us for God's work. In the teaching

of Jesus Christ, prayer is the working of the miracle of

redemption in others by the power of God.

Oswald Chambers

t w o

The eternal truths we have just studied cannot be fully experienced in our life unless we follow the example of our wonderful Lord Jesus, for without following His example, we will not know the power of prayer. Scripture declares that He often went alone to pray: *"And in the morning, rising up a great while before day, he went out, and departed into a solitary place, and there prayed. And Simon and they that were with him followed after him. And when they had found him, they said unto him, All men seek for thee"* (Mark 1:35-37).

The book of Hebrews tells us clearly that when the Lord Jesus walked the earth He offered up prayers and supplications, with crying and tears, to Him who was able to save Him from death:

> *Who in the days of his flesh, when he had*
> *offered up prayers and supplications with*
> *strong crying and tears unto him that was*
> *able to save him from death, and was heard*

in that he feared; Though he were a Son, yet
learned he obedience by the things which he
suffered; And <u>being made perfect, he became</u>
<u>the author of eternal salvation unto all them</u>
<u>that obey him.</u> (Hebrews 5:7-9)

The Lord understood the power of prayer, and
He recognized the importance of calling upon His
Father. And to this moment, He is still interceding for
you and for me. In fact, prayer is so important in the
life of Christ that Scripture says, *"Wherefore he is able*
also to save them to the uttermost that come unto God by
him, seeing he ever liveth to make intercession for them"
(Hebrews 7:25).

If prayer was so vital in His life when He walked
on this earth, and if prayer and intercession is His ministry eternally as our High Priest, then as His people we
must follow His example.

Prayer brought God's glorious anointing upon the Lord's life and ministry.

Now when all the people were baptized, it
came to pass, that Jesus also being baptized,
and praying, the <u>heaven was opened,</u> and the
Holy Ghost descended in a bodily shape like

a dove upon him, and a voice came from heaven, which said, Thou art my beloved Son; in thee I am well pleased. (Luke 3:21-22)

Notice the Scriptures declare that while in prayer during His baptism, the heavens opened and the Holy Spirit descended. It was prayer that caused the Holy Spirit to descend upon His life, anointing Him to accomplish God's will on earth, becoming the substitute for man's sins on Calvary's cross.

Prayer empowered Christ Jesus to defeat the enemy.

It was prayer in the life of Jesus that prepared Him for the battle with the enemy after His baptism. It was prayer that defeated the purpose of satan when Christ was tempted. And it was prayer that caused the Son of the living God to return in the power of the Holy Spirit to Galilee, preaching the Gospel of the kingdom (Luke 4).

God's Word tells us that after His baptism and great victory, the Lord Jesus continued to pray. Mark 1:12-13 speaks of His temptation, but later in verse 35 we read: *"And in the morning, rising up a great while before day, he went out, and departed into a solitary place, and there prayed."*

After the Lord overcame the enemy because of prayer, He knew that only prayer would enable Him to preach the Gospel: *"And he said unto them, Let us go into the next towns, that I may preach there also: for therefore came I forth"* (verse 38).

It was prayer that sustained Him and caused Him to minister with power, and it is prayer that will sustain you and enable you to serve the Lord.

Prayer protected the Lord Jesus from the evil plans of the Pharisees.

It was prayer in the life of our wonderful Lord Jesus that protected Him from the plans of His enemies, for the Word of God declares: *"And they [the Pharisees] were filled with madness; and communed one with another what they might do to Jesus"* (Luke 6:11). The Lord Jesus knew that only prayer would keep Him safe, for verse 12 tells us, *"And it came to pass in those days, that he went out into a mountain to pray, and continued all night in prayer to God."*

All decisions in the life of the Lord Jesus were made by prayer.

Not only did prayer protect His life, but it enabled Him to know the will of God in choosing His twelve apostles: *"And when it was day, he called unto him his disciples: and of them he chose twelve, whom also he named apostles"* (Luke 6:13).

The Lord made no decisions without prayer, and how tragic it is that some of God's precious people will make decisions that involve marriage, business, or family, yet they do not seek the Lord in making such critical choices. Then, when they are in trouble, they cry out to God for help.

Let us learn from the Lord. Before making any decisions that will affect your life and future, make sure you get on your knees and seek the Lord's guidance and perfect will.

Prayer protected His disciples from harm.

It was prayer in the life of Jesus that also protected the lives of His disciples. Matthew 14:23-25 tells us: *"And when he had sent the multitudes away, he went up into a mountain apart to pray: and when the evening was come, he was there alone. But the ship was now in the midst of the sea, tossed with waves: for the wind was contrary. And in the fourth watch of the night Jesus went unto them, walking on the sea."*

In the fourth watch (3–6 a.m.), the Lord came walking toward His disciples in the midst of the storm.

They were in fear, but as the Lord drew near to the ship, they willingly received Him and were saved from harm.

A friend of mine told me of being caught suddenly in a storm on the Sea of Galilee. It is approximately eight miles wide, surrounded by mountains. Although the sea itself is relatively small, it is very deep in some parts. Great storms often occur when the wind blows in a circular pattern. Almost instantly the beautiful, tranquil waters can become turbulent, tossed, and life threatening. So it is not difficult for me to imagine the situation in which the disciples found themselves.

The Scriptures tell us that as the Lord entered the boat, He not only rescued His disciples, but the boat was also transported from the midst of the storm to the safety of the shore (John 6:21).

Prayer revealed Jesus Christ to Peter's heart.

Luke 9:18 speaks of the time when the Lord went to Caesarea Philippi and was alone praying. After that He asked His disciples, "Whom do people say that I am?"

They, of course, answered, *"Some say that thou art John the Baptist: some, Elias; and others, Jeremias, or one of the prophets [risen from the dead]"* (Matthew 16:14).

Then He asked them, *"But whom say ye that I am?"* (verse 15).

Peter answered, "*Thou art the Christ, the Son of the living God*" (verse 16). ☆

Matthew 16 gives us the rest of the story, for after Peter had spoken these words, the Lord said to him: "*Blessed art thou, Simon Barjona: for flesh and blood hath not revealed it unto thee, but my Father which is in heaven*" (verse 17).

This revelation was given to Peter by God the Father as a result of prayer in the life of Jesus.

Prayer saved Peter's life from ruin.

This amazing truth was spoken by the Lord Himself to Peter, for we are told in Luke: "*Simon, Simon, behold, Satan hath desired to have you, that he may sift you as wheat: But I have prayed for thee, that thy faith fail not: and when thou art converted, strengthen thy brethren*" (Luke 22:31-32).

It was satan's will to destroy Peter. It was his plan to sift him as wheat, for the devil had planned to thwart God's plan for Peter's life.

Peter had already confessed Jesus as the Christ. He had been shown that revelation by God the Father in Caesarea Philippi and had been given this promise: "*And I also say to you that you are Peter, and on this rock I will build My church, and the gates of Hades shall not prevail against it*" (Matthew 16:18, NKJV).

It was upon the rock—upon Peter's confession that Jesus was the Christ—that God would build His church. Peter had been given the authority and the promise, yet the enemy had planned to destroy Peter.

It was prayer in the life of Jesus Christ that saved Peter from the enemy. And it was prayer in the life of the Lord that destroyed the enemy's plans. It was prayer that fulfilled the promise spoken to Peter at Caesarea Philippi and caused him to become the pillar in Jerusalem that strengthened his brethren. And it was that Peter who was used so mightily on the Day of Pentecost—all because of prayer.

Prayer will empower you.

As you follow the Lord's example in prayer, you, too, will be anointed to serve Him with power. You, too, will overcome the evil one's temptations, daily defeating the devil's purposes in your life. You will find safety from your enemies and be led continually by the Holy Spirit.

It will be through prayer that you will see your loved ones and friends delivered from sin and harm. And it will be prayer in your life that will cause others to see Jesus in you, bringing great glory and honor to our heavenly Father through His Son, Jesus Christ!

three

RESULTS OF PERSEVERING PRAYER

The Christian should have an appetite for prayer.

He should want to pray. One does not have to force food

upon a healthy child. Exercise, good circulation, health

and labor demand food for sustenance. So it is with those

who are spiritually healthy. They have an appetite

for the Word of God, and for prayer.

Dr. Billy Graham

three

An intriguing story has been passed down through the centuries about one of Greece's best-known philosophers. According to the legend, a young man came to the legendary teacher with an urgent request. "I have walked 1,500 miles from my home to Athens to gain wisdom and learning," the student began. "I want learning, so I came to you. Can you give it to me?"

The great philosopher reportedly spoke without hesitation: "Come, follow me."

The acclaimed teacher led the student to the seashore. He walked into the gentle waves until he and his young follower were in water up to their waists. Then the older man grabbed his youthful companion and pushed his head under the water. In spite of the younger man's frantic struggles, the teacher held him under the surface. After several tense moments, the philosopher pulled the young man out of the water, laid the would-be pupil on the shore and returned to the marketplace. When the young man regained his strength, he walked back to challenge the teacher.

"You are a man of learning and wisdom," the young man yelled furiously. "Why did you treat me so badly?"

"When you were under the water," the teacher asked, "what was the *one thing* you wanted more than anything else?"

"I wanted air!"

Then the great philosopher reportedly said, "When you want wisdom and understanding as badly as you wanted air, you won't have to ask anyone to give it to you. You will get it on your own!"

THIS ONE THING

This account of the philosopher and his would-be student is very cruel. It has nothing to do with our relationship with God. I told the story to make this point: What is the *one thing* you want more than anything else?

Until you answer this one question, and unless you begin seeking God with deep hunger and mighty thirst, literally to be as the deer in search of life-giving water—*"As the hart panteth after the water brooks, so panteth my soul after thee, O God"* (Psalm 42:1)—you will not enjoy a blessed relationship with God the Father, nor will you begin to see results in prayer.

What is the one thing you want more than anything else?

Paul the apostle knew what he wanted, and he knew the one thing that would give him his greatest desire in life. What was that one thing? In Philippians 3:13-14, he writes: *"Brethren, I count not myself to have apprehended: but this **one thing** I do, forgetting those things which are behind, and reaching forth unto those things which are before, I press toward the mark for the prize of the high calling of God in Christ Jesus"* (emphasis mine).

What he wanted most was his death—death to his flesh, death to his desires, death to his past and to all his experiences in the flesh.

What did he long for? What was his greatest desire in life?

It was Christ Jesus and His fullness—the high calling of God was Paul's oneness with Jesus Christ.

Paul's greatest desire was his own cancellation and elimination, for in Philippians 3:10, the apostle wrote, *"That I may know him, and the power of his resurrection, and the fellowship of his sufferings, being made conformable unto his death."* He wanted to be conformed to the death of Christ Jesus. The apostle wanted to die that Christ might live. He wanted to decrease that Christ might increase. He wanted to be fully clothed in the image of Christ Jesus.

He knew the secret to victory in this world, for he understood the words spoken by the Lord in Matthew 16:24: *"If any man will come after me, let him deny himself, and take up his cross, and follow me."* Paul understood that only total death to self would cause a believer to belong wholly to the Lord.

Is that your cry? Is that why you pray? Do you pray to become more like Jesus Christ? Do you pray that self may die?

What is your reason for prayer? Is it that your needs will be met, or is it that Christ's image will be formed in you?

Once we begin to experience prayer in its depth, seeking the Lord with all our hearts, souls, and strengths, then these glorious results will begin to show themselves in our lives:

You will discover that prayer will reveal your true heart and nature.

This is the first step to power with God. In Isaiah we read:

> *In the year that king Uzziah died I saw also the LORD sitting upon a throne, high and lifted up, and his train filled the temple. Above it stood the seraphims: each one had six wings;*

with twain he covered his face, and with
twain he covered his feet, and with twain he
did fly. And one cried unto another, and said,
Holy, holy, holy, is the LORD of hosts: the
whole earth is full of his glory. And the posts
of the door moved at the voice of him that
cried, and the house was filled with smoke.
Then said I, Woe is me! for I am undone;
because I am a man of unclean lips, and I
dwell in the midst of a people of unclean lips:
for mine eyes have seen the King, the LORD of
hosts. (Isaiah 6:1-5)

When Isaiah saw the Lord while in prayer and saw His glory, and when he heard the seraphims cry "holy, holy, holy," it was at that moment that he also saw his own uncleanness. It was at that moment that he saw that he dwelt in the midst of an unclean people, so he cried, *"Woe is me! for I am undone,"* for he knew he was a man of unclean lips.

It was because of prayer that God revealed Isaiah to Isaiah, for prayer is like a mirror. As you pray, God will reveal to your heart your sins and weaknesses in order that you might cry, "Woe is me!" and experience God's power that will purge you and transform you.

Only prayer has the power to reveal what your true heart and nature is. Only prayer causes you to look to God for deliverance!

Prayer has the power to purge and cleanse your heart from all sin.

David the psalmist wrote: *"Who can understand his errors? cleanse thou me from secret faults. Keep back thy servant also from presumptuous sins; let them not have dominion over me: then shall I be upright, and I shall be innocent from the great transgression"* (Psalm 19:12-13).

As you pray for deliverance from sin, you will say with David, *"Then shall I be upright."* When you pray and seek God with all your heart, you will live a life that is upright before God. And then you will walk in righteousness before God.

Hosea 10:12 tells us, *"Sow to yourselves in righteousness, reap in mercy; break up your fallow ground: for it is time to seek the LORD, till he come and rain righteousness upon you."*

In Psalm 119:2-3, David declares: *"Blessed are they that keep his testimonies, and that seek him with the whole heart. They also do no iniquity: they walk in his ways."*

Only as you seek Him with your whole heart will you receive His power to live a holy life. For only then will you experience the promise that you will do no iniquity, and you will walk in His ways. As you pray for deliverance from sin, deliverance from sin will become yours.

Prayer will cause you to walk with God.

The psalmist prayed, *"Hold up my goings in thy paths, that my footsteps slip not"* (Psalm 17:5). Prayer gives you the power to walk with God, for it is His strength that holds you and keeps your footsteps sure and secure.

Walking with God is dependent totally upon prayer. The Word of God says, *"And when Abram was ninety years old and nine, the LORD appeared to Abram, and said unto him, I am the Almighty God; walk before me, and be thou perfect"* (Genesis 17:1).

The Word of God tells us that as we wait upon the Lord, He renews our strength: *"But they that wait upon the LORD shall renew their strength; they shall mount up with wings as eagles; they shall run, and not be weary; and they shall walk, and not faint"* (Isaiah 40:31).

As we wait upon the Lord and seek Him continually, this promise becomes ours. Our strength will be renewed to defeat the enemy. We will mount up with wings as eagles, for the majestic bird stands upon the rock and mounts up when the wind currents are at full strength. Only those who wait upon the Lord are able to discern the currents of the wind of the Spirit and surrender to those winds.

And the promise continues: they shall run and not be weary. Running is redeeming the time. It is impossible to redeem the time without prayer. It impossible to regain all that is lost without prayer, for Joel 2:25 tells us, *"And I will restore to you the years that the locust hath eaten."* Restoration and recovery are the result of prayer.

The promise of God also tells us that we shall walk and not faint. Walking with God is daily fellowship and an intimate relationship—all the result of prayer.

Prayer has the power to fill your heart with God's Word.

The psalmist teaches us when he said, *"Open thou mine eyes, that I may behold wondrous things out of thy law"* (Psalm 119:18).

Only prayer will cause you to cry out, *"O how love I thy law! it is my meditation all the day. Thou through*

thy commandments hast made me wiser than mine ene-
mies: for they are ever with me. I have more understand-
ing than all my teachers: for thy testimonies are my medi-
tation. I understand more than the ancients, because I
keep thy precepts" (Psalm 119:97-100).

Through prayer, hunger is born for the Word of
God. Divine hunger for the Word of God is the result
of prayer.

Prayer has the power to give you wisdom and understanding.

James 1:5-6 tells us, *"If any of you lack wisdom, let him*
ask of God, that giveth to all men liberally, and upbraideth
not; and it shall be given him. But let him ask in faith,
nothing wavering. For he that wavereth is like a wave of
the sea driven with the wind and tossed."

The Lord promised to give us wisdom which
none of our enemies will be able to contradict or resist
(Luke 21:15), but we must ask. Prayer imparts this
depth of wisdom.

The Word of God commands:

My son, if thou wilt receive my words, and
hide my commandments with thee; So that
thou incline thine ear unto wisdom, and

*apply thine heart to understanding; Yea, if
thou criest after knowledge, and liftest up thy
voice for understanding; If thou seekest her as
silver, and searchest for her as for hid treasures; Then shalt thou understand the fear of
the LORD, and find the knowledge of God.
For the LORD giveth wisdom: out of his
mouth cometh knowledge and understanding.
He layeth up sound wisdom for the righteous:
he is a buckler to them that walk uprightly.*
(Proverbs 2:1-7)

Again I emphasize, you must ask for wisdom,
seeking it as for hidden treasures. Only prayer imparts
wisdom.

When the apostle Paul heard of the faith of the
believers at Colosse, he prayed that they would be
filled with wisdom. The apostle wrote: *"For this cause
we also, since the day we heard it, do not cease to pray for
you, and to desire that ye might be filled with the knowledge of his will in all wisdom and spiritual understanding"* (Colossians 1:9).

That is my prayer for you, for as evangelist
Dwight L. Moody once said, "A Christian on his knees
will see more than a philosopher on his tip toes."

Prayer brings the power of the Holy Spirit.

The Word of God declares that as the Lord was assembled with His disciples,

> *He commanded them that they should not depart from Jerusalem, but wait for the promise of the Father, which, saith he, ye have heard of me. For John truly baptized with water; but* <u>*ye shall be baptized with the Holy Ghost not*</u> *many days hence. When they therefore were come together, they asked of him, saying, Lord, wilt thou at this time restore again the kingdom to Israel? And he said unto them, It is not for you to know the times or the seasons, which the Father hath put in his own power.* <u>*But ye shall receive power, after that the Holy Ghost is come upon you.*</u> (Acts 1:4-8)

The Lord Jesus then told His disciples that <u>they would receive power from on high and be His witnesses</u> *"both in Jerusalem, and in all Judaea, and in Samaria,* <u>*and unto the uttermost part of the earth"*</u> (verse 8).

The Scriptures then declare that <u>the apostles and</u> disciples continued in <u>*"prayer and supplication"*</u> (verse

14), for they fully understood that only as they prayed would they receive the promise given to them by the Lord.

Still in prayer, they remained together. Then on the Day of Pentecost the Holy Spirit descended on them with great power, for *"suddenly there came a sound from heaven, as of a rushing mighty wind, and it filled the whole house where they were sitting"* (Acts 2:2).

It was prayer that brought about the outpouring of the Holy Spirit upon the 120 on the Day of Pentecost. And it was prayer that transformed them into mighty witnesses of the resurrection of our Lord Jesus:

> *And when they had prayed, the place was*
> *shaken where they were assembled together;*
> *and they were all filled with the Holy Ghost,*
> *and they spake the word of God with bold-*
> *ness. And the multitude of them that believed*
> *were of one heart and of one soul: neither said*
> *any of them that ought of the things which he*
> *possessed was his own; but they had all things*
> *common. And with great power gave the*
> *apostles witness of the resurrection of the Lord*
> *Jesus: and great grace was upon them all.*
> (Acts 4:31-33)

And it is as you pray that He promises to fill you and empower you with His precious Holy Spirit: *"Verily, verily, I say unto you, Whatsoever ye shall ask the Father in my name, he will give it you. Hitherto have ye asked nothing in my name: ask, and ye shall receive, that your joy may be full"* (John 16:23-24).

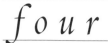

four

ROOTS AND RESULTS OF PRAYERLESSNESS

Sin breaks fellowship with God. A little girl

committed a certain offense and when her mother

discovered it, she began to question her daughter.

Immediately the child lost her smile and a cloud

darkened her face as she said, "Mother, I don't

feel like talking." So it is with us when our

fellowship with God is broken by sin in our lives.

[We do not feel like talking to Him. If you do not

feel like praying, it is probably a good indication

that you should start praying immediately.]

Dr. Billy Graham

four

No power on earth can stand against the man or woman who knows how to pray, yet the Word of God tells us that from the time mankind began to walk upon the earth, the enemy of our souls has used every weapon in his arsenal to destroy our ability to commune with God. Sadly, most have submitted to satan's plan and have become prayerless and powerless against the enemy. This has brought about great ruin and destruction in the lives of so many.

ROOTS OF PRAYERLESSNESS

Prayerlessness began in the Garden of Eden. It is a direct result of the fall of man. In Genesis 3:1-10 we read:

> *And they heard the voice of the LORD God*
> *walking in the garden in the cool of the day:*
> *and Adam and his wife hid themselves from*
> *the presence of the LORD God amongst the*
> *trees of the garden. And the LORD God*
> *called unto Adam, and said unto him,*
> *Where art thou? And he said, I heard thy*

voice in the garden, and I was afraid,
because I was naked; and I hid myself.
(Genesis 3:8-10)

When sin entered into the heart of Adam and
Eve, they hid themselves from the presence of the
Lord. Hiding from the presence of the Lord is prayerlessness. It was sin that caused Adam and Eve to hide
from God.

Notice that they hid *from* the Lord, not *in* the
Lord. Hiding *from* Him is prayerlessness. Hiding *in*
Him is prayer. We are commanded to hide *in* Him,
not *from* Him.

When we hide in Him, we are protected from the
enemy, but when we hide from Him, we cannot be
protected. The Lord becomes our refuge and fortress,
our deliverer and coverer, our shield and our buckler,
only when we hide in Him.

Prayerlessness is the cause of misery and ruin in
the lives of so many. And prayerlessness is a sin, for
God commands us to seek Him, not to hide from
Him. That is why Samuel said to the children of Israel:
"Moreover as for me, God forbid that I should sin against
the LORD in ceasing to pray for you: but I will teach you
the good and the right way" (1 Samuel 12:23).

And today, more than anything else, many need deliverance from this sin. Therefore, before effective prayer can begin, we must repent from the sin of prayerlessness. Just remember, it is not a weakness; it is a sin!

No Delight in God

Prayerlessness is in the heart of so many because the Word of God says they have no delight in God. Job 27 tells us that the wicked and unrighteous man, also called a hypocrite (verses 7-8), does not delight himself in the Almighty or call upon God (verse 10).

Yet God's Word commands: *"Delight thyself also in the LORD; and he shall give thee the desires of thine heart"* (Psalm 37:4). Delighting in the Lord is a choice we make, and those who are wicked have made their decision. But our choice, as God's children, will always be to delight in the Lord.

No Knowledge of God

The prayerless are prayerless because the Scriptures declare that they have no knowledge of God. The psalmist wrote: *"Have all the workers of iniquity no knowledge? who eat up my people as they eat bread, and call not upon the LORD"* (Psalm 14:4). The lack of the knowledge of God results in prayerlessness, and it is because of that lack that so many do not pray.

But as God's people, we are commanded to *"walk worthy of the Lord unto all pleasing, being fruitful in every good work, and increasing in the knowledge of God."* (Colossians 1:10).

The knowledge of God fills our hearts, and the result will always be prayer.

Turned Away from God

Those who are prayerless are the ones who have refused to walk with the Lord. Zephaniah 1:3-5 tells us that the prayerless, who are also called idol worshipers, have given themselves to the will of the enemy and refuse to seek the Lord, for they have given themselves over to rebellion. They have *"turned back from the LORD; and…have not sought the LORD, nor enquired for him"* (Zephaniah 1:6).

RESULTS OF PRAYERLESSNESS

The consequences of prayerlessness are disastrous and frightening, for the Word of God in Job 21 tells us that the wicked (verse 7) say *"unto God, Depart from us; for we desire not the knowledge of thy ways"* (verse 14).

The prayerless, as I said earlier, do not desire the knowledge of God or the knowledge of His ways. They say, *"What is the Almighty, that we should serve him? and what profit should we have, if we pray unto him?"* (verse 15). They are looking for profit. They do not seek God for who He is. Instead, they think they can use Him or get something out of Him, and only then do they call on Him. But the Word of God clearly tells us that this is not true prayer. True prayer is seeking God for who He is, not for what He can do for an individual.

What are the results of prayerlessness? The remainder of Job 21 unfolds before us a frightening picture for the prayerless and the ungodly.

No Goodness

The prayerless will never know true goodness. *"Lo, their good is not in their hand"* (Job 21:16). No good will come to them—only evil. Nothing good will ever be given into their hands.

No Counsel

Further, in the last part of verse 16, we are told that *"the counsel of the wicked is far from me."* Imagine having no guidance, no direction, no clarity of heart and mind. God's counsel will never be given to them. He will never counsel the wicked. They will walk continually in confusion because of prayerlessness.

No Light

Job 21:17 tells us: *"How oft is the candle of the wicked put out!"* Think about it—no light, only darkness. The wicked, the prayerless, will always walk in darkness and belong to the kingdom of darkness, not God's kingdom of light.

Total Destruction

Continuing in verse 17, we read, *"And how oft cometh their destruction upon them!"* What overwhelming misery and destruction follow the prayerless. All that they touch is eventually destroyed. All that they build will end up in ruin. They are left with nothing. Total destruction is their reward.

No Gladness

The last part of verse 17 says, *"God distributeth sorrows in his anger."* Imagine a life of no true joy. Gladness is far from them. There is no contentment, all because the prayerless refuse to seek the Lord.

No Preservation

The first part of Job 21:18 tells us that the prayerless have no preservation: *"They are as stubble before the wind."* Stubble is what is left of the grain stalk and roots when the crop is harvested. Those who do not pray are not preserved. Only as we pray do we become useful and are preserved. This is an awesome truth that the Word of God gives us—only through prayer are we secure. Only through prayer are we established. That is the reason why so many individuals are thrown to and fro by different doctrines. In Ephesians 4:14 we are commanded: *"That we henceforth be no more children, tossed to and fro, and carried about with every wind of doctrine, by the sleight of men, and cunning craftiness, whereby they lie in wait to deceive."* Prayerlessness is the reason so many are easily deceived. They are not established and preserved. Only prayer reveals the Word of God that will establish you. Only prayer enables you to walk and not stumble. But the prayerless are like the stubble left in the field, useless and alone.

No Protection from the Storms

Notice that the Bible mentions in the remainder of Job 21:18 that the prayerless are *"as chaff that the storm carrieth away."* When the grain is harvested, it is separated from the hulls and stalks—the chaff—often by shaking, scraping, rubbing, and tossing it in the air. The grain remains, but the chaff is blown away by the wind. This verse also mentions the storms which come whether you are prayerful or prayerless. If you are prayerful, the storms and wind will not affect you; if you are prayerless, they will. Only as you stay on your knees will you remain unmovable and unshaken by the trials of life.

Sorrow for Generations to Come

Job 21:19 tells us, *"God layeth up his iniquity for his children."* Think about it, his children reap the seed sown by the prayerless. The seed of the prayerless is cursed by God, and the harvest of the prayerless will bring sorrow and anguish to their descendents. But the prayerful will see blessings untold upon their lives and the lives of their descendents. Remember, the Word of God declares: *"Know therefore that the LORD thy God, he is God, the faithful God, which keepeth covenant and mercy with them that love him and keep his commandments to a thousand generations"* (Deuteronomy 7:9).

Witness Suffering

Job 21:19 continues, *"He rewardeth him, and he shall know it."* What a painful experience this will be! The prayerless will see the horrible reward brought upon his life and that of his descendents. He will see pain and suffering. He will see anguish and sorrow. Prayerlessness is a dangerous and destructive practice. Neglecting God is the cause for much pain and suffering in our world.

Experience Wrath

Following in verse 20 we read, *"His eyes shall see his destruction, and he shall drink of the wrath of the Almighty."* In this verse the misery of prayerlessness is clearly described, for he shuts God out of his life and does not lift up his eyes to the hills where his help comes from (Psalm 121:1). And because he refuses to look to God, instead, he will look upon his destruction.

Horrible End of Life

Job 21:21 gives us a frightening picture of the end of his days: *"For what pleasure hath he in his house after him, when the number of his months is cut off in the midst?"* The prayerless will not know a long life, nor will he know the promise of Psalm 91:16: *"With long life will I satisfy him, and shew him my salvation."* Only those who seek the Lord are guaranteed this promise: *"He shall call upon me, and I will answer him: I will be with him in trouble; I will deliver him, and honour him"* (Psalm 91:15). The promise of long life is the result of prayer.

At the End, a Bitter Death

In Job 21:22-25, we read:

> *Shall any teach God knowledge? seeing he*
> *judgeth those that are high. One dieth in his*
> *full strength, being wholly at ease and quiet.*
> *His breasts are full of milk, and his bones*
> *are moistened with marrow. And another*
> *dieth in the bitterness of his soul, and never*
> *eateth with pleasure.*

Concerning the righteous and the prayerful, the Word of God declares he will die in his full strength, wholly at ease, and quiet. When the righteous one dies, God's abundance is still within him (milk), and he has known a life of blessing *("his bones moistened with marrow")*. Yet the wicked—the prayerless—die bitterly and never eat with pleasure.

Prayerlessness is a deadly sin and is the cause of all pain, but prayer is the key that will release all of God's blessings. As R. A. Torrey once said, "Prayer is the key that unlocks all the storehouse of God's infinite grace and power. All that God is, and all that God has is at the disposal of prayer."[1]

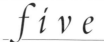

five

OVERCOMING PRAYERLESSNESS

I have been driven many times

to my knees by the overwhelming

conviction that I had nowhere else to go.

My own wisdom, and that of all about

me, seemed insufficient for the day.

President Abraham Lincoln

five

In the previous chapter we dealt with the danger of prayerlessness. The causes are very clear-cut:

- No delight in God
- No knowledge of God
- Turned away from God

In this chapter I want to discuss the vital importance of overcoming prayerlessness and the rewards that will follow.

DELIGHT IN GOD

God's Word commands us: *"Delight thyself also in the LORD; and he shall give thee the desires of thine heart"* (Psalm 37:4). Delighting in the Lord is a choice we make every day.

This means spending time with Him: *"If ye abide in me, and my words abide in you, ye shall ask what ye will, and it shall be done unto you"* (John 15:7).

Years ago, a little boy lived next door to a great artist. Every day the lad would go to the older man's home and watch him paint. The youngster was entranced for hours as the man brushed pungent, colorful oils onto the canvas.

The boy was still quite young when the artist passed away. Sadly, the lad knocked on the widow's door and said, "I really miss your husband. I always loved coming to your house to watch him paint." Then he added, "When I grow up, I want to be just like him. What do I have to do?"

The widow struggled for the right words, not wanting to discourage the boy, yet knowing firsthand the lifelong, bittersweet pursuit for perfection her husband had lived. Her thoughts were interrupted by the boy's determined voice: "Ma'am, can I take one of his paintings home so I can copy it?"

She not only let him borrow the painting, but also gave him a box full of brushes, oils, and a canvas, then watched him proudly march home.

In a few days he dejectedly trudged across the yard with the box of art supplies. "I've tried and tried to do it like he painted," the lad explained, his voice choking with painful emotion. "I just can't do it. I give up."

The widow gave the boy a big hug and said, "You must keep trying. You see, it's not the brush or the paint or the canvas that makes a great work of art. It's not just the talent, though God gives more to certain people than to others. It's the trying again and again. It's learning through all the failures and successes that eventually leads to being able to paint a masterpiece like my husband did. It is inside you! It is the spirit of the painter who keeps going when others quit that makes all the difference."

I have met so many people who are like that child. With the sometimes-wonderful, often overwhelming fervency of the new convert, they want to be the next Elijah, Peter, Paul, Charles Finney, D. L. Moody, or Kathryn Kuhlman. I speak from time to time at Bible schools and universities, and I have often heard a young student exclaim, "Oh, if only I could preach like Billy Graham!"

Every man or woman whom we might call "warriors of the faith" started as new believers with similar fears, mistakes, and tentative steps. They all had struggles that few knew about. They all had their own personal barriers. To be used mightily, they had to go through many trials before God could trust them with leadership.

I sometimes ask people, "What is the greatest desire of your heart?" Many answer, "I want the presence of God in my life. I want to truly know the Lord."

I know of only one way to know Him intimately: You must spend time with Him. There is no substitute. There are no shortcuts to prayers that get results.

If closeness with God is your desire, here is some wonderful news: The Lord desires a close relationship with you, even more than you do with Him. From the time God created Adam, man was created for fellowship. And from the moment sin broke that fellowship, the Lord offered ways to rebuild a loving relationship. Enoch is mentioned in the Bible simply for walking with God. Abraham, Isaac, and Jacob were also known for their fellowship with the Lord, for He continually and patiently looked for those whose hearts were after Him.

Think back for a moment to the time when Moses was given instructions for the building of the ark of the covenant: *"And thou shalt put the mercy seat above you upon the ark; and in the ark thou shalt put the testimony that I shall give thee. And there I will meet with thee, and I will commune with thee from above the mercy seat"* (Exodus 25:21-22). God's greatest desire was to commune with His servant Moses, and His great desire still is to commune with you. For remember, the veil was rent in two and the way unto the Holies was opened. Today, all you have to do is come. And when you approach Him, come with worship in your heart and praise on your lips. Come seeking Him with all your heart, and He promises you will find Him. But you must come: *"And ye shall seek me, and find me, when ye shall search for me with all your heart. And I will be found of you, saith the LORD"* (Jeremiah 29:13-14).

Andrew Murray, a truly great man of prayer, once said that before he prayed, he often said, "Lord, melt my cold heart. Break my hard heart and prepare it for Your touch."

Oh that we would be willing to approach the Father in that way. And when we come with such a heart, the Holy Spirit will meet us as our Helper and prayer Partner, enabling us to approach the throne of grace and touch the heart of God. For He promises as we draw night to Him, He will draw night to us: *"Draw nigh to God, and he will draw nigh to you"* (James 4:8).

You will know when He is present as your heart begins to break and the coldness begins to melt. Suddenly your empty words become life giving.

God wants fellowship with you. He doesn't just want words and formulas. He longs to answer that prayer that comes from your heart. You see, prayer is your heart listening to and talking to the Lord. Listening to the Lord is the key to power in prayer:

Keep thy foot [walk prudently] when thou
goest to the house of God, and be more ready
to hear, than to give the sacrifice of fools....
Be not rash with thy mouth, and let not thine
heart be hasty to utter any thing before God;
for God is in heaven, and thou upon earth:
therefore let thy words be few. (Ecclesiastes
5:1-2)

Be ready to hear the Holy Spirit's voice as you enter into God's presence. Real prayer is not filled with meaningless phrases but is the result of a heart filled with the abundance of God's presence. Therefore, prayer is the overflow of a heart filled with God. The Lord Jesus said, *"But when ye pray, use not vain repetitions, as the heathen do: for they think that they shall be heard for their much speaking"* (Matthew 6:7). And the apostle James wrote, *"The effectual, fervent prayer of a righteous man availeth much"* (James 5:16).

LEARN FROM GOD'S WORD

As God's people, we are commanded to *"walk worthy of the Lord unto all pleasing, being fruitful in every good work, and increasing in the knowledge of God"* (Colossians 1:10). We are commanded to be filled with the knowledge of God, for it is that knowledge of Him, His person, and His heart that must fill our being. And once His knowledge is in us, the glorious result will be a life of prayer.

Prayer will be as easy as breathing. It will be as natural to pray as it is to live. The knowledge of God is the key to that kind of life. Once His knowledge fills us, His Word will empower us, allowing us to pray effectively. And as we come to His throne room, we come filled with His faith and confidence: *"And this is the confidence that we have in him, that, if we ask any thing according to his will, he heareth us. And if we know that he hear us, whatsoever we ask, we know that we have the petitions that we desired of him"* (1 John 5:14-15).

It is confidence in Him—confidence born of Him that gets results in prayer. And it is that confidence that enables you to say, "Father, Your Word says…" And it is at that moment the Holy Spirit will quicken your mind and bring the Word to your remembrance.

This is why we are commanded, *"Be filled with the knowledge of his will in all wisdom and spiritual understanding"* (Colossians 1:9). Prayer is impossible unless we are filled with His knowledge and the knowledge of His Word. Overcoming prayerlessness takes place only when this happens.

And my prayer today for you is that the Word of Christ will *"dwell in you richly in all wisdom"* (Colossians 3:16).

THE POWER OF PRAYER

If only we knew how much God loves us

and wants to communicate with us, we would not

set up impossible standards for ourselves. Nor would

we become discouraged in obtaining good things

from God. After all, it is His earnest intent to give

us good things: "He that spared not his own Son,

but delivered him up for us all, how shall he not with

him also freely give us all things?" (Romans 8:32).

Madame Jeanne Guyon

six

Do you realize that movements on earth govern movements in heaven? Do you realize that a child of God in prayer affects decisions in heaven? The Lord declared, _"Whatsoever ye shall bind on earth shall be bound in heaven; and whatsoever ye shall loose on earth shall be loosed in heaven_ (Matthew 18:18).

So awesome is this power that it releases angels to do God's bidding on the earth and binds demons as it destroys the purpose of the enemy!

PRAYER—A PLACE OF SUPERNATURAL PROTECTION

Job tells us there is a secret place, known and available only to God's children. And when God's children enter into it, only then is the power of God activated on their behalf and on behalf of those in desperate need: _"There is a path which no fowl knoweth, and which the vulture's eye hath not seen: The lion's whelps have not trodden it, nor the fierce lion passed by it"_ (Job 28:7-8).

There is a path, a place which no fowl knows. That place is the secret place, that glorious place so secure and protected that no demonic power can find it. It is a place hidden in God that no vulture's eye has seen. No demon on earth or satan, the enemy of our souls, has seen or knows. It is a place of refuge, a place of safety that no lion's whelps (principalities and powers) pass by—not even the lion, satan. That place is the place of prayer.

The psalmist tells us it is in that secret place that you will find the Lord to be your refuge and fortress, and it is in that secret place that He covers you with His wings so that no evil will befall you nor will any plague come nigh to your dwelling. That secret path, that secret place is prayer.

PRAYER—A PLACE OF DELIVERANCE

Job 28:9 tells us that God puts forth His hand upon the rock and overturns mountains by the roots: It is only as we pray that obstacles are revoked from our path. It is there He makes for us a way of escape and sends His power to bring us out: *"He cutteth out rivers among the rocks; and his eye seeth every precious thing* (verse 10).

It is as we seek Him that He binds floods from overflowing over our lives, protecting and keeping us, revealing to us His love and His will, for the thing that is hid, He brings forth to light: "*He bindeth the floods from overflowing, and the thing that is hid bringeth he forth to light*" (verse 11).

Prayer is the only place of protection, deliverance, and revelation:

> *He that dwelleth in the secret place of the*
> *most High shall abide under the shadow of*
> *the Almighty. I will say of the LORD, He is my*
> *refuge and my fortress: my God; in him will I*
> *trust. Surely he shall deliver thee from the snare*
> *of the fowler, and from the noisome pestilence.*
> *He shall cover thee with his feathers, and*
> *under his wings shalt thou trust: his truth*
> *shall be thy shield and buckler. Thou shalt*
> *not be afraid for the terror by night; nor for*
> *the arrow that flieth by day; Nor for the pesti-*
> *lence that walketh in darkness; nor for the*
> *destruction that wasteth at noonday. A thou-*
> *sand shall fall at thy side, and ten thousand*
> *at thy right hand; but it shall not come nigh*
> *thee.* (Psalm 91:1-7)

Through the prophet Jeremiah, God sent us His royal invitation and said, "*Call unto me, and I will*

answer thee, and shew thee great and mighty things,
which thou knowest not" (Jeremiah 33:3).

I am reminded of the words spoken by U.S. President Abraham Lincoln as he led America through one of its most devastating years: "I have been driven many times to my knees by the overwhelming conviction that I had nowhere else to go. My own wisdom, and that of all about me, seemed insufficient for the day."[1]

Dangers and trials will also come our way, but if we obey the command of Proverbs 27:12, we cannot be defeated or overcome. We will prevail, for none who prays ever fails: *"A prudent man foreseeth the evil, and hideth himself; but the simple pass on, and are punished."*

Only as we hide *in* God—not like Adam who hid *from* God—can we find continual safety from harm. For God in His great love will warn us of coming dangers, yet He expects us to beware and hide in Him. Only the prudent know how to pray. The foolish neglect God and are punished.

I will never forget the time I was invited to minister in a politically unstable nation in Africa. Great pressure was placed on me to accept the invitation, yet in my heart I felt something was wrong. I had no peace. I sought the Lord greatly concerning this, and in His grace He spoke to Oral Roberts who told me if I would go, I would be killed and that God would judge me for dying before my time. Prayer saved my life, and the purpose of God was accomplished: *"And call upon me in the day of trouble: I will deliver thee, and thou shalt glorify me"* (Psalm 50:15).

PRAYER DRIVES AWAY ALL FEAR

David the king said:

> *LORD, how are they increased that trouble me!*
> *many are they that rise up against me. Many*
> *there be which say of my soul, There is no*
> *help for him in God. Selah. But thou, O*
> *LORD, art a shield for me; my glory, and the*
> *lifter up of mine head. I cried unto the LORD*
> *with my voice, and he heard me out of his*
> *holy hill.* (Psalm 3:1-4)

David's enemies had increased greatly. Trouble was all around. They mocked his faith in God and said, "Who can help him now?" But David knew the secret of deliverance from trouble. He cried to the Lord and found Him to be a present help in time of trouble.

You, too, will experience God's power as you call on Him in your time of anguish and fear, for you will find Him to be your shield and the lifter of your head. And as you seek Him, He will fill you with His peace and cause your sleep to be sweet as He holds you in His arms and sustains you.

Oh, the glorious power of prayer! Truly great peace belongs to those who know how to call upon the Lord.

PRAYER GIVES SUPERNATURAL PROTECTION FROM JUDGMENT

Are you bound or oppressed? Are you tired of the bondage that has wrapped itself around your soul?

Oh, if you will only call on Him today, you will find He is looking down from heaven to hear your cry and to loose the chains of death that have held you. You will find Him ready and able, for you will hear His voice saying, "Be not afraid, it is I," and He will lift you out of your storm and cause the sun to shine again.

The prophet Jeremiah said: *"I called upon thy name, O LORD, out of the low dungeon. Thou hast heard my voice: hide not thine ear at my breathing, at my cry. Thou drewest near in the day that I called upon thee: thou saidst, Fear not"* (Lamentations 3:55-57). And like

Jeremiah, you, too, will hear His voice the day you call.

Corrie ten Boom used to say, "There is no pit so deep that Jesus is not deeper still." Only prayer can lift you up and put you back on the mountaintop.

PRAYER HAS POWER TO CHANGE THE PLANS OF GOD

The Bible is filled with examples of prayer changing God's plans. Now, prayer does not change prophecy, but if man cooperates with God, God will answer, and His plans to punish will be changed:

Abraham and Abimelech

One of the first examples is recorded in Genesis:

And Abraham journeyed from thence toward the south country, and dwelled between Kadesh and Shur, and sojourned in Gerar. And Abraham said of Sarah his wife, She is my sister: and Abimelech king of Gerar sent, and took Sarah. But God came to Abimelech in a dream by night, and said to him, Behold, thou art but a dead man, for the woman which thou hast taken; for she is a man's wife. But Abimelech had not come near her: and he said, LORD, wilt thou slay also a righteous nation? Said he not unto me, She is my sister? and she, even she herself said, He is my brother: in the integrity of my heart and innocency of my hands have I done this. And God said unto him in a dream, Yea, I know that thou didst this in the integrity of thy heart; for I also withheld thee from sinning against me: therefore suffered I thee not to touch her. Now therefore restore the man his wife; for he is a prophet, and he shall pray for thee, and thou shalt live: and if thou restore her not, know thou that thou shalt surely die, thou, and all that are thine. (Genesis 20:1-7)

King Abimelech had taken Sarah, Abraham's wife, to be his. The Lord warned him in a dream that if he did not restore her back to Abraham, he would die. The Lord also had closed the wombs of King Abimelech's wives so that none could bear children in his house.

Yet when Abraham prayed, God healed Abimelech, his wife, and his maidservants. The plan of God was changed as Abraham prayed: *"So Abraham prayed unto God: and God healed Abimelech, and his wife, and his maidservants; and they bare children. For the* LORD *had fast closed up all the wombs of the house of Abimelech, because of Sarah Abraham's wife"* (Genesis 20:17-18).

Moses and the Children of Israel

In Exodus, we read how Moses was upon the mount with the Lord. Even after all God had done to deliver, protect, and feed the children of Israel, they turned away from Him and made a molten calf and worshiped it. Then the Lord said to Moses:

> *Go, get thee down; for thy people, which thou broughtest out of the land of Egypt, have corrupted themselves: They have turned aside quickly out of the way which I commanded them: they have made them a molten calf, and have worshipped it, and have sacrificed thereunto, and said, These be thy gods, O Israel, which have brought thee up out of the land of Egypt. And the* LORD *said unto Moses, I have seen this people, and, behold, it is a stiffnecked people: Now therefore let me*

alone, that my wrath may wax hot against
them, and that I may consume them: and I
will make of thee a great nation. (Exodus
32:7-10)

God, in His holy wrath, wanted to destroy Israel,
yet when Moses prayed, the Lord turned away from
His anger, revealing His mercy, all because a man knew
how to pray: *"And Moses besought the LORD his God,*
and said, LORD, why doth thy wrath wax hot against thy
people, which thou hast brought forth out of the land of
Egypt with great power, and with a mighty hand.... Turn
from thy fierce wrath, and repent of this evil against thy
people" (32:11-12).

As a result of Moses's earnest prayer *"the LORD*
repented of the evil which he thought to do unto his peo-
ple" (verse 14). It was God's plan to destroy His people
for their disobedience, but prayer caused Him to
change His plans.

Deuteronomy 9:19-20 even reminds us that God
wanted to destroy Aaron, as well, but as Moses prayed
for his brother, the Lord spared Aaron also: *"For I was*
afraid of the anger and hot displeasure, wherewith the
LORD was wroth against you to destroy you. But the LORD
hearkened unto me at that time also. And LORD was very

angry with Aaron to have destroyed him: and I prayed for Aaron also the same time" (Deuteronomy 9:19-20).

Of this, the great Bible teacher Matthew Henry wrote:

> See here, the power of prayer; God suffers himself to be prevailed with by the humble believing importunity of intercessors. [See also] the compassion of God towards poor sinners, and how ready he is to forgive. Thus he has given other proofs besides his own oath that he has no pleasure in the death of those that die; for he not only pardons upon the repentance of sinners, but spares and reprieves upon the intercession of others for them.[2]

What a mighty, loving God we serve! He keeps His promises. He is ever merciful and full of compassion.

King Hezekiah

Following the death of King Ahaz, his son Hezekiah ascended the throne in Jerusalem. The new monarch abolished the places of idol worship and returned the children of Israel to the worship of Jehovah. Also, for the first time since the kingdom had been split under

Rehoboam, son of Solomon, the remnants of the tribes of Israel were encouraged to renew the Passover feast and pilgrimage.

As the godly King Hezekiah reached the end of his life, Isaiah tells an amazing account of God's plans being changed through prayer:

> *In those days was Hezekiah sick unto death. And Isaiah the prophet the son of Amoz came unto him, and said unto him, Thus saith the LORD, Set thine house in order: for thou shalt die, and not live. Then Hezekiah turned his face toward the wall, and prayed unto the LORD, And said, Remember now, O LORD, I beseech thee, how I have walked before thee in truth and with a perfect heart, and have done that which is good in thy sight. And Hezekiah wept sore. Then came the word of the LORD to Isaiah, saying, Go, and say to Hezekiah, Thus saith the LORD, the God of David thy father, I have heard thy prayer, I have seen thy tears: behold, I will add unto thy days fifteen years.* (Isaiah 38:1-5)

King Hezekiah's prayer was answered. His life was extended.

Jonah and Nineveh

Another powerful example is recorded in the book of Jonah: *"Arise, go to Nineveh, that great city, and cry against it; for their wickedness is come up before me"* (Jonah 1:2). God planned to destroy Nineveh.

You remember the story. God told Jonah the prophet to go to Nineveh and proclaim God's judgment upon the city. Jonah rebelled and went a different direction, but when the storms hit the boat he was riding in, he was thrown overboard and was swallowed by a big fish. God got Jonah's attention. He was delivered from the fish's belly, and when he hit dry land, Jonah headed directly toward Nineveh to preach:

And the word of the LORD came unto Jonah the second time, saying, Arise, go unto Nineveh, that great city, and preach unto it the preaching that I bid thee. So Jonah arose, and went unto Nineveh, according to the word of the LORD. Now Nineveh was an exceeding great city of three days' journey. And Jonah began to enter into the city a day's journey, and he cried, and said, Yet forty days, and Nineveh shall be overthrown. So the people of Nineveh believed God, and proclaimed

*a fast, and put on sackcloth, from the greatest
of them even to the least of them. For word
came unto the king of Nineveh, and he arose
from his throne, and he laid his robe from
him, and covered him with sackcloth, and sat
in ashes. And he caused it to be proclaimed
and published through Nineveh by the decree
of the king and his nobles, saying, Let neither
man nor beast, herd nor flock, taste any
thing: let them not feed, nor drink water:
But let man and beast be covered with sackcloth, and cry mightily unto God: yea, let
them turn every one from his evil way, and
from the violence that is in their hands. Who
can tell if God will turn and repent, and turn
away from his fierce anger, that we perish
not? And God saw their works, that they
turned from their evil way; and God repented
of the evil, that he had said that he would do
unto them; and he did it not.* (Jonah 3:1-10)

God's plans were to destroy Nineveh, but when
the people of that great city prayed, God saw their
hearts as they turned from their evil way. As a result,
God changed His plans: *"He did it not."*

R. A. Torrey, the great American Bible teacher, said, "Prayer moves the hand that moves the world." Richard Trench, a powerful English preacher, once wrote: "Prayer is not overcoming God's reluctance, but laying hold of His highest willingness."

If the Lord can find just *one* person who will seek His face, the tide of events can be turned. He told the prophet Ezekiel, *"I sought for a man among them, that should make up the hedge, and stand in the gap before me for the land, that I should not destroy it: but I found none"* (Ezekiel 22:30). And because He found none who would pray and intercede, the Word of God declares, *"Therefore I have poured out mine indignation on them; I have consumed them with the fire of my wrath; their own way have I recompensed [their own deeds] upon their own heads"* (verse 31).

It is not the Lord's will to destroy. He continues to ask, "Is there anyone who will step forward and stand in the gap?"

God is looking for men and women who, like Moses, will cry to God for deliverance. The psalmist wrote, *"Therefore he said that he would destroy them, had not Moses his chosen stood before him in the breach, to turn away his wrath, lest he should destroy them"* (Psalm 106:23).

Prayer is not meant to overcome God's reluctance. You cannot strong-arm the Lord and force Him to do something. Moses prayed and interceded, and God answered Him for His mercy's sake.

Prayer is partnership with God. Despite being imprisoned for her devotion to God, Madame Jeanne Guyon taught, "Come, then, give your heart to God and learn the ways of prayer. For those who have the desire, it is easy to pray. The Holy Spirit has enabled common men to pray great prayers by His gifts and grace."[3]

GOD HAS PROMISED TO ANSWER PRAYER

Before I discuss the right location, position, and condition of prayer, here is a list of some of God's precious promises from Psalms that will lift your faith, for the One who loves you still hears and answers prayer:

Psalm 18:3—*"I will call upon the LORD, who is worthy to be praised: so shall I be saved from mine enemies."*

Psalm 50:15—*"And call upon me in the day of trouble: I will deliver thee, and thou shalt glorify me."*

Psalm 55:16— *"As for me, I will call upon God; and the LORD shall save me."*

Psalm 86:5— *"For thou, Lord, art good, and ready to forgive; and plenteous in mercy unto all them that call upon thee."*

Psalm 86:7— *"In the day of my trouble I will call upon thee: for thou wilt answer me."*

Psalm 91:15— *"He shall call upon me, and I will answer him: I will be with him in trouble; I will deliver him, and honour him."*

Psalm 99:6— *"Moses and Aaron among his priests, and Samuel among them that call upon his name; they called upon the LORD, and he answered them."*

Psalm 145:18— *"The LORD is nigh unto all them that call upon him, to all that call upon him in truth."*

RIGHT LOCATION, RIGHT POSITION, RIGHT CONDITION

Power will come when

the way is paved by prayer.

That way is available to you and me.

We must tap into it. To do so,

we must travel on a road toward

a life of abiding prayer that is built

on the greatest of foundations.

Harold J. Ockenga

seven

Near Campbellville, Ontario, some thirty miles southwest of Toronto are the grounds of a retreat center called Bezek, a wonderful place founded by Bernie Warren. Brother Warren was affiliated with the United Church of Canada and had launched the ministry at Bezek Center after receiving the baptism of the Holy Spirit. He named the retreat Bezek after the place where the Israelites gathered to be refreshed and encouraged as they faced an important battle (1 Samuel 11).

After my own encounter with the Holy Spirit in 1973, I often attended the Friday night charismatic meeting there. Bezek always seemed to have lots of vibrant Christians, and I felt very welcome there. I knew God had called me to preach the Gospel, yet I felt so inadequate, so unprepared. Even though I had yet to stand behind a pulpit for the first time, I identified with the apostle Paul, who said, *"Woe is unto me, if I preach not the gospel!"* (1 Corinthians 9:16).

On one particular day I arrived quite early and began to walk alone on the grounds of the retreat center, talking to God. I went up the hill and sat on a rock, a hymnal in hand. As I sat, I began to worship the Lord as I waited upon Him, calling His precious name.

And it was in those glorious days, I began to understand the importance of being alone with God, for I began to experience God's presence in a very special way when I was alone and began to practice what I want to discuss in this chapter.

Effective prayer is impossible unless we understand the importance of being in the right location, the right position, and the right condition.

RIGHT LOCATION

When we pray, we must come to the right place. Moses understood this, for we read in Exodus 33:7-11:

> *And Moses took the tabernacle, and pitched it
> without the camp, afar off from the camp,
> and called it the Tabernacle of the congrega-
> tion. And it came to pass, that every one
> which sought the LORD went out unto the
> tabernacle of the congregation, which was
> without the camp. And it came to pass, when
> Moses went out unto the tabernacle, that all
> the people rose up, and stood every man at his
> tent door, and looked after Moses, until he*

was gone into the tabernacle. And it came to pass, as Moses entered into the tabernacle, the cloudy pillar descended, and stood at the door of the tabernacle, and the LORD talked with Moses. And all the people saw the cloudy pillar stand at the tabernacle door: and all the people rose up and worshipped, every man in his tent door. And the LORD spake unto Moses face to face, as a man speaketh unto his friend. And he turned again into the camp: but his servant Joshua, the son of Nun, a young man, departed not out of the tabernacle.

Moses knew where to meet God. The Lord said in Matthew 6:6, *"Enter into thy closet."* This doesn't necessarily mean a physical closet or specific address, for you and I can experience that solitude and oneness with the Lord even in the midst of a crowd. But separating ourselves as the Lord did enables us to come into God's presence, free from the distractions of the world and the things that can so easily harm our communion with the Lord.

That is why Moses entered into the tabernacle (Exodus 33:8-9), away from the multitudes. That is also why the Lord Jesus often separated Himself from the crowds, for He understood this glorious secret to power with God *"And when he had sent the multitudes away, he went up into a mountain apart to pray: and when the evening was come, he was there alone"* (Matthew 14:23).

Even when Peter, James, and John were with Him in Gethsemane at the time He needed them most, He knew the importance of being alone with God the Father: *"Then cometh Jesus with them unto a place called Gethsemane, and saith unto the disciples, Sit ye here, while I go and pray yonder"* (Matthew 26:36).

The Lord Jesus told us, *"But thou, when thou prayest, enter into thy closet, and when thou hast shut thy door, pray to thy Father which is in secret; and thy Father which seeth in secret shall reward thee openly"* (Matthew 6:6).

The Master loved being with the people. He spent much of His time ministering to those in need in public places, mountainsides, and seashores. Yet He knew that only alone could He know and enjoy that glorious intimacy with God the Father. Elijah, too, showed he understood this when the Lord met Him in Horeb (1 Kings 19).

So it is with us. It is impossible to know close communion with God unless we are alone with Him. For it is in that place of quietness and rest that we are able to commune with the Lord. And prayer that gets results must have a location.

RIGHT POSITION

When I talk about position, I do not mean standing, sitting, or kneeling. I am talking about something much more important. The Scriptures tell us that when Moses went into the tabernacle to be alone with God, he came into the Holy of Holies where stood the Ark of the Covenant; he came to the mercy seat and to the blood.

It is impossible to pray effectively without coming to the blood. We pray as we come under the blood at the Cross:

> *And when Moses was gone into the tabernacle*
> *of the congregation to speak with him, then*
> *he heard the voice of one speaking unto him*
> *from off the mercy seat that was upon the ark*
> *of testimony, from between the two cherubims:*
> *and he spake unto him.* (Numbers 7:89)

> *And he shall take of the blood of the bullock,*
> *and sprinkle it with his finger upon the mercy*
> *seat eastward; and before the mercy seat shall*

he sprinkle of the blood with his finger seven
times. Then shall he kill the goat of the sin
offering, that is for the people, and bring his
blood within the vail, and do with that blood
as he did with the blood of the bullock, and
sprinkle it upon the mercy seat, and before the
mercy seat. (Leviticus 16:14-15)

You must be under the blood. As believers, we must come through the work of the Cross:

Having therefore, brethren, boldness to enter
into the holiest by the blood of Jesus, By a new
and living way, which he hath consecrated for
us, through the veil, that is to say, his flesh;
And having an high priest over the house of
God; Let us draw near with a true heart in
full assurance of faith. (Hebrews 10:19-22)

Not only is the right position important, but also the right condition.

RIGHT CONDITION

By the "right condition" I mean the condition of the heart, a heart drawn and touched by God Almighty. It is impossible to pray effectively until the Lord touches your heart and quickens it: *"And their nobles shall be of themselves, and their governor shall proceed from the midst of them; and I will cause him to draw near, and he shall approach unto me: for who is this that engaged his heart to approach unto me? saith the LORD"* (Jeremiah 30:21).

Notice the Word of God tells us *"I will cause him to draw near, and He shall approach Me"* (NKJV). For it is better to have a heart without words than words without a heart.

The Word of God tells us, *"So will not we go back from thee: quicken us, and we will call upon thy name"* (Psalm 80:18). And in the Song of Solomon, we read: *"Draw me, we will run after thee: the king hath brought me into his chambers: we will be glad and rejoice in thee, we will remember thy love more than wine: the upright love thee"* (Song of Solomon 1:4).

Madame Guyon, a mighty woman of prayer, once said:

> The simple requirement is that you must learn to pray from your heart and not your head. The reason for this is that man's mind is so limited in its operation, it can only focus on one object at a time. But the prayer offered from the heart cannot be

interrupted by reason. Nothing can inter-
rupt this prayer except confused affection.
When you have enjoyed God and the
sweetness of His love, however, you will
find it impossible to set your affections on
anything other than Him.[1]

To enjoy the sweetness of His love in your heart,
however, your heart must be pure and contrite, for the
Word of God tells us: *"The sacrifices of God are a broken
spirit: a broken and a contrite heart, O God, thou wilt not
despise"* (Psalm 51:17). God is looking for a broken
heart, a truthful and honest heart. Psalm 51:6 declares,
*"Behold, thou desirest truth in the inward parts: and in the
hidden part thou shalt make me to know wisdom."*

Psalm 145:18-19 is also very clear on this: *"The
LORD is nigh unto all them that call upon him, to all that
call upon him in truth. He will fulfil the desire of them
that fear him: he also will hear their cry, and will save
them."* The Lord is close to the one who calls on Him in
truth, whose heart is full of honesty, and whose spirit
is free from guile: *"Thus saith the LORD, The heaven is
my throne, and the earth is my footstool: where is the
house that ye build unto me? and where is the place of my
rest? For all those things hath mine hand made, and all*

those things have been, saith the LORD: but to this man will I look, even to him that is poor and of a contrite spirit, and trembleth at my word" (Isaiah 66:1-2).

When you pray, God looks on the condition of your heart. Prayer must come from a prepared heart. This is the prayer that touches heaven!

The secret to effective, anointed, powerful prayer is not dependent upon any of the external elements, but upon a **relationship** and **heart**:

> *For I know the thoughts that I think toward you, saith the LORD, thoughts of peace, and not of evil, to give you an expected end [a future and a hope]. Then shall you call upon me, and ye shall go and pray unto me, and I will hearken unto you. And ye shall seek me, and find me, when ye shall search for me with all your heart, and I will be found of you, saith the LORD.* (Jeremiah 29:11-14)

When you are in the right location (alone with God), the right position (under the blood), and the right condition (a prepared, pure heart), God stands ready to honor your prayers with His presence and power!

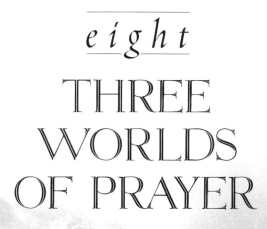

e i g h t

THREE
WORLDS
OF PRAYER

Let us be faithful to our high calling and our heavenly

ordaining, for "I have chosen you, and ordained you," is our

Master's word, "that whatsoever ye shall ask of the Father in

my name, he may give it you" (John 15:16). Let us not fear,

but let us pray. Let us not doubt, but let us pray. Let us not

murmur, but let us pray. Let us not faint, but let us pray.

Let us not struggle so hard to try to do it all ourselves, but

let us recognize it all as but a greater opportunity for proving

the all-sufficiency of God and the power of prayer.

A. B. Simpson

eight

It has been more than three decades since the early days of our ministry in Toronto, yet I can recall many scenes as if they happened yesterday. One incident that happened in April 1974 is indelibly etched in my mind. I was having a wonderful time of prayer in my bedroom, enjoying God's presence. His presence had been so real to me since I had attended a Kathryn Kuhlman service in December of 1973.

As I was in prayer, I remember asking the Lord, "Why am I experiencing Your presence in such a glorious way?" I knew God had a divine purpose in all that had been happening to me.

Standing in my room, I suddenly had a vision. I saw someone standing in front of me. That person was enveloped in tormenting flames. I couldn't tell if it was a man or woman. The person's feet weren't touching the ground. As I looked at this being's face, his or her mouth was opening and closing, making a horrible sound, just as Matthew 13:42 describes: *"And shall cast them into a furnace of fire: there shall be wailing and gnashing of teeth."*

I was horrified as the person was completely engulfed in tormenting flames, and I began crying, "No! No! No!"

At that moment, the Lord spoke to me audibly: "Preach the Gospel."

"But Lord," I said, "I can't talk." I had had a stuttering problem all my life. How could I possibly preach?

Sometime later I had a vivid dream. An angel appeared, carrying a chain that was attached to a door so huge that it seemed to fill heaven. As he pulled on the chain to open the door, I suddenly saw a multitude of people stretching as far as the eye could see. Then the angel called me and took me to a higher place. As I looked down, I saw the same multitude slowly walking forward. To my horror, the shuffling throng was moving toward a billowing inferno. Fire blazed from the abyss, and I saw people at the front of the line being pushed over the precipice, disappearing from sight. And the same happened to those following as the crush of humanity behind them kept pushing them over the edge and into the raging flames.

Again, I heard the Lord's voice say clearly, "Preach the Gospel. If you do not preach, every soul that falls will be your responsibility."

The words cut through me like a jagged sword. From that moment, I knew I had to preach the Gospel.

Shortly after that dream, the doors began opening for me to preach. As I stood to preach for the first time, the Lord healed my stuttering tongue!

Though it has been nearly three decades since then, the reality of that terrible vision is still as vivid to me as the day it happened.

It was because of prayer that the call of God was made so real and clear to my heart. It was prayer that opened my eyes to a heavenly vision and prayer that enabled me to hear the voice of the Lord at a young age.

And it was in those early days that I began to understand and experience the power of prayer.

THREE WORLDS OF PRAYER

When we study the subject of prayer, we should always go to the Source. In Matthew, the Lord Jesus said: *"Ask, and it shall be given you; seek, and ye shall find; knock, and it shall be opened unto you. For every one that asketh receiveth; and he that seeketh findeth, and to him that knocketh it shall be opened"* (Matthew 7:7-8).

In this truth, the Lord presents to each one of us three worlds of prayer: the world of asking, the world of seeking, and the world of knocking. Each has a unique purpose in developing direct access to the throne room.

When Moses, under God's direction, built the tabernacle in the wilderness, he built it with three distinct areas:

- The outer court, which was surrounded by a linen fence, and within it stood the altar of sacrifice and the laver
- The Holy Place, where stood the candlestick, the table of shewbread, and the table of incense
- The Holy of Holies, where he placed the ark of the covenant and the golden censor

In the tabernacle are revealed the three worlds of prayer:

- The outer court is the world of asking.
- The Holy Place is the world of seeking.
- The most sacred place behind the veil—the Holy of Holies—is the world of knocking.

The World of Asking

Matthew 7:8 tells us, *"For every one that asketh receiveth."* Asking is where you begin, and asking is the

result of abiding in Christ: *"If ye abide in me, and my*
words abide in you, ye shall ask what ye will, and it shall
be done unto you" (John 15:7).

Asking begins in the outer court. This is where we
make our requests known: *"Be careful for nothing; but*
in every thing by prayer and supplication with thanks-
giving let your requests be made known unto God"
(Philippians 4:6).

This is where we ask and receive. This is where we
come to the Lord and make our desires and needs
known to Him.

This is also where we are cleansed by the blood as
we confess our sins. This is where we find Him faithful and just to forgive us, as promised in 1 John 1:9—
"If we confess our sins, he is faithful and just to forgive us
our sins, and to cleanse us from all unrighteousness"—for
it is in the outer court that we find the altar of sacrifice, where the work of the Cross and the blood of
Jesus avails.

And remember, the outer court is also where we
find the laver, the Word of God, and it is in this world
of prayer that we remind the Lord of His promises. We
do this by asking according to His will, according to
His Word: *"And this is the confidence that we have in*
him, that, if we ask any thing according to his will, he

heareth us" (1 John 5:14). This is why David cried, "*Blessed are they that keep his testimonies, and that seek him with the whole heart*" (Psalm 119:2).

It is in this world that we must prevail in prayer as we wait upon the Lord. And as we overcome in this world of prayer, we are granted the privilege of entering into the next.

The World of Seeking

In the Holy Place, the seeking world of prayer, stood the candlestick on one side and the table of showbread on the other. As you looked toward the veil, you would see the table of incense.

It is here in the seeking world of prayer that the Holy Spirit grants you the power to seek the Lord. In Jeremiah 29:13-14 we read:

> *And ye shall seek me, and find me, when ye shall search for me with all your heart. And I will be found of you, saith the LORD: and I will turn away your captivity, and I will gather you from all the nations, and from all the places whither I have driven you, saith the LORD; and I will bring you again into the place whence I caused you to be carried away captive.*

It is in this world of prayer that you find the Lord and receive liberty from all captivity. It is here that God Almighty gives you illumination through His Word. It is here that you receive the truth of God's Word. And it is also here that you will be nourished and satisfied by the promises of God, for it is here that you find the table of showbread.

Only in this world of prayer can you experience true worship, for the table of incense stood in the Holy Place.

Seeking the Lord, finding Him, and finding the fullness of your liberty will cause your heart to be filled with His Word. It will cause you to erupt in worship and prepare you for the greatest privilege a Christian will ever know—the knocking world.

The World of Knocking

This knocking world of prayer, the Holy of Holies, is the place of partnership with God. Intercession, the deepest form of prayer, takes place only here.

It was in the Holy of Holies that the high priest entered once a year to intercede for the children of Israel. It was here that he offered the blood of the sacrifices for himself and for the sins and errors of God's people.

And it was here that Moses interceded continually for Israel, for the Holy of Holies is the place of intercession.

And it is in the Holy of Holies in heaven today that Christ Jesus still intercedes for you and me: *"Wherefore he is able also to save them to the uttermost that come unto God by him, seeing he ever liveth to make intercession for them"* (Hebrews 7:25).

Charles Spurgeon was England's best-known preacher for most of the second half of the nineteenth century. He wrote:

> We will now remember that our Lord presents us with a promise. Note that the promise is given to several varieties of prayer: "I say unto you, Ask, and it shall be given you; seek, and ye shall find; knock, and it shall be opened unto you" (Matthew 7:7-8). The text clearly asserts that all forms of true prayer will be heard, provided they are presented through Jesus Christ and are for promised blessings.... To each of these stages of prayer there is a distinct promise. He who asks will have; what more did he ask for? But he who seeks will go

further; he will find, will enjoy, will grasp,
and will know that he has obtained. He
who knocks will go further still, for he will
understand, and to him will the precious
thing be opened.[1]

The Lord today is asking us to come into the
outer court to make our requests known and to receive
from His giving, loving hands. He is asking us to come
into the Holy Place, seeking Him until we find Him.
And He wants us to come into the Holy of Holies,
interceding for others, where we will find Him able to
save to the uttermost.

INCREASING YOUR PRAYER LIFE THROUGH FASTING

If we would pray with power, we should pray

with fasting. This of course does not mean that we should fast

every time we pray; but there are times of emergency or special

crisis in work or in our individual lives, when men of downright

earnestness will withdraw themselves even from the gratification

of natural appetites that would be perfectly proper under other

circumstances, that they may give themselves up wholly to prayer.

There is a peculiar power in such prayer. Every great crisis

in life and work should be met in that way.

R. A. Torrey

nine

As He walked on the earth, the Lord Jesus was very clear on the subject of fasting: *"I say unto you, If ye have faith as a grain of mustard seed, ye shall say unto this mountain, Remove hence to yonder place; and it shall remove; and nothing shall be impossible unto you. Howbeit, this kind goeth not out but by prayer and fasting"* (Matthew 17:20-21).

If fasting was that vital to the Lord, it should be no less important to us. It has been to me for many years. I have learned a lot about prayer and fasting by reading the works of many great people of faith from the past. I have also witnessed firsthand the incredible, dynamic results of fasting by both my wife, Suzanne, and my mother.

Years ago, my mother began the practice of fasting every Friday. It was not something she was told to do by a parent or minister, nor was it a custom she learned as a young girl raised in the Greek Orthodox Church.

"God led me to do it," she told me. In ways too numerous to mention, fasting had a profound impact on her spiritual life and mine.

Suzanne, on the other hand, grew up in a pastor's home. I have always been amazed at how committed she has been to prayer and fasting. Over the years she has fasted more times than I can count, and I have watched her experience incredible spiritual breakthroughs.

From both of these extraordinary women, I have learned many things that have led to spiritual victories for me. More than ever, I am of the opinion that believers must have a proper understanding of fasting. Only then can each of us be equipped to break down the barriers and open the floodgates of heaven. First, we must learn why and how to fast.

QUESTIONS TO ASK BEFORE FASTING

It is important to know that there are special fasts for specific purposes. Before we begin, here are five questions to ask yourself.

Is this fast God directed?

Are you fasting because God has led you into it? Is it ordained by Him? Some people fast so they can boast about their spiritual piety. When Jesus told the parable of the Pharisee and the publican, He said, *"The*

Pharisee stood and prayed thus with himself, God, I thank thee, that I am not as other men are, extortioners, unjust, adulterers, or even as this publican [tax collector]. I fast twice in the week, I give tithes of all I possess" (Luke 18:11-12). The reason the Lord Jesus <u>condemned</u> the <u>fasting of the Pharisee</u> was because it was done in the flesh, led by <u>pride and tradition</u>.

It is vital to follow God's leading regarding prayer and fasting. Otherwise it may lead to bondage. Be certain you are prompted by the Holy Spirit and that your actions will please, honor, and glorify Him.

What are your motives for fasting?

I have known people who treat fasting as a hunger strike, attempting to push God into a corner to have Him respond to what they want accomplished in their life. Others go without food, calling it a spiritual fast, but they mostly want to shed a few pounds.

The person who does anything for the flesh is an idol worshiper. We are warned, *"Neither be ye idolaters, as were some of them; as it is written, The people sat down to eat and drink, and rose up to play"* (1 Corinthians 10:7). Their bodies were their gods. True fasting, on the other hand, always crucifies self. We must become as Paul, who brought his body into subjection (1 Corinthians 9:27).

Adam and Eve fell in the Garden of Eden because of the lust of the flesh, and the flesh is something satan will attempt to arouse in you. When the devil came to the Lord Jesus, he said, *"If thou be the Son of God, command that these stones be made bread"* (Matthew 4:3). Why did the evil one use those words? He wanted to see if the Lord would bow to the temptation of the flesh. Jesus answered, *"It is written, Man shall not live by bread alone, but by every word that proceedeth out of the mouth of God"* (4:4).

Jesus would not yield. Neither should we.

What specific needs are you fasting for?

In Scripture, when people fasted, it was usually because of a specific need: <u>deliverance, healing, ministry challenges, or personal problems.</u> No one fasted "just to fast."

What about you? When you fast, can you state specifically why you feel led to enter this time of self-denial?

What results are you expecting?

When your time of fasting is completed, how will your life be different? Do you expect to be closer to the Lord? What prayer do you believe will be answered? Will your actions affect the life of someone else?

Remember, you are not going through a ritual or routine. It is not out of place to establish a "goal setting" aspect to your fast. When the fast is completed, what will be the results?

Will you minister to the Lord while fasting?

Often, we get this backward. We fast, fully expecting God to minister to us. He will, but it is more important for you to minister to Him. During this time you are ministering to God Himself. The believers at Antioch *"ministered to the Lord, and fasted"* (Acts 13:2).

The Lord wants to know, "Are you fasting for My purpose?" That is what God said through the prophet Zechariah: *"Speak unto all the people of the land, and to the priests, say when ye fasted and mourned in the fifth and seventh month, even those seventy years, did ye at all fast unto me, even to me?"* (Zechariah 7:5).

Above all, a fast is more than a personal spiritual exercise, more than religious gymnastics. It must have a purpose. Then you can move confidently toward the purpose of your fast.

SEVEN TYPES OF FASTS

In Scripture there are seven unique types of fasts for distinctive purposes. Some are to be observed for one day, others for three days, three weeks, or even forty days and nights. These are not given as a rigid formula, but as examples of how God works.

Fasting in a Crisis

In the Old Testament there is a fascinating story of Esther who became deeply troubled when she learned that Haman, the prime minister of the land, was determined to eliminate the Jewish race from Babylon and plotted to kill Esther's older cousin Mordecai by publicly hanging him from the gallows. Esther gave these instructions to Mordecai:

> *Go, gather together all the Jews that are present*
> *in Shushan, and fast ye for me, and neither eat*
> *nor drink three days, night or day: I also and*
> *my maidens will fast likewise; and so will I*
> *go into the king, which is not according to the*
> *law; and if I perish, I perish.* (Esther 4:16)

Esther entered the three-day fast because there was a crisis that needed to be solved. She prayed that God would turn the situation around, and that is exactly what happened. The king not only granted her request, but when he learned of Haman's evil plans *"they hanged Haman on the gallows that he had prepared for Mordecai"* (Esther 7:10).

It is not the only time in Scripture that God directed a fast of three days because of impending danger. Saul of Tarsus, who had persecuted the church, had his life-changing conversion to Christ on the road to Damascus. The experience was so powerful that he was blinded by the light from heaven that shone around him. As a Pharisee, his conversion would surely mean death. Saul *"was three days without sight, and neither did eat nor drink"* (Acts 9:9).

It was after that time of fasting that Ananias laid hands on Saul, later called Paul. His sight was restored, and Paul began to proclaim the Gospel of Jesus Christ to the world.

Fasting for Revelation

The second fast described in God's Word is a twenty-one day partial fast so that God would reveal the future. The prophet Daniel wrote, *"In those days I Daniel was mourning three full weeks. I ate no pleasant bread, neither came flesh nor wine in my mouth, neither did I anoint myself at all, til three whole weeks were fulfilled"* (Daniel 10:2-3). This was not a total fast since he mentions only the food he did *not* eat. No dessert, no meat, no wine.

The purpose became clear when the angel Gabriel appeared to Daniel and said, *"Now I am come to make thee understand what shall befall thy people in the latter days, for yet the vision is for many days"* (Daniel 10:14). Daniel's twenty-one day partial fast was for revelation. God pulled back the curtain and unveiled what would happen in the coming days.

The same thing happened to Daniel earlier. He shunned food for the same purpose, and there was an identical result: *"And I set my face unto the LORD God, to seek by prayer and supplications, with fasting, and sackcloth, and ashes"* (9:3). Soon after, God gave him a revelation: *"At the beginning of thy supplications the commandment came forth, and I am come to shew thee; for thou art greatly beloved: therefore understand the matter, and consider the vision"* (9:23).

Fasting for Reexamination

In the Old Testament, God asked His people to set aside one day each year—the Day of Atonement—to take a better look at their spiritual state: *"Also on the tenth day of this seventh month there shall be a day of atonement: it shall be a holy convocation unto you; and ye shall afflict your souls, and offer an offering made by fire unto the LORD"* (Leviticus 23:27).

How did King David afflict his soul and humble himself? With fasting. He wrote, *"But as for me, when they were sick, my clothing was sackcloth: I humbled my soul with fasting"* (Psalm 35:13).

God directed His people to use a specific day for denial of self. The prophet Jeremiah wrote, *"Therefore go thou, and read in the roll, which thou hast written from my mouth [at my instruction], the words of the LORD in the ears of the people in the LORD'S house upon the fasting day"* (Jeremiah 36:6). It was a specific day. God wanted His people to reexamine their spiritual state on a particular day. They were to ask, "Where do I stand with God?" The New Testament church continued the practice of fasting, not out of duty or custom, but because it was a way of drawing closer to the Lord.

With your own fasting day, as with every aspect of your life, let God direct you in these matters. Then you can be certain it is of Him.

Fasting for Deliverance

The book of Judges relates a dramatic story of Israel as they engaged in a battle with the tribe of Benjamin for a sin that had been committed. God specifically told His people to fight against this one tribe. Here is what took place.

The children of Israel asked God, *"Which of us shall go up first to battle against the children of Benjamin? And the* LORD *said, Judah shall go up first"* (Judges 20:18).

So the men of Judah prepared themselves to battle Benjamin at a place called Gibeah. The results, however, were not what Israel expected. Scripture records that the children of Benjamin came out of Gibeah, and on that day cut down twenty-two thousand men of the Israelites (verse 21).

It is amazing that God told them to go into battle, yet they were sorely defeated. Those who returned were distraught, and with bitter tears they cried, *"Shall I go up again to battle against the children of Benjamin my brother? And the* LORD *said, Go up against him"* (verse 23).

So the next day they reorganized and headed again into battle*: "And Benjamin went forth against them out of Gibeah the second day, and destroyed down to the ground of the children of Israel again eighteen thousand men"* (verse 25).

In two days Israel lost forty thousand men. Most people would say, "God can't be in this! If we try one more time we'll all be dead!" However, there was something missing in their prayer prior to the first two battles. They had not fasted. The Scriptures record, *"Then all the children of Israel…came unto the house of God, and wept, and sat there before the LORD, and fasted that day until even, and offered burnt offerings and peace offerings before the LORD"* (verse 26).

One of the leaders stood before the ark of the covenant and asked God: *"Shall I yet again go out to battle against the children of Benjamin my brother, or shall I cease? And the LORD said, Go up; for to morrow I will deliver them into thine hand"* (verse 28).

They should have known to fast from the beginning. Moses and the prophets had given them God's clear instructions on fasting, yet they waited until two major defeats before they saw the importance of fasting unto the Lord for deliverance.

It was only after total obedience that God told them precisely when the battle would be won. It would happen "tomorrow." God kept His promise. The Word says, *"The LORD smote [defeated] Benjamin before Israel"* (verse 35). On their first two attempts, the Israelites tried to fight the battle by themselves. They lost. When they fasted, the Lord won the battle for them!

Fasting for Freedom from Judgment

God's principles regarding keeping His ordinances are universal. There are examples in Scripture where even the sinful were spared judgment because they followed the Lord's command.

Ahab, the husband of Jezebel, is one example of this. God let His displeasure be known against this evil king of Israel:

> *And it came to pass, when Ahab heard those words, that he rent [tore] his clothes, and put sackcloth upon his flesh, and fasted, and lay in sackcloth, and went softly [in mourning]. And the word of the LORD came to Elijah the Tishbite, saying, Seest thou how Ahab humbleth himself before me? because he humbleth himself before me, I will not bring the evil in his days.* (1 Kings 21:27-29)

Fasting lifted judgment from the life of Ahab. It can do the same for anyone who discovers this powerful spiritual principle.

Fasting for Health and Healing

For years many nutritional doctors and health practitioners have known that fasting promotes a cleansing and healing process because it helps eliminate toxins from the body.

In the Bible we read of <u>an Amalekite who went without food for three days and was healed:</u>

> *And they found an Egyptian in the field, and brought him to David, and gave him bread, and he did eat; and they made him drink water. And they gave him a piece of a cake of figs, and two clusters of raisins: and when he had eaten, his spirit came again to him [his strength returned]; for he had eaten no bread, nor drunk any water, three days and three nights.* (1 Samuel 30:11-12)

Some may conclude that it was the food that made him well. I believe it was fasting that brought him back to health. There have certainly been hundreds of other examples around the world of people who have benefited spiritually, emotionally, and physically from fasting.

Of course, I recommend that you always talk with your personal physician before going into a fasting-for-health program. I do this. In fact, one of the best fasting practitioners I know of is my friend Don Colbert, M.D., who has a medical and nutritional practice in Longwood, Florida. He has written numerous books on the subject, including *Walking in Divine Health* and *Toxic Relief.* I recommend anything he writes or teaches on the subject, and for good reason: Dr. Colbert has been my personal physician and nutritional teacher for many years.

Fasting for Dominion

In Scripture there were only three individuals who fasted forty days: Moses, Elijah, and the Lord Jesus.

- Moses went without food forty days before he received the law (Exodus 24:18).
- Elijah, as he slept under a juniper tree, was awakened by an angel who cooked a meal for him: *"And he arose, and did eat and drink, and went in the strength of that meat forty days and forty nights unto Horeb, the mount of God"* (1 Kings 19:8).
- The Lord Jesus was *"led by the Spirit into the wilderness, Being forty days tempted of the devil. And in those days he did eat nothing"* (Luke 4:1-2).

I don't recommend fasts that last this long for anyone! In the natural, you cannot live that long without food or water.

FASTING SPECIFICS

I have often been asked, "How do you begin a fast, and how do you end one?" As mentioned earlier, my advice is that you first check with your doctor before you begin any fast. Some physicians may not understand what you are trying to do, but there are a growing number of medical and nutritional practitioners who do recognize the physical, mental, and spiritual advantages of fasting. As Dr. Don Colbert has been to me and my family, a spirit-filled physician is a Godsend.

Regardless of your situation or the availability of anointed medical personnel, your current spiritual, emotional, and physical condition must always be taken into consideration. For example, if you are on a medication to be taken with food, you should not be fasting. That one is simple enough, but your situation may be much more complex. Whatever you do, use wisdom.

Once you have consulted with a doctor, begin a fast by entering into it slowly. I suggest you start by skipping just one meal. The next time, miss two meals. Eventually you may feel comfortable with fasting for a few days or even a week.

One man told me, "God is directing me, and I know He will take care of any problems no matter how long I fast." That is simply not sound judgment. Again,

I urge you to consult with your physician regarding any fast you are contemplating for any length of time. And be more careful about ending your fast than beginning it. Anyone who has fasted for any length of time knows that your body actually becomes accustomed to not eating. The last thing you want to do is run out to a restaurant and scarf down a big steak with all the trimmings. Drink fruit and vegetable juices (just don't mix them!) after completing the fast. Then on successive days, add fruit, soup, salads, and whole-grain breads until your body is ready for meats such as fish or chicken. Control your food quantities. Get plenty of rest. Be wise in your pursuit of reasonable goals.

I am convinced more than ever that fasting should be part of your normal Christian walk. It will strengthen your relationship with the Lord. The presence of God will become closer, and your prayer life will take on added power.

Fasting in the name of the Lord Jesus will build a stronger, more potent faith. And fasting will intensify your prayer life.

ten

STEPS TO EFFECTIVE PRAYER

*Prayer is
releasing the
energies of God,
for prayer is asking
God to do what
we cannot do.*
Charles Trumbull

t e n

This story reportedly happened during World War I: A British soldier was caught one night while creeping secretively back to his tent from a nearby wooded area. He was immediately hauled before his commanding officer and charged with holding communications with the enemy. The man pleaded that he had gone into the woods to pray. That was his only defense.

"Have you been in the habit of spending hours in private prayer?" his officer asked roughly.

"Yes, sir."

"Then get down on your knees and pray now like you've never prayed before!" the commander ordered.

The young man knew he could be shot at sunrise for the crime he was accused of committing. He knelt and poured out his soul in prayer that could have only been inspired by the Holy Spirit.

"You may go," the officer said in hushed tones after the soldier finished praying. "I believe your story. If you hadn't drilled often, you couldn't have done so well at review."[1]

The young man had a breakthrough that saved his life. He did so because he had prepared for that breakthrough for some time, not knowing what challenges he would face.

Oh, that believers today would "drill" often in preparation for the times which lie ahead. Our lives would be so different.

PREPARATION FOR EFFECTIVE PRAYER

James 5:16 gives every believer this powerful truth: *"Confess your faults one to another, and pray one for another, that ye may be healed. The effectual fervent prayer of a righteous man availeth much."* Becoming an effective (another word for effectual) prayer warrior is a practical, attainable goal that every child of God can attain. Hopefully we will not have to have a death threat over our heads, as did the British soldier, when we are called upon to pray for a breakthrough, but we should be ready, nonetheless.

Everything begins with preparation. Becoming an effective prayer warrior begins by preparing yourself every day for serious, intimate communion with God. It only happens when you spend time with Him. Only then can breakthroughs happen in every area of your life.

We must prepare our hearts for prayer. Everything starts by creating an atmosphere that makes it easy to commune with God. Let me share five simple ways to help you develop a conducive atmosphere for spending effective time with the Lord.

Find a Quiet Place

Do you want freedom in prayer? Do you want breakthroughs? Find a quiet place to be alone.

As I have mentioned several times in this book, especially in chapter 8, it is important to get away from distracting influences because you cannot commune with the Lord as effectively in a busy, loud atmosphere surrounded by people. Certainly there are times when you pray with your family, church, or friends, but you must also find a quiet place during those all-important times you want to be alone with God.

Wait Quietly Before the Lord

I have mentioned this before, but it bears repeating. You must learn to come into the presence of God, then wait until you feel Him near. You may ask, "What if that doesn't happen?"

Then you wait!

Don't worry. God is already there, waiting for your heart and mind to become in tune with Him.

Our number one problem is emptying our thoughts from the clutter of the day and calming our hectic pace of life. Get on your knees and just wait quietly before Him. Moses, Ezekiel, and the prophets came into God's presence with stillness, calmness, and serenity. You can, too.

Play Worship Music

Perhaps like me, you sometimes know you need to spend time with the Lord, but you feel empty and low, not really ready to pray. I have learned that worship music changes everything. I find that as I put on my earphones and begin to play a CD of worship music, within minutes I find myself enraptured by the glorious presence of the Holy Spirit. All the outer influences and the inner hindrances leave, the praise lifting me to new heights.

I find that even after the CD ends, songs and melodies keep flowing out of my heart. This has happened to me more times than I can count, so I can tell you from personal experience that it is very important that the music you play has been written and produced for worship.

So much music today is designed to stir our emotions, tell a story, or deliver a message. There is nothing wrong with any of those, and there is a time and place for those tunes, but music of this nature probably will not help create the atmosphere you need for worship. You need songs that usher you into the very presence of the Lord. This is why the apostle Paul wrote, *"Speaking to yourselves in psalms and hymns and spiritual songs, singing and making melody in your heart to the Lord"* (Ephesians 5:19).

Worship and praise prepares you for victory, for what lies ahead. Remember how the Lord Jesus and the disciples shared the Last Supper together, then as they prepared to leave, the Bible says, *"And when they had sung an hymn, they went out into the mount of Olives"* (Matthew 26:30). Christ Jesus then won the victory!

This is why we emphasize praise and worship music during our broadcasts and crusades. There is something about this music that lifts you up, sets you on a firm foundation, and prepares you for victory—no matter where you are in life.

Paul, writing under the inspiration of the Holy Spirit, told the church to teach and admonish each other with these powerful words: *"Let the word of Christ dwell in you richly in all wisdom; teaching and admonishing one another in psalms and hymns and spiritual songs, singing with grace in your hearts to the Lord"* (Colossians 3:16).

"God is a Spirit," we are told in John 4:24, *"and they that worship him must worship him in spirit and in truth."* Likewise, Psalm 29:2 declares, *"Give unto the LORD the glory due unto his name; worship the LORD in the beauty of holiness."* Enter into worship with music and see how much more effective your prayer life can be!

Become Totally Dependent upon the Holy Spirit

When left to our own devices, we have a difficult time preparing for breakthroughs. The phone rings, the kids start crying, the doorbell chimes, the dog begins to bark, our stomach tells us we are hungry, and suddenly we drift off in a thousand different directions.

For some people, the moment they get on their knees they start to yawn and have to fight drowsiness. Instead of praying, they try reading a chapter from the Bible and fall asleep.

Every believer needs God's help in becoming an effective prayer warrior. In fact, the psalmist was so reliant on the Lord that he asked God to guide his footsteps. He prayed, *"Make me to go in the path of thy commandments; for therein do I delight.… Turn away mine eyes from beholding vanity; and quicken thou me in thy way"* (Psalm 119:35, 37).

In Psalm 80:18, David wrote, *"So will not we go back from thee: quicken us, and we will call upon thy name."* What was he saying? "I can't do it on my own. Can you help me?" We should make the same request when we pray.

There comes a time when we must die to self and surrender totally to the Lord. Remember, the Lord became weary of the hollow prayers of the children of Israel. God said, *"And when ye spread forth your hands, I will hide mine eyes from you: yea, when ye make many prayers, I will not hear"* (Isaiah 1:15).

Why was the Lord so displeased? Because the flesh cannot please God, nor can the flesh pray. We need to say, "Holy Spirit, I can't pray. Help me. Pray through me. Holy Spirit, I can't even worship in my own strength. Help me worship the Lord as He deserves to be worshiped and adored. Be reminded that *"God is a Spirit: and they that worship him must worship him in spirit and in truth"* (John 4:24).

Open Your Heart to God

It is futile to enter God's presence while attempting to impress Him. He knows your heart and wants you to pour out your heart to Him, telling Him your deepest desires. You must confess your need and your sin, for without confession, there can be no forgiveness: *"When I kept silence, my bones waxed old through my roaring all the day long. For day and night thy hand was heavy upon me: my moisture is turned into the drought of summer"* (Psalm 32:3-4).

The psalmist also declared: *"I acknowledged my sin unto thee, and mine iniquity have I not hid. I said, I will confess my transgressions unto the LORD; and thou forgavest the iniquity of my sin"* (Psalm 32:5).

David continues: *"For this shall every one that is godly pray unto thee in a time when thou mayest be found"* (Psalm 32:6). Likewise, it is impossible to pour your heart out to the Lord without first confessing your sin, and once He cleanses you, there will be intimacy that words cannot express.

REVELATIONS TO EFFECTIVE PRAYER

Once sin is confessed and the Holy Spirit has touched your heart to pray, He will lead you into the seven revelations of prayer.

Confession

True prayer begins with confessing who God is. After the apostles were threatened by the Pharisees and told not to speak in the name of Jesus Christ, Peter prayed, and the apostles came into God's presence by confessing who He is:

> *And being let go, they went to their own
> company, and reported all that the chief
> priests and elders had said unto them. And
> when they heard that, they lifted up their
> voice to God with one accord, and said,
> Lord, thou art God, which hast made
> heaven, and earth, and the sea, and all
> that in them is....*
>
> *And now, Lord, behold their threatenings:
> and grant unto thy servants, that with all
> boldness they may speak thy word, By stretch-
> ing forth thine hand to heal; and that signs
> and wonders may be done by the name of thy
> holy child Jesus. And when they had prayed,
> the place was shaken where they were assem-
> bled together; and they were all filled with
> the Holy Ghost, and they spake the word of
> God with boldness.* (Acts 4:23-24, 29-31)

Before asking the Lord to heal and do signs and wonders and before the place was shaken, the apostles said, *"Lord, thou art God, which hast made heaven, and earth, and the sea, and all that in them is"* (verse 24).

When Moses approached God's throne, he confessed who God is. The Scripture tells us, *"Enter into his gates with thanksgiving, and into his courts with praise: be thankful unto him, and bless his name"* (Psalm 100:4). True prayer begins by confessing who He is. We confess His glory. We confess His holiness. We confess His majesty.

When I enter prayer, I always begin by telling God who He is: "Lord, You are God Almighty. You are just. You are pure. You are holy." I begin to magnify His holy name.

"The heavens declare the glory of God," the psalmist cried (Psalm 19:1). He always began with exaltation.

How can you approach God and immediately begin telling Him your needs until you tell Him how mighty He is to meet those needs? You begin by confessing how mighty He is. Prayer begins with declaring the glory of God. You cannot begin true prayer until you declare who God is.

Supplication

Not only do we declare the sovereignty and power of God, but we also must present our needs to Him. This is called supplication. After the apostle Paul told us to put on the whole armor of God (see Ephesians 6:11-17), he declared that we should be *"praying always with all prayer and supplication in the Spirit"* (verse 18).

Literally, take your requests to the Lord. Don't hesitate to say, "Lord, here is the need I am bringing to You today." Paul wrote, *"Be careful for nothing; but in every thing by prayer and supplication with thanksgiving let your requests be made known unto God. And the peace of God, which passeth all understanding, shall keep your hearts and minds through Christ Jesus"* (Philippians 4:6-7).

He knows our petitions before we even ask, yet God is waiting to hear the cry of our heart. Unfortunately, many people end their time of prayer at this point. They never move beyond supplication. They present their requests and say, "Well, I feel better now. That's it. I am finished." They rush to turn on the news, read a newspaper, or phone a friend, not realizing that God is still waiting.

Adoration

Supplication always leads to adoration. After you confess who God is, and after your petition has been presented, then peace begins to fill your soul, and you will enter into worship: *"Give unto the LORD the glory due unto his name; worship the LORD in the beauty of holiness"* (Psalm 29:2).

Communion

From adoration, we always move into communion and intimacy with the Lord. Intimacy is where words become inadequate. As we worship Him, He will fill us with His presence, and as a result, our hearts will be filled with His abundance. This results in holy silence and intimacy.

Intimacy is the result of abundance, not lack. The presence of God begins with quietness and intimacy, which will impart to you the quietness and confidence wherein you will find your strength: *"For thus saith the Lord GOD, the Holy One of Israel; In returning and rest shall ye be saved; in quietness and in confidence shall be your strength"* (Isaiah 30:15).

The apostle Paul prayed: *"The love of God, and the communion of the Holy Ghost, be with you all"* (2 Corinthians 13:14). Intimacy is the key that will lead you to intercession.

Intercession

Often I have met people who tell me, "I'm an intercessor." Yet when I talk with them it becomes clear they simply see their role in ministry as "praying for others." True intercession has a far deeper meaning and is the result of a relationship with the Lord that is immeasurable.

Intimacy with the Lord prepares the heart for intercession and victory. It is in intimacy with the Lord that the Holy Spirit takes over our hearts and intercession is born. For it is He who intercedes. We become vessels for the Intercessor: *"Likewise the Spirit also helpeth our infirmities: for we know not what we should pray for as we ought: but the Spirit itself maketh intercession for us with groanings which cannot be uttered"* (Romans 8:26).

Praise

After intercession, praise will erupt out of your soul, for the Holy Spirit, the great Intercessor who knows the will of God, who has wrought great victories in the heavenlies as you were willing to surrender to His presence, will cause praise. Praise is the result of intercession, and it brings about the will of God into this world and into the lives of many. It is in praise that the enemies of God will be bound:

> *Let the high praises of God be in their mouth, and a twoedged sword in their hand; To execute vengeance upon the heathen, and punishments upon the people; To bind their kings*

with chains, and their nobles with fetters of iron; To execute upon them the judgment written: this honour have all his saints. Praise ye the LORD. (Psalm 149:6-9)

Thanksgiving

Because of the victories wrought in praise, thanksgiving will follow. Thanksgiving seals the work which was wrought in praise.

Paul the apostle told us we are to be *"abounding therein with thanksgiving"* (Colossians 2:7). He also tells us, *"In every thing give thanks: for this is the will of God in Christ Jesus concerning you"* (1 Thessalonians 5:18).

Prayer is not overcoming God's reluctance, but laying hold of His willingness.
—Martin Luther

Groanings which cannot be uttered are often prayers which cannot be refused.
—Charles Spurgeon

Prayer does not fit us for the greater works; prayer is the greater work. We think of prayer as a common sense exercise of our higher powers in order to prepare us for God's work. In the teaching of Jesus Christ, prayer is the working of the miracle of redemption in others by the power of God.

—Oswald Chambers

The greatest power that God has given to any individual is the power of prayer.

—Kathryn Kuhlman

If you live in the neglect of secret prayer, you show your good will to neglect all the worship of God. He that prays only when he prays with others, would not pray at all, were it not that the eyes of others are upon him. He that will not pray where none but God seeth him, manifestly doth not pray at all out of respect to God, or regard to his all-seeing eye, and therefore doth in effect cast off all prayer. And he that casts off prayer, in effect casts off all the worship of God, of which prayer is the principal duty.[2]

—Jonathan Edwards

I have so much to do that I must spend
several hours in prayer before I am able to
do it.

—John Wesley

Many persons, being told that God answers
prayer for Christ's sake, overlook the condition of obedience. They have so loose an
idea of prayer, and of our relations to God
in it, and of His relations to us and to His
moral government, that they think they
may be disobedient and yet prevail through
Christ. How little do they understand the
whole subject! Surely they must have quite
neglected to study their Bible to learn the
truth about prayer.[3]

—Charles G. Finney

When God intends to bless His people, the
first thing He does is to set them a-praying.

—Matthew Henry

Is prayer your steering wheel or your spare
tire?

—Corrie ten Boom

notes

Introduction
1. www.Lifeway.com

Chapter 1
1. Eleanor Doan, *The Speaker's Sourcebook* (Grand Rapids, MI: Zondervan, 1971), 193.

Chapter 4
1. R. A. Torrey, *How to Study the Bible* (New Kensington, PA: Whitaker House, 1999), 349.

Chapter 6
1. Abraham Lincoln, as quoted in Albert M. Wells, comp., *Inspiring Quotations* (Nashville: Thomas Nelson, 1988), 159.
2. Matthew Henry, *Matthew Henry's Commentary on the Whole Bible* (1706–1721; p.d.).
3. Jeanne Guyon, *Experiencing God Through Prayer* (New Kensington, PA: Whitaker House, 1984), 20.

Chapter 7
1. Guyon, *Experiencing God Through Prayer*, 21.

Chapter 8
1. Charles Spurgeon, *The Power of Prayer* (New Kensington, PA: Whitaker House, 1996), 18–19.

Chapter 10
1. "Sunday School Promoter," *Speaker's Sourcebook*, 195–6.
2. Jonathan Edwards, *Hypocrites Deficient in the Duty of Prayer* (1742).
3. Charles G. Finney, *The Way of Salvation*.

We must know the power of the Blood if we are to know the power of God. Our knowing experimentally the power of the Word, the power of the Holy Spirit, and the power of prayer is dependent upon our knowing the power of the Blood of Christ.

—R. A. Torrey